The Therapeutic Nursery School

The Therapeutic Nursery School

A Contribution to the Study and Treatment
of Emotional Disturbances in Young Children

Edited by

Robert A. Furman, M.D.

and

Anny Katan, M.D.

INTERNATIONAL UNIVERSITIES PRESS, INC.

NEW YORK   NEW YORK

This book is dedicated by all the research participants to Dr. Anny Katan in grateful acknowledgment of her thoughtful, unassuming leadership, her profound understanding of small children and their mothers and her great patience as a wise and effective teacher.

Contents

Preface
ANNY KATAN, M.D.   1

1. Introduction
ROBERT A. FURMAN, M.D.   4
     I. GENERAL ORGANIZATION   4
     II. HISTORICAL REVIEW   6
     III. RESEARCH METHODOLOGY   8
         Accumulation of Basic Data   11
         Assimilation and Presentation of Basic Data   17

2. Educational Program
LOIS ARCHER and ELEANOR HOSLEY   21
     I. PHYSICAL PLANT   21
     II. ADMINISTRATIVE POLICIES   24
         Staff   24
         Lines of Communication   25
             1. Teaching Staff   25
             2. Therapist   26
             3. Parents   27
         Selection of Cases   27
             1. Types of Problems Accepted   27
             2. Balance of Groups   27
             3. Parents   27
         Application Procedures   27
             1. Referral Agencies or Persons   27
             2. Intake Procedure   28
     III. EDUCATIONAL PROGRAM   33
         General Structure   34
             1. Transitions   35

2. Changes in Program   35
3. Visitors-Observers and New Children   35
4. Holidays and Parties   35
5. Handling and Routines   36
Verbalization   40
1. Initial Separation and Adjustment Period   44
2. Anger and Aggression   49
3. Instinctual Gratifications   52
4. Curiosity   54
5. Jealousy and Rivalry   56
6. Discipline   57
IV. SIMILARITIES AND DIFFERENCES BETWEEN THIS AND
OTHER SCHOOLS   59

3. Treatment via the Mother
ERNA FURMAN   64
I. HISTORICAL BACKGROUND AND REVIEW OF THE LITERATURE   64
II. THEORETICAL AND CLINICAL CONSIDERATIONS IN THE
ASSESSMENT OF PARENTS   66
Assessment of Parents   67
Parenthood as a Developmental Phase   67
Motivation   71
Capacity for Identification   73
Role and Assessment of the Father   77
III. TECHNIQUE OF WORKING WITH THE MOTHER   79
Initial Stage   79
Middle Stage   86
1. Prevention of Interferences   87
2. Discussion of Interferences   90
Final Stage   94
IV. THE ROLE OF THE NURSERY SCHOOL IN THE WORK
WITH THE MOTHER   98
Observation   98
Education   101
Support of the Mother in Times of Stress   103
Disadvantages of the Nursery School   104
V. LIMITING FACTORS IN THE MOTHER
"Unsuitable" Mothers   105
Mothers with Limited Ability   107
1. Difficulties with Direct or Indirect Drive
Manifestations   107

2. Cases of Mother and Child Sharing
   Important Conflicts or Prominent Defenses   108
3. Disturbances in the Libidinal Cathexis of
   the Child   109
4. Gross Educational Inconsistency   110
5. Pathological Guilt   111
6. Inability to Integrate Means and Aims of
   Educational and Therapeutic Principles   111
   Discussion   112
   Case 1   114
   Case 2   114
   Case 3   115

VI. SPECIAL APPLICATIONS OF THE WORK WITH THE MOTHER
   —PREPARATION FOR THE CHILD'S TREATMENT   117
   *The Parents' Role in the Direct Treatment of
   Under-Fives*   117
   *The Impact of Direct Treatment on the Early
   Mother-Child Relationship*   118
   The Mother's Contribution to Direct Treatment   121

4. Case Reports
ROBERT A. FURMAN, M.D., EDWARD J. SCHIFF, M.D.,
J. BENKENDORF, and ERNA FURMAN   124
   CASE 1: SALLY   124
   CASE 2: JILL   138
   CASE 3: MARTIN   156
   CASE 4: JANIE   180

5. Diagnosis
ELIZABETH DAUNTON   204
   I. REVIEW OF THE LITERATURE   204
   II. DIAGNOSTIC CONSIDERATIONS   208
   III. DIAGNOSTIC CLASSIFICATION   211

6. Description, Evaluation and Follow-up of Cases
   Treated via the Mother
ELIZABETH DAUNTON   215
   I. USE OF PROFILE MATERIAL IN ASSESSING CHILDREN
   TREATED VIA THE MOTHER   215
   Study of Individual Cases   215
   II. COMPARISON OF RESULTS OF TREATMENT VIA THE
   MOTHER IN DIAGNOSTIC GROUPS I-IV   218

III. DISCUSSION OF RESULTS OF TREATMENT VIA THE MOTHER
     FOR CHILDREN IN DIAGNOSTIC GROUPS I-IV   229
IV. CONCLUSIONS   230

7. Psychosomatic Disorders
ROBERT A. FURMAN, M.D.   231
  I. DIAGNOSTIC ASSESSMENT   231
         Definition   233
         Theoretical Considerations   234
         Areas for Further Study   234
         Evaluation of the Studied Areas   240
         *The Diagnostic Assessment vs. the Developmental
           Profile*   242
         The Literature   244
  II. CASE EVALUATIONS   247
         Diagnostic Assessment   249
           1. Organic Factor   249
           2. Relationship Factor   249
           3. Psychic Factor   250
           4. Profile Diagnosis   251
  III. INDIVIDUAL CASES   253
         Gretchen—Allergic Rashes   253
         Craig—Asthma   257
         Chuck—Eczema   260
         Yvonne—Asthma   264
         Timothy—Asthma   267
  IV. DISCUSSION OF THE INDIVIDUAL CASE MATERIAL   270

8. The Role of the Nursery School with the Children Who
   Received Direct Treatment
RUTH OPPENHEIMER   274
  I. CASE MATERIAL   276
         *Beginning of Treatment in Relation to Nursery
           School*   276
         Diagnostic Categories   277
         The Psychotherapy Cases   278
         *Looking at the Diagnostic Profiles
           Retrospectively*   279
  II. ROLE OF THE NURSERY SCHOOL IN PREPARATION FOR
      TREATMENT   280

Contents

III. ROLE OF THE NURSERY SCHOOL DURING THE CHILD'S
TREATMENT 287
    Helping the Child 287
    Helping the Parents 289
    Helping the Therapist 290
IV. SOME DIFFICULTIES INHERENT IN THE NURSERY SCHOOL
SETTING 291

9. Role of the Nursery School in Relation to Total Child
    Analytic Program
EDWARD SCHIFF 293

10. Appendix
ERNA FURMAN
SCHEMA OF LINES OF DEVELOPMENT AND MASTERY OF TASKS 298
SUMMARY OF INFORMATION ABOUT THE ROLE OF THE NURSERY
    SCHOOL IN CASES OF TREATMENT VIA THE MOTHER 309
STUDY OF PARENTAL FACTORS HELPFUL OR LIMITING TO
    THE WORK 311
DEVELOPMENTAL CHART 316
PHASE DOMINANCE CHART 321
CHART FOR ASSESSMENT OF PSYCHOSOMATIC DISORDERS 325

Bibliography 326

Preface

ANNY KATAN, M.D.

In introducing this book, I would like to describe briefly our nursery school in Cleveland.

Hanna Perkins School is on university grounds, directly across from the School of Medicine. It is therefore easily accessible and can be used extensively for teaching students and graduates who work with children. Originally we had only a nursery school attended by 15 children. Four years ago, a kindergarten was added to provide an opportunity to observe children between the ages of three and six, or from the time of the main phase of their preoedipal development until the beginning of latency. The nursery school children are taught by three teachers; two teachers are assigned to the kindergarten. An educational director supervises and teaches both groups.

The children all have emotional problems of various gravity, and all need treatment. Thus treatment is an integral part of the school system. We apply two different forms of therapy, depending on the assessment of the child's pathology. One is psychoanalysis. In the other, the child is not in direct contact with the therapist; rather, the therapist helps the mother to treat her own child.

The larger number of children are treated by the second method. If you wonder about treatment of a child via the parent, recall that this method was applied many years ago in a classic case known to everyone—the case of Little

1

Hans, treated by his father under the guidance of Freud. As you all know, a follow-up of the case showed that the treatment was extremely successful. We have long wondered why this very instructive and successful form of treatment was not adopted earlier and elaborated upon and used with the preschool child more intensively.

I think this method of treatment was not taken over by anyone in Vienna at the time, because we were all too busy learning about child analysis. When I went to Holland in 1937, I was for a while the only child analyst in a wide area, and accordingly I received consultations from people that lived at quite some distance. One day a mother came to consult me about her daughter, age four. The mother had traveled on foot. taken a streetcar. then a train, then another streetcar and again had walked in order to reach my office. Her travel time both ways amounted to three and one half hours. She told me that her child had been completely toilet-trained at the age of two, without a relapse until just the week before when the little girl suddenly started wetting at night and had wet every night since. The mother suggested she might bring me the child once a week for treatment.

Many things flashed through my mind: the three-and-one-half hours necessary to get the child to and from my office, where she would meet a complete stranger; the many sessions it would take to establish in the child the minimum of confidence necessary before anything even remotely resembling treatment could be started; and the fact that all through these weeks the child would continue wetting every night. And I suddenly heard myself saying to the mother, "Don't bring your little daughter. Rather, come yourself once a week and together we will try to understand what started her wetting."

This was the first such treatment I undertook, and, as it was successful, I did several more. They were my first experiences with the type of treatment that will be presented in detail in the pages that follow.

Follow-up studies of the graduates of our nursery school, which were the immediate stimulus for this book, were made possible by the generous support of the Grant Foundation, graciously assisted by the New Land Foundation. The co-directors of these studies at their inception were myself and Dr. Marvin Ack, the latter soon succeeded by Dr. Robert A. Furman. Nineteen different therapists were involved over the years and all have contributed to the work. This group includes Drs. Willard Boaz, Marvin G. Brook, David Crocker, Robert A. Furman, Jane Kessler, Edward J. Schiff; Joanne Benkendorf, Catharine Berwald, Mary Flumerfelt, Erna Furman, Charlotte Haspels, Alice W. Rolnick, Marion J. Barnes, Mary Bergen, Elizabeth Daunton, Eleanor Fieldler, Eleanor Hosley, Marie McCann and Ruth Oppenheimer. The social service work in the follow-up studies was performed by Mrs. Miriam Jaffee.

Our secretarial work has been done by Mrs. Louise Smith, Mrs. Sarah Swancar and Mrs. Eleanor Whiston. All the work described has drawn heavily on the observational reports written daily by many devoted teachers. The only direct representative of the teaching staff, however, is Miss Lois Archer, current Educational Director of the Hanna Perkins School, who has co-authored the chapter on educational techniques.

The completion of this volume has been possible only because of the devoted and conscientious efforts of each participant.

1. Introduction

ROBERT A. FURMAN, M.D.

The purpose of this book is to describe in detail the concept of the therapeutic nursery school as it has evolved in Cleveland over the past 15 years. An integral part of this concept is the therapeutic approach known to us as treatment of the child under five years of age by way of his parents. A very large share of what is to be presented will be devoted to the exposition and evaluation of this approach.

The stimulus for this publication was the opportunity afforded us by the Grant Foundation and the New Land Foundation to do follow-up studies in depth on the graduates of the nursery school program. These studies involved us in extensive utilization of Miss Freud's Developmental Profile and yielded findings which seemed to merit exposition. A full description of our total therapeutic program must accompany the presentation of the results of these studies if they are to be meaningful.

The purposes of this introductory chapter are threefold: (1) to outline a general organization of this publication; (2) to present a brief historical review of the development of the nursery school; (3) to describe the research methodology used in the follow-up study.

I. GENERAL ORGANIZATION

The chapters immediately following this introduction, "Educational Program" and "Treatment via the Mother,"

4

are primarily focused on the technical problems inherent in our work. Discussion of the problems faced by the educator and the therapist seemed the best way to acquaint the reader with the nature of our approach. The second chapter details not only the theoretical basis and technical aspects, but in addition begins an exposition of the findings of the follow-up study by describing the factors in the mother that proved crucial to successful work.

Chapter 4 presents four case reports so that the technical questions of the preceding chapters can immediately be seen in clinical perspective. These reports were selected to highlight different aspects of the program.

The next three chapters (Chapters 5, 6, 7) deal most specifically with the follow-up studies of the children who had been treated only by way of their mothers within the setting of the therapeutic nursery school. The chapter on Diagnosis introduces this part of the book so that the reader will have full familiarization with the terminology used throughout the follow-up report.

Chapter 8 describes the role of the nursery school program with those children who received direct individual treatment, either psychotherapy or psychoanalysis. Although we did not follow up these children to study their current functioning, meaningful information seemed available from review of the data covering their time in school. Perhaps a brief explanation is warranted about Chapter 9, on the relation of the nursery school to the child analytic program in Cleveland. The school, from the start, has served as the central or focal point for Cleveland child analysts for child analytic training and child analytic research. This unusual function of the therapeutic nursery school seemed sufficiently significant to warrant special consideration.

Last we have included an Appendix which presents the various forms used in the follow-up, plus tables relevant to certain chapters.

II. HISTORICAL REVIEW

To create a milieu in which to study treatment of the child under five years of age by way of his parents, Dr. Anny Katan was instrumental in establishing, in 1951, a nursery school, Children's House, as part of the Child Psychiatry Division of University Hospitals of Cleveland under the auspices of the Division of Psychiatry of Western Reserve University School of Medicine. The school was planned as an optimal educational setting for small children whose emotional problems would be treated either via their mothers or by direct psychoanalysis, as well as a place for the observation of small children by medical students and physicians in psychiatric or psychoanalytic training. Initially children without specific difficulties were also admitted to the school.

From the outset the aim was to correlate the therapist's work with the mothers and children with the work of the teaching staff. The evolution of the concept of treatment via the mother led to an ever increasing coordination of the educational and therapeutic programs. Soon the only children admitted to the school were those whose emotional disorders were to be treated within the school setting either by psychoanalysis or by treatment via the mother.

It is pertinent at this point to explain the evolution of the term, "Treatment of the Child under Five via His Parent." At the outset we had used the phrase, "mother guidance" to describe our work to visitors and to analytic and psychiatric colleagues. We increasingly became aware, however, of the great difference between what we were doing and that usually connoted by mother guidance. This led to frequent misunderstandings. But it was not until the presentations of our work at the Worcester meetings (E. Furman, 1957) that the phrase "treatment via the mother" was introduced. We have used it since to distinguish our approach from that more appropriately characterized as mother guidance.

Children's House was founded during an era of expansion in the program of the Division of Psychiatry at Western Reserve. In the Child Psychiatry Section a Child Guidance Clinic recently had begun operation within University Hospitals and a special house for child therapists had just been acquired. Initially the child therapists in the program were those trained in the Hampstead Child Therapy Course and Clinic who had recently come to Cleveland. The overall director was Dr. Anny Katan and the administrative director for nearly the first two years was Mrs. Emma Plank.

The child analysts both in what was called the Therapy House and in the nursery school in Children's House occupied older frame residences across the street from one another, adjacent to the hospital medical school complex. These converted homes retained enough of their original atmosphere to make them most appropriate for work with small children. The school capacity was limited to 15 children and the staff consisted of the administrative director, head teacher, two assistant teachers, one of whom served as a secretary, and a cook.

In spring 1953 a new administrative organization emerged for the school, which was then beginning to be more generally known as the University Hospitals Nursery School. Miss Eleanor Hosley, Executive Director of the Day Nursery Association of Cleveland, took over the administrative direction of the school, although it remained completely under the jurisdiction of University Hospitals. At the same time Miss Lois Archer became Head Teacher or Educational Director, a position she has since occupied except for a four-year absence.

In spring 1956, the Psychiatry Department moved into its new hospital building, Hanna Pavilion. The therapists also moved into the new facility. In line with continuing expansion in the Division of Psychiatry, the number of therapists at the nursery school increased. Over the years seven therapists have come from Hampstead and they have been joined by seven analysts whose training has mainly been in Cleveland. In recent years participants of the Cleveland Child Therapy Course have also worked within the school program, four of them cooperating with this study.

Autumn 1961 saw the last major steps in the evolution of the school. Administrative responsibility for the school changed from University Hospitals to the Day Nursery Association, the psychoanalytic or therapeutic aspects of the program remaining under the Department of Psychiatry of Western Reserve University. The change was prompted by the move to a new building shared with the Day Nursery Association and by expansion of the school to include a kindergarten as well as nursery school. The new building is adjacent to the original location, allowing the school to preserve its physical proximity to the university and hospital complex. With the new building the name was changed to the Hanna Perkins School.

But despite the changes in name, administration and physical plant, there have been no changes in the school's basic philosophy, and the overall direction has remained with Dr. Katan (see footnote at end of chapter).

III. RESEARCH METHODOLOGY

As we considered different methods for reviewing the cases available for the follow-up study, we realized that our research problem contained a number of unique aspects. We wished to study the effect of a specific treatment approach on a large group of children who were young when treated but had now grown into latency or adolescence. A number of persons have worked in a manner similar to ours (see Chapter 4), but no group has utilized these techniques over a long period. The Child Research Council at the University of Colorado under John Benjamin (1959) and the Child Study Center at Yale University established by Ernst Kris

(1953) and Milton J. E. Senn have in their longitudinal studies developed methods of intensive observation of small children over many years, but neither group has focused on the effects of a specific therapeutic intervention. Augusta Alpert (1953, 1954), Peter Neubauer (1960) and others from the Child Development Center in New York City have described a number of cases with whom they have worked, but the approach they have utilized within their therapeutic nursery school is quite different from ours (see Chapter 2), and they have not yet described any long-term follow-up. As the following pages are intended to clarify, we have relied heavily on Miss Freud's developmental profile. Despite the availability of this invaluable research tool, however, many adaptations and new study techniques were required because of the nature of our clinical material.

In the first meetings the participating therapists decided that for our study to make any significant evaluation of a child's current status in relation to his previous nursery school experience, at least one year should have elapsed since he left either nursery school or kindergarten. It was also decided that it would be necessary for the child to have participated in the program for at least six months. The last children eligible for inclusion in the study were those who had left school in 1962.

Going back to 1951 we found that 106 children were possibly available for study. Forty-four were eliminated for the following reasons: 11 were in school for less than six months; nine had not participated in any therapeutic program; eight had moved out of town and we could not establish sufficient contact to make a meaningful follow-up evaluation possible; six sets of parents refused to cooperate; six children were in situations which the therapists felt contraindicated a follow-up study; four were excluded for reasons of confidentiality.

A word might be in order about each group except the first, which is self-explanatory. For many reasons we wished to include the children who had not participated in therapy at all, perhaps as a type of control group, but we found that in the early days of the school almost no daily records had been kept of the behavior of these apparently problemless children. Since there were hardly any recorded interviews with their parents it was felt there was no possibility of evaluating their status when they either entered or left school. It was known in a few instances the children had not been as free from symptoms as the parents had felt, but we now had no way to explore the extent of their original difficulties.

As for children who had moved out of town, some *were* included in the study. In two instances they had moved to communities close enough to allow them to come to Cleveland for follow-up interviews, and to allow someone from the study to explore their school situations. One follow-up was conducted by long distance correspondence when a mother of known veracity and insight wrote at length about her daughter's situation. The daughter, an adolescent, had herself maintained a contact with the therapist and she, too, wrote extensively. In addition, the school records were made fully available to us and it was possible for one of our staff to interview the teachers.

The parents who declined to cooperate did so for reasons not clear enough to allow a meaningful assessment of the factors underlying their wish not to participate. Of the six children whose current situation contraindicated a follow-up evaluation, three were in psychotherapy with people not connected with our group and three were in the midst of family crises, such as the very recent death of a parent. In the four instances, where confidentiality precluded participation, the individual therapist's judgment was accepted without question. A number of children were included in the study whose parents are members of the local professional group, so this factor itself was not deemed adequate reason for exclusion.

The remaining 62 children are listed in Table 1 (see Appendix), grouped according to the diagnostic evaluation of their pathology at the time of entry into nursery school. At this point it might suffice to say that 34 were treated via their parents and that 28 received direct treatment, four in psychotherapy, 24 in psychoanalysis. The development of the study of these 62 children has had two distinct phases: (1) accumulating the basic data; (2) assimilating them and presenting the resulting conclusions and observations.

Accumulation of Basic Data

It was most fortunate that at the time the study began Miss Freud and the Hampstead Group had completed their first papers regarding the developmental profile, and most kindly made them available to us prior to publication (1962, 1963). The value of the profile to our research group was immediately obvious: it offered an ideal way to compare the complete emotional status of a child at different stages in his development and to compare the status of one child with another in a systematized fashion. It was decided to construct retrospective profiles for the time of the child's entry into school and for the time of his leaving school. Comparison of these profiles would reveal the changes, if any, that had transpired. A third profile would be constructed from follow-up interviews with the mother and child which, in comparison with the second profile, would reveal whether the previous gains had been maintained and the changes, if any, that had occurred since.

Many members of the research group were apprehensive at the start about their ability to construct a profile retrospectively for the time of entry into school with the proper objectivity, for they felt they were too keenly aware of the subsequent course of the child's development. The decision was made to have this initial profile cover the child's first two months in school, enabling the therapist to use, not his memory nor impression, but the detailed daily observations of the nursery school teachers, his own records of his interviews with the mother and the teacher's notes of his weekly conference sessions. In addition we found that almost every child had been discussed in a group seminar with Dr. Katan sometime during his first two months, and this conference focused on an assessment of the child's developmental status at the time and was fully recorded by the teachers. These same sources of information were available for the construction of the profile at the time of leaving school—a profile that covered either the child's last two months at our school or the last month with us and the report of his entry to regular school if the information for that period was sufficiently available.

Although the availability of these detailed written observations greatly allayed the group's anxieties, there is no way of knowing how successful they were in eliminating distortion from the profile. The advantages in utilizing the retrospective profiles, however, seemed to outweigh any possible disadvantages.

The participating therapists then discussed who should do the follow-up profile. Should it be the therapist familiar with the mother and child? Should it be someone who did not know them and could therefore be more objective? Or should we attempt to have two parallel follow-up studies, one by the therapist familiar with the case and another by a therapist not familiar with the case? The initial conclusion was that the advantages of an unfamiliar observer's neutrality would be more than counterbalanced by the mother's and child's lack of relationship with him, which would preclude certain communications, and by his lack of familiarity with the weak spots of the mother's and child's personality and the particular form that their defenses might take. The neutral observer might be warned that a certain mother used denial a great deal, but he might not recognize its use as readily as the familiar therapist. For example, he might not know that when a particular mother responded positively to a certain situation, the chances were that a difficulty was being denied, whereas if all were really going well, the mother might pause, consider and apparently present positives and negatives alternately. In similar fashion, the omission of a topic with a familiar therapist would have a significance he would at once recognize, but its absence would have little recognizable meaning to an unfamiliar person. It was decided therefore to have the follow-up done by the familiar therapist. Ilse Hellman (1962) came to essentially the same conclusion about the importance of the preceding relationship to the accumulation of meaningful follow-up data.

Again, regarding objectivity, it was decided that for a few cases we would have a second, parallel follow-up done by a neutral observer. But this inclination was short-lived, as it promised only confusion for mother, child and therapist, as well as for the neutral observer. The concerns about objectivity in the third profile were greatly abated by the social worker's evaluation of the child's school performance. With the parents' written permission and the advance consent of the school authorities, she visited the child's school, interviewed as many of his teachers as were available and either had full access to his school records or could question and discuss them with some member of the school administration. These school visits sometimes required half a day to complete and led to very detailed, extensive reports that were of great value. In addition to the information she usually sought, the social worker could, if the therapist so wished, explore any areas that were deemed particularly significant because of a child's prior difficulties or a mother's known propensity to deny certain problems.

Again, as with the retrospective profiles, perhaps there is no completely objective method of obtaining the desired data, but the method selected seemed clearly to have advantages far outweighing the possible disadvantages. And this impression increased with our experiences in assimilating the data, as described below.

Before discussing other data accumulated for each case and the modifications of data collection employed for the cases that had direct treatment, it would seem advantageous to detail some problems encountered in the application of the developmental profile to our group of cases and how these difficulties were approached. The entire group shared some initial apprehension about their ability to construct developmental profiles, which were then completely unfamiliar to all but one or two. The first profiles were discussed and reviewed by the entire group, seeking a uniformity of terminology about items such as "object constancy" or "progressive vs. regressive factors" or "superego precursors." Subsequent publications of the Hampstead group, as well as Miss Freud's generous communications with us before and during her 1964 visit to Cleveland, were of great assistance. Nagera's report (1963) of the stimulation and improvement of analytic thinking that ensues from work with the developmental profile has been confirmed by our experience.

Application to children under five years old of the diagnostic categories proposed by Miss Freud in her initial communication posed problems for us that are extensively reported in Chapter 5. The formulations presented there were first discussed by a small group and then reviewed by the entire group of participating therapists.

In Miss Freud's New York lectures in 1960 she had presented as an example of task mastery the developmental lines involved in entry into nursery school. For our initial profile covering entry into our nursery school and in some second profiles that covered entry into regular school, this example was most useful. The lack of a similar developmental line for children in latency and adolescence was sorely felt. Two committees were subsequently formed: one on latency under Dr. Jane Kessler and another on adolescence under Mrs. Benkendorf and Mrs. Furman, which developed comparable situations of task mastery for latency and puberty. These committees also abstracted from these formulations the specific areas that the social worker was to evaluate in her school visits. The schemata developed by these committees are included in the Appendix.

The last item of basic data acquired about the children was a summary of the work with the parents. This was written by the therapist active with the case while the child was in school and was based on three sources: (1) the therapist's notes of his weekly conferences with the mother; (2) the summaries of all seminar discussions of the case while the child had been in school (the children were usually discussed in seminar two or three times yearly); and (3) the case summary written by the therapist at the time the child left school.

The summary written for the follow-up study included these specific areas: (1) assessment of the mother, her strengths and weaknesses, as well as a description of the father's role in relation to the work; (2) the child's problems that seemed to have been worked through; (3) the remaining areas of difficulty that had not been worked through; (4) the role of the nursery school in assisting or hindering the treatment of the under-five by way of his mother. Although no specific predictions of the child's future functioning were made when this summary was written, an element of prediction was inherent in the therapist's evaluation of the extent the child's difficulties had been resolved.

This summary was written for all cases regardless of whether the child went into direct treatment, unless he began such treatment within six months of entering school. The data on each child who received only treatment via his mother consisted then of three developmental profiles for the time of entry into school, the time of leaving school, the follow-up visit, the raw data of the follow-up visit (report of interviews with mother and with child and report of the school visit) and the summary as detailed above.

It was difficult at first to decide exactly which data was to be accumulated on the cases that went into analysis or psychotherapy. To evaluate the work done via the mother, a profile was constructed for the time of entry into school and, if more than six months elapsed before direct treatment was started, a second profile was constructed for the time of beginning treatment and a summary was written of the work done via the mother. These were all written by the therapist active with the case to this point. The therapist who treated the child in analysis or psychotherapy (sometimes a different person), was then asked to write a special report on the relationship of the school program to the child's direct treatment. In the report the analyst was asked to cover these points: (1) the role of the school in preparing the child and the parents for his treatment; (2) the effects of the school program, both positive and negative, on that portion of the child's treatment concurrent with his attendance at school; (3) an evaluation of the preceding profiles in the light of the understanding which emerged from the analysis or psychotherapy.

The data available on the children in treatment obviously would vary, depending on when they began their individual work. The children who started their analysis before school had but one profile constructed—from the information available at their original evaluation. For the children whose individual therapy began after they left school, the section of the analyst's report dealing with the role of the school in conjunction with a concurrent analysis was omitted.

For various reasons (see Chapter 8), it was decided not to have follow-up studies on the children who had individual treatment. Though those studies would be intriguing and challenging, it seemed important to maintain our original focus on the therapeutic nursery school and treatment of the young child via his parents.

Assimilation and Presentation of Basic Data

As the tremendous amount of information described above began to accumulate, a group of six therapists,[1] in conjunction with Dr. Katan, met to discuss the utilization of the material. As soon as any therapist had completed his profile and summary work, he was most welcome to participate in these discussions, but as the work evolved, the group's composition did not expand. The six therapists had done approximately 60 per cent of the basic data accumulation and had been directly involved in over two thirds of the cases.

The first task the group set for itself was a review of all profile diagnoses, no therapist reviewing a case in whose study he had participated. This meant a total review of each profile, a consultation with the original therapist whenever a discrepancy seemed apparent and then a discussion within the group of doubtful points. This rather tedious work was most helpful in assuring some uniformity of approach to all profiles, in familiarizing the group with all the individual cases and in pinpointing certain areas, such as those involving the diagnostic categories, that needed further revision or clarification. In addition, the group discussions inevitably became the starting point for our thinking about the optimum utilization of the material available to us, as well as the overall organization of the final report.

It was decided that different members of this smaller group, which soon became known as the research group, would individually assume primary responsibility for various aspects of the study, the remainder of the group working at his

[1] Elizabeth Daunton, Ruth Oppenheimer, Joanna Benkendorf, Erna Furman, Edward J. Schiff, and Robert A. Furman.

direction on that part of the study. The person who accepted
this responsibility acted as chairman of the group whenever
his section was under discussion and ultimately became the
author for that section or chapter. For all the chapters dealing with the clinical material, the same general approach was
used by all the chairmen, any modification being dictated
either by the complexity of the material or by the chairman's
preference for working independently or within the group
at different stages of the work.

In general it was necessary to begin with some method of
abstracting comparable data on the cases involved either from
the developmental profiles or from the different summaries
prepared by all the participating therapists. The author of
each individual chapter feels keenly his indebtedness to his
colleagues. This abstracting involved the preparation of
forms which either the chairman prepared and presented
to the group or the group evolved in a general discussion.
These forms all are included in the Appendix, both as examples of our research methodology and as possible aids for
others. Once the forms or charts were worked out they were
applied to the available data by the research group, abstracting from the profiles and summaries the selected facts and
impressions. Any problems were referred back to the research group for further discussion and amplification. Their
completion usually required additional consultation with the
therapist who originally prepared the profile or summary.

Once the data had been collated, the chairman undertook
its study and from his study prepared an outline of his section of the report. This, too, was presented to the research
group and thoroughly discussed before the actual writing
began. The drafts of each chapter were also reviewed in detail
by the research committee, in regard both to form and
to content. Thus each section chairman constantly had his
thinking and work reviewed by a group most familiar with

the clinical material from which he was working. At the same time, each member of the research group was constantly kept informed of the progress and findings that emerged from each section of the study.

There are three areas related to the clinical material where we went beyond the full descriptive assessment of the work of the total nursery school program, which was the primary focus of the study. They deal with "Diagnosis" (Chapter 5), "Treatment via the Mother" (Chapter 3) and "Psychosomatic Disorders" (Chapter 7). Our special and intensive focus on the under-five indicated a need to modify the diagnostic categories available in Miss Freud's initial publication about the Developmental Profile and a new diagnostic group is formulated and described in that section. In describing the treatment via the mother the chairman of that section developed fully the concept of motherhood as a developmental phase, a concept not only crucial to understanding our particular work but also one that has provided a basis for a new method of evaluation of mothers. Our wish not to omit the special group of children with psychosomatic diseases and our inability to adequately describe and discuss them on the basis of existing diagnostic classifications prompted the formulation of a new diagnostic assessment for those disorders. In each instance these new formulations have been included because they arose at least in part from the clinical material and because they are necessary to the full comprehension of this report.

This description of our research methodology has been included not only to familiarize the reader with our approach to our material, but also to emphasize the following points: (1) the means by which we tried to insure the reliability of our observations; (2) our experiences with the research application of the developmental profile, the modifications necessitated by the age group in our study and the adaptability of the profile to these ends; (3) the factors that led to our including contributions regarding these three areas (diagnostic classification, parenthood as a developmental phase, the psychosomatic disorders) where insights have evolved primarily from the treatment of under-fives via their parents within the setting of the therapeutic nursery school.

After the completion of this manuscript, further administrative changes evolved. Beginning in 1968, the responsibility for the psychoanalytic therapeutic aspects of the program were increasingly assumed by the Day Nursery Association itself and by the newly created Cleveland Center for Research in Child Development.

2. Educational Program

LOIS ARCHER and ELEANOR HOSLEY

In this chapter we will describe the physical setting and educational program of Hanna Perkins School. Because most of the children included in the follow-up study attended the original school, we will portray our original building as well as that to which we moved four years ago. We will next describe our administrative policies, including staffing, lines of communication, selection of cases and application procedures. Then we will present the educational program in sufficient detail to make its philosophy clear, outlining first the general program structure, then focusing on verbalization, its abuses and appropriate educational utilization. And finally we will make comparisons between ours and other nursery schools.

Please note that throughout the material on educational handling certain examples are presented to illustrate technical points. These are in no sense formulas to be used for each such situation, but are rather examples of approaches that might be used with the children dependent on their current, individual situation as discussed and reviewed by the teachers with the head teacher or therapist.

I. PHYSICAL PLANT

Originally Hanna Perkins School was in a small remodeled house. At that time, there was only a nursery school group of 15. In 1961, the school was moved to a building designed for it, and a kindergarten, with a capacity of 15 children, was added.

The teaching staff has always felt that certain advantages of the original building were lost in the larger, more formal structure. In the first building, the children entered through a front door. The front hall served as an office where the director had her desk and telephone. There were two play-rooms downstairs, each approximately 25′ x 15′, with a broad passage between, off which was the bathroom. Adjacent to the front room was a small observation booth. There was a locker room off the front hall and a kitchen on the far side of the locker room.

Upstairs there was a meeting room and a room used for music; both were also used as nap rooms. There was also an interviewing room and a bathroom. The staff thought that having rooms associated primarily with sleeping was a great advantage at nap time. The space, divided into small compartments, offered flexibility in grouping children plus a reassuring homelike atmosphere.

Outside was a small playground and a two-car garage that could be used as a sheltered play area or for carpentry.

In the new building the appearance and atmosphere is more institutional; there are more children, and there is a second floor where there are three therapy offices and the main office of The Day Nursery Association of Cleveland. In addition there is a lower floor with therapy offices and a large meeting room. Nevertheless, every effort was made to construct a building with an air of informality. The nursery school children have their own entrance directly into their room. The lockers are directly by the entry but open to the room so that a dawdler can be watched without a teacher's being in absolute attendance. The kindergarten children also have their own entrance, but it is near the back of the building and the children have to walk up a few stairs and across a hall to reach their room. In the nursery, lockers are marked with symbols, such as a circle, simple enough for a three-year-old to "write" himself to identify his own work. In the kindergarten, children print their first names on locker labels.[1]

The nursery and kindergarten each have a large room, approximately 32' x 38', with an alcove at one end. They share a third room 26' x 26' 10". There is a railed platform in each room whose original purpose was for observation. Because we believed that children should know about observers, it seemed appropriate to have them in the open. In practice, however, the platforms have rarely been used as observation areas. Observers move freely about the room instead. The platforms have become housekeeping units, special places to play games, and have been used for a variety of other purposes.

Each large room has a sliding and folding wooden partition which splits it into two rooms if needed. The cots are set up on one side before lunch.

In the old school there were three toilets and two washbowls. There were no doors to the individual toilets, although the lavatory had a door. A separate toilet on the ground floor was primarily for adults but could be used by a child who particularly needed privacy. In the new building, there are three washbowls and three toilets in the bathrooms, plus a door to each toilet.

In the new school, the doors from the play room open directly onto a sheltered area, which runs the length of the building. Halfway down, running from the door of the center room, is a sheltered walk leading to a sheltered storage and carpentry building.

The director of the school has an office across the hall from the center room. A mothers' waiting room next to it doubles as an isolation room for separating a child who de-

[1] Refer to Appendix for floor plan.

velops symptoms of a contagious illness, and next to the waiting room is a kitchen and laundry. A unit for the exclusive use of the children at one end of the kitchen includes burners, an oven and a sink at child height.

In the old school, during the period of the child's initial adjustment, the mother stayed in an upstairs room. A child was free to go to her and usually could manage it on his own. In the new school the waiting room is halfway down the hall, easily accessible to a child who needs to see his mother during this period.

II. ADMINISTRATIVE POLICIES

Staff

The staff of Children's House is referred to in the Introduction. The staff at Hanna Perkins includes an educational director, a head teacher and two assistants in the nursery school and a head teacher with one assistant in the kindergarten. A therapist serves as Kindergarten Consultant, meeting weekly with teachers about general program. The Administrative and Medical Directors are shared with the Day Nursery Association. There has always been a part-time cook, selected because of her warm interest in children. For example, she is able to have in the kitchen a child who had had to be separated from the group. With guidance, she can handle children appropriately. The maid, custodian, receptionist and other supportive staff are shared under the general administration of the Day Nursery Association.

It has not always been possible to procure appropriately trained people for the teachers' positions. However, three who turned out to be most successful teachers were college graduates whom the school trained on the job. All teachers have regular conferences with the therapists, and weekly seminars under the direction of the clinical director. All young teachers, whether specifically trained in early childhood education or not, require a considerable period of adjustment to the multiplicity of conferences and material discussed.

Hours of attendance are from 9:00 a.m. to 2:30 p.m.

Lines of Communication

Perhaps the greatest practical problem, once the appropriate personnel has been found, is the scheduling of time for the essential communication between them, outside of school hours, and without interfering with programming for the children themselves.

1. Teaching Staff

(a) Weekly teaching staff meetings for program planning and general discussion.

(b) Weekly joint staff meetings to coordinate kindergarten and nursery school planning.

(c) Individual conferences, weekly, director with head teachers (nursery and kindergarten); head teachers with their own assistant teachers; other director-teacher conferences as requested at intervals for specific problems.

(d) Daily parent-teacher-director informal contacts.

(e) Occasional parent-director or parent-teacher conferences.

In the nursery school, these are usually with the director and deal with practical problems. In the kindergarten, there are always twice-a-year conferences with teachers following written progress reports, as well as occasional conferences with either director or teacher on request.

(f) Weekly therapist conferences. This means that before 9 a.m. or after 2:30 p.m., each therapist meets for one-half to one hour with teachers concerning the children whose mother(s) he sees. With 14 therapists working with 30 families, this has meant a minimum of nine hours a week.

(g) Weekly seminar (clinical director with teaching and

therapy staff) for presentation of cases. This lasts one and a half hours.

(h) Written records. Time must be found for daily recording or weekly summaries done by the teachers for each child. In the nursery, each teacher records for five children—in the kindergarten, the division is seven and eight children to each teacher. The recording teacher also writes and presents seminar reports, each summarizing six to eight weeks. She includes the weekly discussions at therapist conferences and the seminar discussions. At the end of the school year, she writes a concluding summary. Records are checked at intervals by head teacher, director or therapist. Photographs of the nursery children are included in their folders, as well as test results (Stanford-Binet and [for kindergarten] reading readiness tests done each spring).

(i) Observers. We have found that occasional observation is insufficient for real learning and we therefore schedule observers mostly on a long-term basis (one morning a week, plus seminars for a six-month period). Also, unless the observer has a supervisor with whom to discuss what he sees, many distortions or misunderstandings result. (Psychiatric fellows and pediatric interns do have weekly discussions with supervisors.) The teaching staff, which has a full work load without visitors, is often baffled and frustrated about how best to help, and also get along with, this rotating population which varies so widely in perceptiveness and personality.

(j) Service staff. Some time is spent in discussion and planning with cook, maid and custodian, although this is not regularly scheduled.

2. Therapist

Besides seeing mothers an hour a week (sometimes every other week in the kindergarten) therapists visit the nursery to observe and meet weekly with the teaching staff, and attend the weekly seminar (1½ hours). Some of the therapists devote time to supervision conferences for observers, also.

3. Parents

Besides daily informal contact with the teaching staff and weekly interviews with therapists, parents have occasional individual conferences with director or teacher at their or the school's request.

Selection of Cases

1. Types of Problems Accepted (see Chapter 5 and Appendix, Table 1)

2. Balance of Groups (age, sex, types of problems)

In both nursery and kindergarten we try to keep a balance between boys and girls. In the nursery, we try to have an age span from three to five years. In both groups, we try to avoid having more than two hyperactive hyperaggressive children, or a preponderance of one type of problem.

3. Parents

Insofar as possible, the ability of the parents to cooperate with the program is ascertained before a child is accepted. However, a really accurate assessment may not be possible beforehand, except for the ability to arrange practical details like amount of time to be devoted, transportation and tuition payments. (See Chapter IV, "Treatment via the Mother.")

Application Procedures

1. Referral Agencies or Persons

(a) *Pediatricians.* Referrals from a few well-informed doctors are sensitive and appropriate. Other physicians, however, refer reluctantly, often only on the insistence of the mother that she must have help. Some pediatricians assure the mother a child "will outgrow this phase", so that an application may not be filed until a child reaches school age.

(b) *Other agencies,* such as Family Service Association, Cleveland Speech and Hearing Center (when speech problems seem emotionally, rather than organically, based), Mental Development Center (when tests show appearance of retardation is probably on an emotional basis), hospital clinics, child guidance clinic.

(c) *Other nursery schools.* More commonly, such referrals tend to be of children with hyperactive or aggressive behavior, which interferes with the school routine, rather than shy or withdrawn behavior, which does not.

(d) *Psychoanalysts.* Occasionally, an analyst working with an adult will incidentally learn of serious problems in the parent-child relationships and make a referral. The therapist's work with the parent can then be focused on behavior and handling of the child and the analysis can proceed in dealing with the parent's personal problems.

(e) *Other parents.* Some people learn of the school through contact with parents whose children are already enrolled. Often there seems to be some reassurance in seeing that socially acceptable people can enter their children in a school for "problem" children and speak positively of it.

(f) *Publicity.* Articles in newspapers or magazines have not usually resulted in appropriate inquiries directly, but have had educational value for referral sources.

2. *Intake Procedure*

(a) *Initial inquiry.* This is usually made by phone and may be brief or long, depending on how clearly the person has understood the school's purpose and his own reasons for applying. In some instances, it becomes clear at this point that the parent has not understood what the school is, or, learning about it, is no longer interested. In others, it seems clear that another facility is indicated (such as child guidance clinic, checking speech, hearing or I.Q., consulting a family service agency or using a day care center). Both for applicants who seem appropriate, and for those about whom we cannot be sure, the next step is an initial interview.

(b) *Initial interview* (usually 1-1½ hours). This is to clarify the procedure and requirements of the school, as well as to obtain information about the presenting problem(s) and developmental history. It may involve one or both parents.

Hopefully, enough information can be obtained in one interview (supplemented by an observation visit) to ascertain whether the application should be presented to the admissions committee. The Admissions Committee consists of the Clinical, Educational, Administrative and Medical Directors and Kindergarten Consultant. Psychological testing or a physical checkup may be requested before presenting the application.

Ordinarily, a morning observation visit of one or both parents to the school (without the child) will follow. Most parents are apprehensive about the "problem" children with whom their child would associate, and worry about how they will look and act. This fear is better quieted by visiting than by words alone. Less directly stated or realized is their concern about themselves, since in coming with a child's problem they have failed to solve, they all feel guilty to some degree. This is true even if a traumatic event outside their control is the main cause. During a first interview, if the parent himself does not bring up these questions or feelings, an attempt is made to state the school's appreciation of responsible parents who can early recognize and come for support, and to stress the amount of cooperative effort (plus expenditure of money and energy) necessary to achieve progress. Parents are also reassured that the school expects to offer a good academic program, careful supervision and strong support to strengthen the family and family relationships, but that the parents are the people who effect changes and are the most important personages in the child's life. They are also told that most parents at first have the idea a stigma is attached (either for them or the child), and the opportunity to discuss this further is offered.

(c) *Child's visit*. For many reasons, a preliminary visit of a child may not be required before acceptance of the application. First, we may already have a report from the referring person who has seen him, or we may have the opportunity of observing him in the school he is then attending. Second, most applications are made far in advance of entrance, and it may be confusing or disappointing to a child to visit and then not be able to attend or have to wait for months. Third, a single visit may be quite unhelpful in learning what the child will be like in the school situation. For instance, some of our most aggressive children have not exhibited this behavior until after some weeks of school attendance. Likewise, an initial visit, or even more, seldom gives us knowledge of which children will interact with each other once they have joined the group. Fourth, visits of a strange child to an established group in attendance are always upsetting to the children to some degree. Since one or more visits will take place for all children before entrance, just those visits alone are enough for the group to absorb, as a rule.

When the child does come, the mother is helped to explain the visit and prepare him for it in advance. From her own visit she can tell him specific comforting physical details and answer his questions more clearly. She can explain the separate entrance door, the individual lockers for clothes and belongings, the various play materials indoors and out, the bathroom, the progression of the morning from indoor activities to music, to juice, to outdoor play. She can speak of the other children, and of the teachers and their names. (First names are used for both children and adults, as more natural in a situation where the young child stays through a day that includes eating and sleeping, and the teachers take on more maternal functions than in a half-day program.) The mother assures him she will remain with him the whole time. More importantly, the mother also tells him the purpose of the school and the reasons for his attendance. It is essential that not only do the parents recognize that they want help with a problem, but that the child understands their concern and their explanation of how the school can help him. Most parents need help to discuss this with their children, many preferring instead to portray the "nice" school, with the fine teachers, playmates and lots of toys. They can be helped to tell a child that Daddy and Mummy have been concerned that he has so much trouble with, say, his worries, and since he's ready to go to school, they looked for one where the teachers understand about helping children with these things as well as playing with other children and toys. It is a school, too, where the mother will stay as long as necessary for the child to be comfortable staying alone. They will explain that mother will have someone to talk to every week, too, so that she can help him more at home.

(d) *Admission committee's discussion—nonacceptance.* If the initial material seems unclear or inadequate, further tests or interviews may be suggested before a final decision on admission is made. If the evidence suggests that the child could not be helped here or the parents' capacities or cooperativeness seem insufficient, alternative referrals are discussed to offer to the parent. Decisions against acceptance may be made also on the basis of group imbalance which would result from a disproportion of boys and girls, too many children with one type of problem, etc. Availability of appropriate therapists is also a factor (see also Chapters 3 and 4).

(e) *Admission committee's discussion—acceptance.* For children who are accepted, notification is followed by making financial arrangements, providing a medical blank to be filled out by the pediatrician, arranging for contact with the therapist and visits of the child.

Eventually, an admitting date is set and plans outlined for a gradual adjustment period. A typical first three days is described below. It should be stressed that starting schedules are individualized for each child and also may be modified as our understanding of the child increases. It helps mothers with their practical planning to have at least a tentative schedule.

First Day—9:15-11:05 a.m. (before stories). Mother stays with child entire time, as much as possible allowing teacher to help him into play, but being there for him to turn to. Before going home, mother shows the child the mothers' waiting room where she will be waiting after juice time next day. He can visit her there as often and as long as he pleases. Second Day—9:15-11:30 a.m. (through story time). Mother stays with child through juice time, then in waiting room. Before leaving, mother, teacher and child speak of schedule for next day.

Third Day—9:15-11:30 a.m. Mother stays in waiting room whole time after child has taken off jacket and settled in. Go over next day's schedule before leaving.

In most cases, the half-day separation will be completed by the end of two weeks (10 sessions). Extension of the day through the afternoon comes as the child seems ready (as decided by joint assessment of teachers, parent, therapist, as well as child's expressed wish, when valid). For this, the mother's return is not necessary. The first extension is for one or two visits in the nap room for the first 15 minutes of settling in and hearing a story, and the child then stays through the afternoon, with his mother coming earlier to visit on the first days. (Further discussion of this important period will be found below, in the section on verbalization.) This is a flexible arrangement, varied according to individual indications.

Mothers have stayed part of the morning for up to nine weeks and children have stayed for half days only for up to nine months before extending the day (particularly young three year olds), although a month would be more usual.

(f) *Introduction to therapist.* Ordinarily the parents are given the responsibility for making their own appointments directly with the therapist, who may see them for a few or many times before the child enters school. However, no child enters before this contact has been established (for further details, see Chapter 4).

(g) *Medical examination.* A medical blank is filled out before entrance and annually while the child attends school. Some of these requirements are specified and checked by the City Health Department. Each family has its own pediatrician. In cases of contagious disease, we check with our medical director concerning notification and recommendations to parents. There is no formal daily "inspection," but each child is greeted individually, with alertness for signs of possible illness or difference in behavior. We give the mother, as closest to the child, a great deal of responsibility for observing and determining preliminary signs of illness as well as reporting them. While all of our children have some of the childhood diseases, colds, viruses, etc., we have often wondered why our attendance record is so high in comparison with other nursery schools and hope some day to investigate this further.

III. EDUCATIONAL PROGRAM

We would hope for all children in our school as elsewhere, to develop healthy personalities, using to the fullest their innate potentials for work, play and constructive relationships and satisfactorily moving through each developmental phase. To this end, we expect to help children become acquainted with themselves and their feelings so that they can learn to cope with and control them responsibly; to offer appropriate academic tasks that build ego strength, develop skills, build up self-esteem and offer gratification at varying levels of ability.

General Structure

We have found that all young children, but especially those with an emotional disturbance, profit from knowing clearly what to expect during the day and their limitations within it. Definite, dependable classroom routines, specific tasks and work standards set in accord with individual developmental abilities, all foster a sense of security which eventually leads to increasing self-discipline and ability to work independently.

During the nursery school period the child is more dependent on the teacher as an extension of a warm adult home relationship and at first has one of the staff teachers as his "special teacher" to turn to for comfort in times of stress. As he progresses through his nursery years he extends his adult relationships to the other teachers, so that by the time he enters kindergarten the teacher-child relationship can have more emphasis on academic learning and less on personal emotional needs.

The kindergarten program is designed gradually to increase expectations and foster intellectual skills, with reading readiness, beginning mathematical concepts and broadening of social studies. Above all, its aim is to foster an attitude of enjoyment of learning and detect any possible blocks to future academic learning so that later school experiences will be successful and gratifying.

Joint staff discussion at regular meetings is necessary to schedule program content and daily routines. While weekly time is set aside for this purpose, many informal discussions must supplement them. Examples of these considerations follow:

1. *Transitions*

The moves from one activity to another present opportunity for disturbance, if not chaos, when not carefully planned for smooth handling and adequate supervision. Such times are clean-up after indoor play before moving on to music or juice periods, dressing to go outdoors, finishing lunch, starting nap, and so on. These must be thought through and carefully supervised to keep the atmosphere pleasant and productive.

2. *Changes in Program*

A walk or a trip are appropriate and included, but are unsuccessful unless planned for in detail.

3. *Visitors-Observers and New Children*

Both are carefully scheduled to avoid too many in one day, since inevitably their presence makes for interaction and some tension, both for children and teachers. Since the children are not observed without their knowledge, they are introduced to visitors and we explain who they are—"a lady who teaches in another nursery school"—"a man who is interested in how children play and what they learn"—"a talking doctor who helps people with their worries"—"a mommy and daddy looking for a good school for their little girl—just as your parents did before you came here." Children visiting with parents in advance of entrance usually constitute a potential threat as rivals and one must be watchful that they be treated politely, even if some coolness is unavoidable, and that our children are helped to recognize and deal with their feelings around the visitors.

4. *Holidays and Parties*

These are kept as simple as possible to make them enjoyable occasions, rather than hotbeds of excitement and exhaustion. Birthdays are celebrated as the dessert part of lunch, with ice cream and birthday cake, singing to the child, favors for everyone and a school present for the child. Other holiday celebrations usually are fitted in as extensions of a regular juice and music time, with extra treats, decorations, special songs, stories, puppet plays or perhaps films or slides of the children themselves. The children help in preparing for these parties, making decorations, learning songs, etc. and know how the time will proceed, rather than being "surprised" by an occasion prepared and carried out by the adults. There always are some children more distractible and excitable than others for whom extra preparation is done in advance and it is planned that an adult will stay close to them.

5. *Handling of Routines*

(a) *Dressing.* This is an extremely important learning situation for the children and one of the most time-consuming, potential sources of irritation for both children and teachers. Especially in late fall, when the whole regalia of jackets, pants, boots and mittens appears with cold weather, extra time and patience must be provided throughout the day until the children have mastered the process. Helping a child to help himself is much more difficult than doing the task for him, and in addition we always have a few children who bring with them a difficulty in this area. Often individual dressing locations must be provided, as well as supervisory help for the child (and perhaps for the parent who is often involved). By the time the child enters kindergarten it is expected that he can carry out all steps independently, though even here an adult presence is needed as a preventive for inappropriate interactions.

(b) *Eating.* There are three eating situations daily—the mid-morning juice and crackers, noon lunch and afternoon milk and cookies. Children learn to serve themselves at each time, with their own appetites to guide their choice and quantity of food. The attitude fostered is one of food and eating being enjoyable, as well as nourishing, with the children themselves choosing and eating for this purpose, rather than to please or displease another person. They themselves must assume the responsibility of making their choices and deciding on amounts, with the requirement that they finish what they have put on their plates. There is no special premium on desserts, nor restriction of extra helpings of any food. The children are encouraged to taste new foods, as a grown-up way of extending their tastes and experience—but there is no struggling over this. Children are expected to use appropriate utensils and table manners. They may sit wherever they wish at snack times, but at lunch tables have regular places (from four to six children with an adult).

The preceding statements outline the goals for the children. Obviously, there will be many different stages of progression. Many children arrive with mild to severe eating problems, which may have served as a focus in a mother-child interplay (just as a focus may be in dressing, toileting, going to bed) and may take a long time to correct, even with the greatest cooperation from parents. A disturbance may be based on an inhibition of aggression (reluctance to chew foods, for instance), general clinging to a more infantile stage (messing with food, eating with hands), a loyalty conflict between school and home, or an internalized disturbance not reachable by educational methods. Behavior at the table may reflect behavior at home (the child who tries to command exclusive attention at all times, or to cause disruption between parents or incite a sibling to misbehavior). Besides stating general realistic standards for everyone, a teacher will be helping the child to become aware of and correct what he is doing through her individual verbalization. (Ex: "What a pity you aren't enjoying this lunch—one day you'll understand better what bothers you and be able to enjoy eating like the others."—"This seems such a restless time for you—

do you find mealtimes hard at home?"—"It's all right to chew food and swallow it."—"I'm going to help you not take too much today and maybe tomorrow you'll remember to decide for yourself."—"Would you like me to remind you for a day or two until you can remember?")

(c) *Toileting.* This is an area where careful planning and individual help leads to eventual independence in self-care, but where many disturbances may be evident. A child is expected to take responsibility for knowing when he needs to to go to the toilet, as well as managing the process independently—but he may enter the school expecting the adult to remind him and demand help each step of the way. Or he may use wetting or soiling to express anger or fear. His sexual curiosity or excitement will often be shown at these times and provision must be made by teachers for adequate supervision and general awareness.

(d) *Rest periods.* Children have their own cots, sheets and blankets, with nap screens between for coziness and privacy. A teacher is with them throughout the period (an hour for nursery school and a half hour for kindergarten). For many children, it is the most uncomfortable division of the day, since feelings of loneliness or worry cannot then be pushed away or alleviated by social or physical activity. It is also a time when teachers feel most strained about how best to supply wise supervision and comfort. Children are not necessarily expected to sleep or lie down, or even remain still if they don't wish to—only to be reasonably quiet and not disturb others who do wish to sleep. They can sit or lie down, on or under their cots, and there is an assortment of nap toys to choose from, including soft animals and rubber cars, books, paper and pencil, paper dolls, puzzles, lacing boards, and various plastic building sets. The teacher reads a story after they've settled in, then plays appropriate records, and is available for giving out more paper, supplying a piece of kleenex, or covering the sleeper. However, even with careful preparation and arrangements, there is never a nursery group without at least one child who cannot tolerate being quiet for the period, who teases the teacher or others, pushes over a screen or destroys materials, starts jumping about or talking loudly. In this school, there has never been less than one, sometimes up to four. This makes necessary separate arrangements—an alcove that can be shut off by a sliding door, the use of a supply room or waiting room. In addition, there must be an adult within call in order that the child not feel abandoned, and the rooms must be cleared of breakable furniture or materials when the child is one who shows his anxiety by being messy or destructive. It is a time of day when the teachers have a great deal else to do preparing for afternoon activities, writing daily notes on children and getting together material for therapist conferences, as well as needing relief from the constant wearing responsibility and pressure of such a group of children. Hopefully, one could give them separate activities, but this scarcely solves the problem of the child whose energies already are directed to getting the exclusive attention of one adult.

At the kindergarten age, this period is much more attractive, partly because many of their initial difficulties have been cleared up or modified, partly because most of these children use this time for avid learning—practicing writing of letters and numbers or beginning reading or making series of extensive, proficient drawings. As in the nursery school, there is a wide selection of materials although at this age soft animals and rubber cars are not offered. The end of a rest period here may be greeted by "Ah, that was too short—I didn't have time to finish."

(e) *Safety.* School should seem a safe and comfortable place to the child, and one guarantee is appropriate safety rules based on his level of development, helping him take on responsibility for himself and considering others. If he disregards the rules he loses the opportunity to use the equipment.

Ordinarily, these limits are welcomed by the children and soon become habitual. This will not be so for an "accident-prone" child, or one whose defiance carries him to do the opposite of what is required, but the majority find them supportive, even while they may test or protest them.

Example 1. Indoors: One does not run—running is for outside. Aprons are used for messy materials or painting. The amount of water in the doll corner is limited to that which can be used constructively (pouring, washing, etc.) Paint, crayons, pencils are used only on paper or materials provided for the purpose. Toys brought from home should be shared, otherwise kept in lockers.

Example 2. Outdoors: Hold on with both hands for seesaw, swings, jungle gym. Only children go down slides, or up on jungle gyms, not toys. Wait for turns—don't crowd or push. Buildings are limited to three blocks high (with double hollow blocks) unless supervising teacher arranges otherwise. Only balls may be thrown; never throw sand, toys, tools. In the pool, no pushing is permitted at any time. No splashing except for "splashing time." Woodwork is done only when a teacher is present. Saws are put down when not in use. Hammers are used only for nails.

Verbalization

A. Katan (1961) in discussing verbalization, cited three points: (1) verbalization of perceptions of the outer world precedes verbalization of feelings; (2) verbalization leads to an increase of the controlling function of the ego over affect and drives; (3) verbalization increases for the ego the possibility of distinguishing between wishes and fantasies on the one hand, reality on the other. In short, verbalization leads to the integrating process, which in turn results in reality testing and thus helps to establish the secondary process.

Before going on to examples of how verbalization might be used, it would be well to consider some potentials for misuse.

Many attitudes and techniques basic in a good program for young children, including observation and understanding of nonverbal communication, are well presented and described in the literature. We have chosen, therefore, to focus specifically upon verbalization about which much less has been written, and have included numerous examples of both its appropriate and inappropriate use.

Parents and teachers often begin the work not fully understanding the appropriate use of verbalization. Mothers are asked to report daily anything different or unusual occurring with the child himself or in the family life which might affect his behavior that day. These might include a restless night, dawdling about dressing, a planned trip to the doctor or dentist, the illness of a sibling or visit of a relative. The mother would give us the facts, how they were handled and perhaps the information that she or the family had been irritable, impatient or overly sympathetic with the child. Such information is helpful in understanding the child's behavior and talking with him during the day. Spilling out many personal feelings at great length does not belong in the school, but should rightly go to the therapist. A mother may do this out of anxiety, out of a need for personal attention, or for other reasons. In any of these instances, the teacher may be able tactfully to call it to the mother's attention and redirect it with—"Have you discussed this with Dr. So & So?"—or excuse herself to tend to a child's need. If this is not sufficient, she can discuss with the therapist a different way to handle it. For example, mothers who themselves have difficulties separating from their children—or the school—may demand extra attention through talking just before vacation periods—or at morning leave-taking. Occasional instances are human and can be handled simply, but a regular pattern would necessitate the therapist's intervention or advice. Some mothers seem to be in competition with their children for teacher attention. Some talk more about another sibling than the one in school.

Teachers, on the other hand, may have difficulty knowing what or how much to say in reporting to a mother, listening or sympathizing (whether with mother or child). For some teachers, the parent may represent their own parents and personal reactions creep in. In general their comments should be factual ones concerning the child's behavior and progress, or any unusual event, without becoming more involved. When the parents look to teachers as the "experts" with "the answers" they may feel forced into offering more than is appropriate of theoretical speculations or hypothetical conclusions.

In relation to the children, teachers must regularly be on guard against using certain expressions repeatedly so that they become devoid of real meaning, for instance, "If you're angry, you can put it into words—you don't have to show it that way," or "You don't have to like it, but I expect you to manage anyway," or "That's too teasey." One tries to avoid a mechanical repetition.

Sometimes teachers who have labored to help a child put into words a real wish, have the idea that as a reward that wish must be gratified. An example was careful planning for a change of places at lunch tables for more appropriate combinations of children. The teachers anticipated that the children involved would have both pleasurable and sad feelings, and all but one child stated these appropriately—("I miss being at S's table but it's nice to be at J's too.") The exception, however, denied anything but great pleasure, yet her eating dropped off and she was restless. The teacher, concerned, inquired in a number of ways what might be wrong; after a week, the child burst out with her wish to return to her previous place. The teacher's first reaction, then, was to allow the return as a reward, rather than consider the situation now available for direct discussion.

Both teachers and parents must guard against a common overestimation of "the magic of words"—the expectation that verbalization will cancel out or more than alleviate painful feelings.

Example 1. One mother was distressed that her child's school behavior the day before the parents left for a week-end trip reflected his objections to being left and feeling lonely—"But I prepared them so well." It was hard for her to accept that the preparation would not cancel out feelings, only help deal with them.

Example 2. Sometimes teachers, who worked on helping a child express in words how much he missed his mother found that he still suffered from the feeling of sadness, even though there was some relief from sharing it in words. The adults themselves found the feeling intolerable if they identified with the child. It is extremely difficult to maintain warm empathy, leaving the feelings with the child, while giving him the support of understanding and encouragement. Often, one's tendency is to *share* the feeling oneself, which then in effect adds to the child's burden and decreases one's ability to support him effectively.

Example 3. Some adults expect that verbalization of anger will dissipate the emotion itself. It is hard to accept that verbalization is often only a step in alleviating this intense feeling, and there is still a great surge of energy to be diverted, channelized, or drained off by acceptable physical means. It is here that one is most challenged to find and develop the sublimations appropriate and effective for each child. In addition, the adult may be struggling with a similar personal problem, which may interfere to some extent with her ability to deal with aggression in the child.

Children as well as teachers and parents often need help in understanding the proper use of verbalizing. A familiar misuse of verbalization is "talking" at inappropriate times and places to get attention. One of the most common instances is the child who has been encouraged to "don't show me—tell me" and picks going-to-bed time or the middle of the night to tell his fears or worries to the parent. In school, this may occur at naptime or when a teacher is busy with another child or children. Such misuse must be pointed out to the child and redirected by the adult.

Often children who begin to express anger in words instead of physical aggression will then turn the words into a form of hurting others. Then an adult must make the distinction between appropriate verbal expression of anger and misuse of words for sadistic purposes. Restrictions are put on the latter just as on physical attacks.

Some children will express with real affect a great fear (perhaps that the father who is away will not return) and then go on to say the same thing without affect, having turned the words themselves into a defense against the feeling. This is sometimes hard to detect at first and the therapist may become aware of it only through the teachers' observations. Afterwards, it may take a prolonged period of working together to effect any real change.

Now here are examples of appropriate educational verbalization:

1. Initial Separation and Adjustment Period

Most parents of our students need a great deal of explanation about the gradual separation period we require for children entering school. Many mothers will accept the time requirement but not be convinced about the necessity or the importance for their own children until later—sometimes very much later. One of the common attitudes we encounter among mothers might be stated as, "Oh, my child won't have any trouble leaving me; he's very adaptable"—with the implication that she would have failed as a mother if her child missed her. This must somehow be countered with the assurance that the better the mothering has been, the more the child is bound to miss her if plunged too suddenly into a place with unfamiliar adults and children for several hours a day.

The mother may go on to describe instances that show how comfortable the child is without her—what poise he displayed when left at a birthday party, or how he never pays attention to her or looks for her when he is playing with friends in the neighbor's yard. In reply, one discusses the difference between a brief, one-time situation, and exposure to an entire new set of children and adults for five days a week. (Even though one suspects, or has some evidence, that the child's behavior at another time has shown he was under too much strain, the mother has usually not developed enough in her work or insight to appreciate this yet.)

Another familiar attitude is the one of "Oh, but he's used to separations—I've left him lots of times"—as though the best preparation for a difficult experience is to have sustained many of them from infancy on. This attitude is also difficult to cope with initially, since full realization would overwhelm a mother with guilt. In such cases we may say in effect that we expect the parent to go along with the gradual adjustment, even though it seems unnecessary to her, as a tactic we have instituted as a form of insurance against later reactions. We will also emphasize the opportunity and value of becoming acquainted with her and she with us during that period, and what a basis for comparison it will give her when she returns to visit later in the school year.

Again, a mother may feel that because a child has been attending another nursery school, he will quickly adjust to a new nursery school, overlooking the fact that the important difference is not in activities and equipment but in a whole new set of children and adults. Indeed, it may be even harder to adapt to the second school when it seems probable (at least to us) that he never satisfactorily resolved the first separation.

Once the mother has accepted the need for staying and her child's feelings of sadness or loss at her leaving, the next hurdle is to have her accept the accompanying feelings of anger. Most mothers find sadness much more acceptable than anger—particularly if the anger is directed toward them. They will interpret excessive clinging as a great love and need, when it may well stem from an intense anger that makes the child too anxious to let the mother out of his sight even briefly. The fear that she will not return or that his anger will cause something to happen to her while she is away is often difficult for mothers to understand. A milder and more common reaction is the child who manages the time alone well but pretends to ignore the mother or protests about leaving when she comes for him. The mother will usually interpret this as an indication of his warm attachment to the school, rather than his "turning the tables" because he's angry that she has caused him painful feelings of sadness by being away.

The mother also needs to be prepared in advance for a child's possible loyalty conflict when he begins to like his teacher—his fear that his mother will abandon him if he extends loving feelings to another adult. The mother can be helped through this period by assurance that only a child who has experienced a warm relationship can make other such relationships, and that the teachers are there to support and supplement, not replace the mother. She can also be given ways of helping her child by telling him such things as, "At home, mothers help you—at school, the teachers do," and, more directly, "We looked for a school where there would be teachers you would like, who could take the best care of you when I'm not with you."

It will not be until a child has established some degree of relationship at school that he will be able to separate from his mother for even brief periods, or eventually to work through the separation successfully. (This process is not always completed by the time the mother leaves the school after the initial period, of course. It may go on for a period of time, or the child may set up a series of defenses against the painful separation feelings that enable him to function temporarily, putting off the real working through until weeks or months later.)

To facilitate this first step, the child is introduced to his "special teacher" when he arrives, with the explanation that all the teachers will be helping him, but this one will spend more time with him; he can ask for her when he needs her, and she will take him back and forth to his mother. (She will also be the main teacher reporting to the mother, along with the director and will be the person keeping daily records and making seminar reports on him.) This teacher will usually continue to seem "special" to the child even after he has moved on to accept more adults and children. Her initial assurances to him will include the information that most children feel a bit shy and strange at first—this is why mommies stay until they feel safe and comfortable. She may explain also that he is not expected to like everyone and everything about the school for awhile; later he'll feel more at home there. In the meantime, we will keep him safe and help him learn new things.

The teachers, too, need this early period of the shorter day at first, with the mother close by, to get to know the parent and child better, to observe the mother-child relationship and exchange information. Each child will deal with the experience differently—one pretending to be big, blustery, unafraid—another hiding behind skirts or even under a table. One hopes gradually to help the child relinquish defenses that can only interfere with his functioning, substituting a healthier, realistic awareness and means of coping with his feelings. If the feelings are bypassed temporarily they remain to be lived through later. He is informed in advance about each new step or change—"Tomorrow your mother will go to the waiting room before juice time. You can take her there if you like and stay as long as you want to." When it comes time for the mother to leave the building for the first time, probably for a 15-minute walk, with her car remaining where the child can see it, we may get an idea of how the child (and the mother) will handle longer separations. He may cling and cry, asking to be taken along. For such an instance the mother has been told to assure him it's all right to cry if he feels badly—the teacher will be there to comfort him. On the other hand, he may feign overcasualness apparently so engrossed in play that he supposedly can scarcely look up to say goodbye. Such children a few days later may reveal their defense by asking to go to the waiting room when the mother is not due back there for another hour.

For extra comfort and support, children may bring special toys or objects from home that provide a physical link while the mother is away. We have had several children who for awhile were comforted by carrying a snapshot of the mother in their pockets. Or a mother may leave a purse or keys in the child's locker as additional tangible proof that she will return. None of these are in place of words, but do serve as reinforcements.

A child may seem to be settled in at school and still be showing extra strain by home behavior, such as irritability, tantrums, wakefulness or bad dreams, return to some wetting, etc. Or there may be a much less noticeable sign. A very common one is inability to recognize his own or other children's identifying symbols, or to remember names of teachers or children. While he is still staying only a half day he may avoid going to the bathroom until he goes home—or he will use the bathroom for urination, but not elimination. When such things are noted, they are brought to the attention of both mother and child and commented upon—"I'm puzzled that you still don't seem to recognize your own symbol."

Then—if this does not change or increase awareness—one might add that maybe there's part of him that still finds being at school pretty hard. The aim is to have the child become aware of and discuss the feeling so he can better deal with it.

Sometimes a child will continue to hold onto his mother in a controlling way after we are sure he is able to carry on without her. After discussing the situation with his mother, we would join in explaining firmly to the child that we think he is really able to manage her leaving, even though it still seems a bit difficult—and that we will expect it of him. He does not have to like it and may protest, but will feel better when it has been accomplished and he finds he can do it.

2. *Anger and Aggression*

A child or an adult will normally—and appropriately— have angry or aggressive feelings in certain situations—when he is hurt, attacked or restrained, or when his rights are infringed upon in any way. Assuming he recognizes his feelings, the main educational task is to help him express or act upon them appropriately.

Some children, however, are fearful to have or recognize such feelings because they are considered "bad" or because their very intensity frightens them. Such a child may need definition and proof of acceptance by the adult before he can gain any control over his feelings. If a child allows another to grab away a special toy without protest, his teacher would ask what he thought of the action. If he "didn't care" she would wonder how this could be—"most children would be angry if their toys were snatched away." If the child progresses to saying he "didn't like it very much," it would be suggested that "you could say so"—with the offer—"If you don't think you can do it alone, I'll be there to help you." A child may be too frightened of retaliation to express his anger at first, but this lays the groundwork for recognition and acceptance of the feeling, with the future hope of a better solution. It is of little lasting help to have the grownup "tell" for him. The relief comes when he can "say" for himself.

Many of the children who act out such feelings most tempestuously are least able to put their angry feelings into words. Somehow the consequences of the uncondoned behavior seems less threatening than the verbal expression of his feeling. For instance, a child may be afraid that putting into words his intense anger at his mother might result in her abandoning him, whereas the temper outbursts only involve her in interaction, however unpleasant that may be. Another child with much separation anxiety admitted after a stormy series of outbursts that she was afraid to say her father was not coming back (he was away on a business trip) because then he really wouldn't. In both instances, the child's belief was in the "magic" aspect of words—that the saying would make them come true. There is the same belief often in the magic power of wishes—stated or unexpressed—with the child convinced that his bad wishes alone ("Go away—I hate you") will produce the reality. This can cause a child great fear and anxiety when someone he loves becomes ill or goes away. Until he learns to recognize and verbalize this fear, his anxiety cannot be relieved. Yet the more intense it is, the more he will need adult help. This may sound relatively simple, yet just explaining this to him might be like an accusation that he must defend against, accentuating his denial. It is usually necessary first to assure him indirectly that such feelings are not uncommon or bad—for instance, "Did you know that lots of children think their angry thoughts might make their mothers leave them?"—or—"I remember a little girl at this school who used to worry that her mother wouldn't come for her when she'd been angry at her." If the child becomes very interested and questioning about such other children, he can often go on to say "once I thought so, too," and in asking about what happened to "the other" learn different ways of handling for himself.

With all the children, the general teacher attitude is one of accepting the feelings (and consequently accepting the child himself with all his negative aspects as well as his positive ones)—but refusing to accept the inappropriate behavior. Nor is it enough to stop the behavior. She has to offer alternates and carry them through. The children will not learn self-control until outer, external controls are firmly established. Thus, the "school rules" and teachers' statements like —"It's alright to be angry, but I won't let you hit him—it hurts too much."—"At this school, we don't let children hurt each other."—"These are rules to protect you and keep you safe." That the children are relieved to have such assurances (even as they may protest or defy) shows up in their play and conversation. For instance, the new child at lunch who announced a discovery—"I know why there's a teacher at every table—so the children won't be naughty." This same child said angrily after a ladder had tipped over—"I thought this place was supposed to be safe." In the kindergarten, a new boy had entered, loudly announcing to a play rival that he was going to bring his gun and shoot him. A seasoned veteran of the nursery school, overhearing, deflated him by her matter-of-fact statement: "No, you can't. The teachers don't let the children shoot each other here."

Children who have acted badly often show their concern that they will be physically punished by becoming extremely anxious when another child has been isolated and is crying. The teacher will pick this up and perhaps mention that he looks worried over the crying—what does he think is happening? Usually he can't say and the teacher goes on to explain the crying ("Because she's sad" or angry or worried or whatever,) and the isolation ("Because it's too upsetting to the other—she'll come back as soon as she feels better.") Sometimes this is enough, but more often there comes a time when direct assurance is needed—"We don't spank or hit children here."—and to the further question of why—"We don't think it helps them learn how to manage better. We try to help them find better ways."

What are those better ways? It varies with individual children, but for everyone the first step is definition by verbalization. Particularly with angry feelings, however, words alone seldom serve to dissipate the aggressive energy. Constructive choices must be offered to drain it off. A very young child may use a "transitional object," like a Teddy bear, to spank and hit. However, by nursery age, one hopes to move on to other methods, such as sawing and hammering, throwing balls, climbing, or jumping rope. If a punching bag is suggested, it is not in the sense of pretending it is the person, but rather as an object to use instead and to practice using skillfully.

Still, we often see a child who has never hit nor in any way defended himself appropriately. His parents want him to learn to hit back if necessary and one is in a quandary about how to reconcile this with the more common admonitions to the overaggressive children. Such strong inhibition of physical aggression is usually accompanied by inhibition of other muscular activity, and building up confidence in those areas can be helpful, as well as reminders that he doesn't have to put up with being set upon. He also needs the feeling he will be protected from being overwhelmed by his own strong feelings if they are ever unleashed—that the teacher will be close by to help if necessary.

3. Instinctual Gratifications

For each developmental phase, specific ways of obtaining gratification will appear. The oral phase brings sucking, the anal phase messing, the phallic phase masturbation, sex play and so on. However, in all children—especially those where there is discrepancy in developmental progress—there will be overlapping, such as undue thumbsucking persisting in a four-year-old. Often the persistence of the instinctual gratification is a reliable indication of where the child is "stuck."

Teachers can help, first, by accepting these manifestations as part of normal development, and then go on to helping the child transform the instinctual energy into sublimated channels for gratification. For instance, a child prone to mess can be given materials like clay and finger paint, but with restrictions on their use, so that he is led to the constructive satisfaction of sculpture and design rather than the more primitive satisfaction of destructive messing. This may take some firm control and verbal definition. "I can't let you mess that way—it doesn't help you. If you can't use the clay to make something we'll find something else for you today." In fact, for some children such materials may constitute such a strong regressive pull that even their supervised use must be postponed until more ego development has been achieved.

Persistent thumb- or fingersucking (other than at times of extra stress or tiredness, as one four-and-a-half-year-old girl returning from a museum trip said, "I suck my thumb so you'll know I'm tired,") can be remarked upon and interfered with gradually and gently if the child can be helped to recognize its inappropriateness and be actively enlisted in moving on to another stage. Just making him feel ashamed or naughty would only increase his need for more infantile comfort.

When the child gets to masturbation and sex play, which in themselves show developmental progress, our aim is again acceptance and management. About masturbation we may say, "Most children enjoy touching themselves like that sometimes, but it is something one does only in private," for instance. Sometimes the child who masturbates compulsively and publicly after such realistic suggestions is showing that he is worried and anxious and may need further prohibition to stop long enough to find out what bothers him. One child would masturbate in a driven way for long periods at nap, getting no relief or satisfaction. He had to be told he must stop now because it only made his worries worse, and that instead of showing his trouble, he should be talking to his mother so she could help him.

Sex play—playing "doctor," wanting to see and touch other children or be touched, wanting to try out "what parents do together," all need adroit supervision to change normal curiosity into verbal questioning and learning without condemning the interest and curiosity itself. Management may mean turning doll corner play from excited exploring of naked dolls to bathing, dressing and caring for them—or admonitions of "just pretend" to the "doctor and patient." Adequate supervision of the bathroom and the small dark houses of tents, blocks or barrels are necessary to avoid physical exploration in lieu of verbal questions, as well as to protect the children from frightening themselves.

4. *Curiosity*

Curiosity is essential to learning, and the child deals with the most profound questions of our lives. It is of permanent importance to encourage curiosity appropriately, not stifle it. This is particularly so in the sexual area, where a child will normally want to explore actively, peek and look. Our problem is to divert the acting into words and to be ready with correct, simple, factual explanations appropriate for the questions, following the lead of the parents who should be the first to answer them. There was a period when parents (teachers, too) thought that if a child were given freedom to look (free access to bedroom and bathroom), his curiosity could be fully satisfied. However, it soon became apparent that seeing was not necessarily comprehending. What he saw was distorted or misunderstood, or he was overwhelmed by his feelings to such an extent that he could no longer see at all. This could lead to the sort of difficulty over seeing and recognizing similarities and differences in other areas that becomes a serious learning block at a later age. One might think, then, that instead of letting him look, one could simply provide a child with all the answers, but that doesn't work, either. First, he has to ask the questions—his own questions—and the answers must be specific for him. In order to ask a question, one must be able to formulate it, and if children could always do this they would already be well along toward a solution. However, they seldom are this clear and their questions may come so indirectly as to be missed completely if one is not alert and sensitive. The therapist can increase the mother's awareness (as well as the teacher's) as they discuss the child's play and words. The teachers can help the mother by bringing their daily observations to her and by pointing out to the child that he should take his questions to his mother—"When you have to crawl under the bathroom door and peek this way, you show me there's something you don't understand. Have you asked your mother about this?"

Parents vary considerably in their ability to talk of birth, death, and the differences between boys and girls, and it is important that teachers do not rush into doing a "better" job than the parent can do. (Occasionally when a mother is so uncomfortable with a subject that she really cannot discuss it, she may turn it over to the teacher, giving her child permission to ask questions at school, and then limiting herself to confirming the answers at home.) It should be clear between teacher and parent just what is said and how to say it in order not to confuse the child with conflicting information. Again, teachers must discuss and be clear among themselves about what they are saying and doing. This involves facing their own attitudes and feelings and reviving childhood feelings and reactions that may be confused or painful. (The most difficult subject for teachers to discuss seems to be masturbation, whereas parents seem to find the most difficult questions those dealing with sexual intercourse.)

The recognition of differences—whether sexual or between material objects—is important for academic learning. Other important differences to be recognized and discussed are racial, cultural and religious ones.

5. *Jealousy and Rivalry*

Children will transfer to the school setting the jealousy and rivalry that originate at home. In diluted form will come the antagonistic feelings and actions toward siblings, the feelings toward mother and father and the attempts to keep one adult exclusively to themselves, which to some degree are natural to all human beings. We expect to help the child recognize and accept such feelings in order to handle them realistically and successfully. Everyone is familiar with plaints like—"You *always* call on him first."—"You *never* do anything for me." —"She always gets the biggest piece." Every child wants to control affairs—as B. and L. once expressed it in this dialogue.

B. "I want to be boss sometimes."

L. "No, I am—"

B. "Well, but you always are and I want to have a turn."

L. "Well, you can be second boss."

B. "No, I want to be first boss."

L. "We can have two first bosses you know."

B. "But I want to be the first boss who tells the other first boss what to do."

There is a delicate balance between making a child ashamed to show his selfish wishes—so that he feels "bad," denies them, but shows them indirectly—and recognizing and handling them fairly and adequately. Parents may say, "Of course, you love your brother and want to share with him," or go to the other extreme of stressing the negative: "I know you hate your brother and don't want to share." But some-where between comes helping the child with, "Part of the time you enjoy playing with Tommy and sharing with him. You don't always have to like him, though. I do expect you to share fairly even when you don't."

The child who constantly tries to separate the parents and keep one to himself will do the same thing with teachers. Here it is often easier to define and modify the behavior. Teachers may say, "I notice that the time you want to tell me things is usually when I'm busy talking to one of the grown-ups. Maybe we could decide on a different time for you so you wouldn't have to interrupt." Linkage to the home situa-tion ("Sometimes children like to keep a mummy or daddy to themselves instead of having them talk to each other or do things together") is usually made later, after the child's awareness.

Teachers must be constantly alert to avoid indicating there are certain situations or children they can handle better than another teacher, since children will quickly sense and use this feeling to divide authority. Regular communication, com-paring of observations and joint decisions about guidance are invaluable. Inevitably, teachers will relate differently to different children and children themselves will often differ in behavior depending on the situation. These differences must be compared so that each teacher can see the total pic-ture and not judge only on the basis of her own contact or observation.

6. Discipline

When parents are asked what they have found effective in disciplining their children, they often reply in terms of physi-cal punishment—spanking or smacking. But frequently they go on to say, "It doesn't seem to work—he just goes back and does it again." In many cases, too, the older child who is spanked simply transfers these physical attacks to his younger sibling. This type of punishment for "bad" behavior may be accompanied also by rewards for "good" behavior—or bribes. Our interest at school is in making discipline a means of learning, with a clear cause and effect relationship understandable to the child so that gradually he will take over his own limits and controls. Initially, we try to define rules and limitations and the reasons for them, so that the children are clear about what is expected of them. Aggressive or destructive behavior thus might result in the child's being admonished, removed, or assigned some repair work. Disciplinary measures *must* be tailored to the individual age and child. For one child, being barred from the playground for 10 minutes might be enough. For another child, it would have no effect at all. For still another, being restricted to one area for a period would serve the purpose. A young child only gradually develops a broad time concept, and cause and effect must come close together for this understanding. A restriction should not persist so long that it seems "forever."

When children are destructive, every attempt is made to find a way they can make restitution. It is not always easy. A broken object sometimes cannot be repaired, and perhaps cannot be replaced. It is not our aim to burden a child with excessive guilt, but to show him realistic methods to alleviate it. This includes restitution in words—not the adult's requirement "tell me you're sorry"—but a planning with the child of what he may say, sincerely and voluntarily, to a person he has hurt.

In the case of the very aggressive child, it may not be possible to avoid some physical handling or restraint, yet this may be the very thing that will make him more fearful and wild—or that will prove stimulating and exciting for him. The teacher is responsible not only for protecting the child from hurting himself, other children or property, but for seeing to it that she is not hurt in the process. She is dealing with a child who is already overwhelmed by his own loss of control; if he can then really hurt the adult, it confirms his fear of the danger of his own strong feelings. Consequently, teachers are taught how to carry a child in such a way that he is not hurt but is unable to land a blow or bite. He is assured that she will be able to control him until he can control himself and that she will hold him only until he is able to do so. For some children, it is enough to be in a room by themselves until the outburst is over, with the teacher waiting nearby. But others may need to be restrained from hurting themselves or furniture, walls and windows. If it is necessary to hold a child, we try to do so firmly, and with a minimum of physical stimulation. Seemingly this is best done if a teacher can hold a child's shoulders from behind while he is sitting down. In this way he cannot hit, kick, bite, scratch or spit at her, or destroy property. It is not a time to talk or reason with a child, although the teacher may assure him that when he feels calmer she will be able to talk over with him what made him feel so very upset.

In every case of misbehavior, the goal is to help the child find and use better methods in the future, although the immediate preoccupation may be with practical handling. Underlying causes for the behavior may not be clear to teacher or child until months later, but different coping or controlling methods can be worked on in the meantime.

The feelings which produce the behavior are not con demned *per se*—only the behavior itself, and the educational work comes in offering other acceptable outlets for the energy.

IV. SIMILARITIES AND DIFFERENCES BETWEEN THIS AND OTHER SCHOOLS

Nursery schools have proliferated in recent years. They vary widely in purpose and function, in hours and days open, in auspices, size, staffing, kinds of children accepted, and in educational method and theory.

There is a considerable mixture in purpose and function. Except for so-called "play schools" run by nonprofessionals, most nursery schools, even rather poor ones, are inclined to believe they have something of a therapeutic or preventive purpose. This is evidenced by the common feeling of nursery school teachers that they have failed when they have to refer a child for help. Perhaps this is partly because nursery schools in this country were from the start frequently associated with the study of child development. Far greater attention has always been given to individual needs than in regular school. It is not surprising that in the development of nursery schools there was very early interest in preventive mental hygiene and the treatment of incipient disturbances. In fact, the two trends developed almost simultaneously. For example, the Day Nursery Association of Cleveland set up its own behavior clinic in 1926 not long after nursery school education had become an integral part of its program. Although so far as we know therapeutic nursery schools, whose primary function was the education and/or treatment of children with emotional problems, did not evolve until the '40's, nursery schools, including day nurseries, were sometimes used as therapeutic milieux before that time. Many still are. In Cleveland, the centers of the Day Nursery Association have continued to be used occasionally for children with particular problems. Although the behavior clinic had to be given up during the Depression because of lack of funds, psychiatric consultation was always available. The Jewish Day Nursery in Cleveland also takes children with emotional problems. A few day nurseries across the country have functioned in this way, usually under the guidance of a child guidance clinic or an individual psychiatrist.

For example, Margaret Lovatt (1962) writing about the West End Creche in Toronto, Ontario, describes a very carefully worked out procedure for working with children diagnosed as autistic. This institution limits itself to introducing one such child at a time into their day nursery which otherwise serves normal children. He is assigned a special teacher so long as he needs one. In general, even the best day nursery whose primary purpose is providing day care is not set up for helping more than an occasional child with a severe problem. However, day nurseries that are well staffed with trained teachers and caseworkers can sometimes be helpful to children who would not be considered suitable for our school. For example, a four-year-old boy who did not talk and would only play by himself was originally referred to the therapeutic nursery school. He was not accepted because of the violence and instability in the home which made parental cooperation impossible. The father, intermittently unemployed, deserted at intervals. A day nursery could offer him the protection from the home atmosphere which he needed for long hours each day, a good educational program and guidance for the mother. He was eventually able to enter public school and make a reasonably successful adjustment.

Because of the lack of resources for young children with problems, nursery schools have been used indiscriminately by pediatricians and others who hope that a "nursery school," regardless of its function, staffing, or abilities, will help the child grow out of his problems. "He needs to play with other children," they say. Slow learners, nontalkers, aggressive children, and very shy children are frequently referred to schools. Nursery schools are not always aware of their limitations and sometimes consider themselves therapeutic when they are not.

Hence, one cannot differentiate our school or any other therapeutic school solely on the basis of its goals, its hours, or of its educational philosophy. There are other schools with similar educational philosophy and program. For example, ours is similar to that of the School for Nursery Years in Los Angeles, whose program is described in the pamphlet "Practices and Beliefs." A number of others emphasize the importance of the verbalization of feeling along with the provision for a rich educational program. There are, however, also schools with very different educational programs. Some schools try to resolve problems by giving children the opportunity to act them out. A dummy to hit, and clay and paint to smear are given major emphasis. Rules may be minimized and permissiveness extreme. At the other end of the line are schools that are rigid in structure and whose goal may be intellectual learning in a narrow sense. Many have grown out of the current emphasis on the importance of science and knowledge. They are to an extent a reaction against the overpermissive, somewhat intellectually sterile nursery schools that existed in many places. The revival of Montessori schools is another reaction. Here the emphasis is on the child's ability to be self-directing and learn from carefully thought out equipment and materials. Creativity and interpersonal relationships are stressed to a lesser degree.

While there is no sharp distinction between our educational program or the children served and those two factors in certain other good nursery schools, we do differ in several ways from a number of therapeutic schools. For example, we accept children with a wide range of problems. Some accept only those with a severe disturbance—for instance some of the groups of the Putnam School in Boston, which has done a great deal of work with the atypical child. Their program is necessarily affected by the degree of disturbance the children have. Pfeiffer (1959) has described the program at Bellevue and has stressed that it is conditioned by serving children disturbed enough to be in a hospital and already separated from their families, who come for diagnosis and short-term treatment. Schools that serve children whose primary problem is mental retardation, such as the Mental Development Center in Cleveland, have to adapt their actual program to the special characteristics of the slow learner. Other schools, similar to ours in some respects, may have experimented with special techniques not used by us. For example, Alpert has described therapeutic-educational techniques employed at the Nursery of the Council Child Development Center, called guided regression, persistent stimulation, dosing and structuring of new experiences. Although there may be elements in common with some of our techniques, we have never used anything like guided regression or corrective identification. In this, a special teacher helps the child retrace his life experience and through a corrective relationship achieves a more healthful starting point for new experiences and achievements. This work was described by Augusta Alpert (1954). A number of centers, therapeutic and other, use various forms of play therapy. Generally this is done by a caseworker. We have not used play therapy. Several schools have experimented with different kinds of group therapy sessions for parents, but we have not.

To summarize, we consider that the special features of our school are the separation of education and therapy and the close teamwork of teachers and therapists in conjunction with treatment via the mother.

3. Treatment via the Mother

ERNA FURMAN

I. HISTORICAL BACKGROUND AND REVIEW OF THE LITERATURE

Treatment of the under-five via the parent was first practiced and described by Freud (1909) in the case of Little Hans. Subsequently the interest of child analysts in this method of treatment abated and did not revive till the special conditions during and after World War II brought a new need and opportunity. In Holland A. Katan (1947) described a mother's analysis of her young child. In England M. Ruben (1946) and A. Bonnard (1950) gave accounts of similar cases. In this country L. Rangell (1950) recorded the parent's treatment of an older boy. During this period also, several authors reported on their work with mothers of young children. M. Ruben and R. Thomas (1947) and, later, M. Ruben (1960) oriented their consultations toward helping mothers with the education of their children's drives and feelings. E. Buxbaum (1946), K. Friedlander (1947) and L. Jacobs (1949) used work with the mother specifically to handle and treat developmental difficulties in children under five years of age. D. T. Burlingham (1951) used case material to compare the understanding of the mother-child relationship gained during advisory work with the mother with that gained during the child's later analysis.

It was A. Katan's interest and experience with the work of mothers with their young children that led her to organize

64

the Cleveland center (see Chapter 1). The therapists on her staff had been trained in methods of work with mothers in the Hampstead Child-Therapy Course.

Since many theoretical and practical aspects of treatment via the mother were not known, the early years were spent in gaining extensive experience with different cases and in comparing and evaluating the data under A. Katan's direction. J. Benkendorf and A. Rolnick met with us regularly to discuss our ideas and eventually reported them in writing (1955).[1] Some years later we described the method of treatment of the under-five via the parent, summarizing our experiences and conclusions up to that time (E. Furman, 1957). Since then all therapists in our center have worked together to contribute a better understanding of the subject through their clinical experience. They have shared and discussed their experiences in the weekly nursery school seminars and have made them available in the context of this follow-up study by constructing the personality profiles and special summaries for all their cases (see Chapter 1).

The methods used in work with mothers were from the start related to theoretical concepts. The mother-child relationship has always been important in psychoanalytic theory. Many authors have attempted to investigate and understand different aspects of it at different genetic levels. Those writers come closest to the thoughts expressed in this article who have considered the parent-child relationship from the point of view of its effect on the parent's development. Thus, G. L. Bibring (1959) discussed pregnancy as a developmental crisis in the life of the woman. R. W. Coleman, E. Kris, and S. Provence (1953) described the development of the mother's attitude in terms of an interaction between her personality makeup and her actual experiences with her child. T. Bene-

---

[1] Some of the thoughts contained in this paper remained valid in the light of later experience and are incorporated in part III of this chapter with the kind permission of the co-authors.

dek (1959) spoke specifically of parenthood as a developmental phase.[2]

The concept of parenthood as a developmental phase was stimulated by the clinical work with parents of children in all age groups, including work with pregnant mothers. It derived, however, primarily from the observations of and experiences with mothers and young children in Hanna Perkins Nursery School. It has been applied mainly in the work with parents of under-fives. Theory and practice thus are intimately linked and influence each other.

II. THEORETICAL AND CLINICAL CONSIDERATIONS IN THE ASSESSMENT OF PARENTS

In our efforts to help a child by treatment via the parents, the mother is the most important partner in the triangular teamwork of parents, therapist and teachers. The work with the parents aims at: (1) helping the parents as educators (furthering all aspects of ego development, lending age-adequate support to the child's ego in dealing with internal and external demands); (2) enabling the parents to help their child with conflicts between the child and his environment (external conflicts); (3) helping the parents to do therapeutic work with their child when the child has internalized conflicts, whether these are phase-adequate or not. The successful pursuit of these aims also implicitly results in an improved and strengthened parent-child relationship.

Obviously, not all parents can cooperate in achieving these goals and not all children can be reached effectively in this way. Selection of suitable children has to take place. How this is done is discussed in detail elsewhere. May it suffice here to repeat that those children are selected for treatment

---

[2] T. Benedek's article came to my attention only some time after we had completed this paper. We concur with her concept of parenthood as a developmental phase but, since my concept is based on different clinical material, we note different manifestations and mechanisms in describing it.

via the parent whose disturbances are diagnosed as categories I, II, or III. For use of work with parents in cases belonging to other diagnostic categories see the section on special goals below.

Assessment of Parents

The assessment of suitable parents is less clearly categorized. The following formulations do not represent a circumscribed theory but rather our current working principles in assessment of parents.

It must be stressed that we are not trying to assess—or work with—the parent's total personality but only with the aspect that functions as a parent and manifests itself in the parent-child relationship. We ourselves were puzzled at first by this differentiation and apparently arbitrary division within a personality. But experience repeatedly showed us that the overall functioning of a person's personality did not necessarily affect his functioning as a parent in all respects. Some well-adjusted adults proved to have severe difficulties as parents, while others with considerable personality disorders were able to progress and develop as parents, and often could keep their neurotic traits or symptoms out of their relationship with their child. This became more understandable when parenthood was viewed as a maturational phase.

Parenthood as a Developmental Phase

As in other developmental phases, marked inner changes occur and bring new elements to bear on the individual's intrapsychic balance and adaptation. As adolescence particularly shapes the person's adult sexuality, so the experiences of conception, pregnancy, birth, and care for the young child shape the adult's role as a parent. It is a period of great flux and mental flexibility. The parent's early experiences of being mothered and fathered come closer to consciousness, frequently stimulated by, and interacting with, the daily experiences with his own child. Similarly early infantile fantasies of being a mother or father are reactivated and brought in line with the current realities. A new aspect of identification occurs with his own parents, and additional new figures are sought to supplement, and coordinate with, these more basic identifications. In integrating these various factors many trial adaptations are made, and eventually a flexible equilibrium is established.

In parenthood as a developmental phase principles apply similar to those of other periods of maturational change. Previously existing personality makeup strongly influences the course of development but does not solely determine it. The maturational forces of the phase itself and the individual reality experiences during the phase play an important and usually unpredictable part. The preparenthood personality may inhibit the maturational forces so that no phase-adequate manifestations can occur. The difficulty is similar to that of the disturbed latency child who does not reach the maturational phase of adolescence. Such an individual cannot truly function as a parent. In other cases the preparental personality may be of such a pathology that the maturational phase can only extend the old conflicts instead of influencing and rearranging existing attitudes. Again there is the parallel of the teenager whose adolescent urges become an inextricable part of his previously established neurosis. Similarly, with some disturbed adults the new experiences of parenthood are only drawn into the orbit of their neuroses so that their functioning as parents and their relationship with their child is patterned solely on their pathology and cannot be influenced by new urges and realities.

In the population at large such instances of pathology are not too common. For the most part, adults are able to enter the developmental phase of parenthood and come to terms with the new inner and outer demands. To these adults the reactivation of their own early experiences and infantile

fantasies serves as an essential and helpful background towards achieving a new inner equilibrium.

The phase of parenthood is probably never quite completed, but its strongest urges and most intense inner struggles occur in its earliest years, when the child is an infant and
under-five. While the child's transition into latency and later
into adolescence always creates the need for new inner read-
justments, it is in the earliest years of parent-child relationship that the parent's inner flexibility is at its peak and the
attempts at a new realignment of inner forces are most intense. It is therefore not only the time when early experiences of and fantasies about mothering and fathering gain a
new importance, but also it is the time when real experiences
with the child himself, or with outsiders concerned with the
child, are most influential. The first five years of life, the
period of greatest emotional growth for the child, is also the
most important one for the parent's development. The child
changes rapidly and presents the parent almost daily with
new demands and reactions. All of these affect the inner life
of the parent and usually require an immediate reaction on
his or her part. It is to be expected that during these years
the parent sometimes veers either to the extreme of drawing
solely (even inappropriately) on his own earlier experiences
and conflicts or to the other extreme of only acting upon the
advice (again often inappropriate) of hastily sought new
models of identification. Most of these trial adaptations to
parenthood are soon discarded in favor of a more reality-
adapted selection and integration of parental attitudes. It is
during this period of rapid shifts that a parent's capacity to
establish himself as a parent can be most fruitfully influenced
—and most readily jeopardized.

The maturational forces as well as the actual experiences
of parenthood are different for men and women. The mother,
through her bodily closeness to the fetus, baby, and young
child, and through her constant exposure to the child's be-

havior, is much more intimately affected by all the internal and external forces. Fathers receive much less immediate bodily and psychological stimulation during the earliest years with their child. Our aims in assessing, and working with, mothers and fathers therefore differ. For the purpose of our work it is essential that the mother have entered the developmental phase of parenthood, while this is not so essential in the father.

The fact that the mother of the under-five is herself in a developmental phase makes it possible for the worker (therapist or teacher) to address himself to that part of her that is distinct from the rest of her personality. The functioning of the mother as a mother implicitly carries certain important qualifications for her work with her child: She is internally unusually flexible and sensitively attuned both to her own early experiences and feelings and to those of her child, more so than at any other time in her adult life. Further she has an intimate lifelong acquaintance with her child and is almost constantly in his presence, able to observe, understand and respond to him. By contrast, therapists and teachers often feel themselves handicapped by lack of intimate knowledge of a young child and by the time limits of their contact with the child.

Our primary task in assessing a mother's ability to pursue the aims of working with her child is to assess whether she has entered the developmental phase of motherhood at all, and if so, whether her flexibility is grossly and rigidly impaired by her previously established character structure.

From initial contacts it is difficult enough to establish whether the mother is functioning in her maternal role. It is much more difficult to assess how grossly and inflexibly her functioning is impaired. In the cases studied, the overt pathology of the child and of the maternal handling told us little about that, in fact they were often misleading (see part V of this chapter). We have therefore tried to investigate other areas of motherhood for diagnostically helpful signs. These may be grouped under two major headings—motivation and capacity for identification.

Motivation

One hallmark of self-acceptance as a mother is the feeling of responsibility for the child's bodily and mental welfare. A mother feels badly when her child's development is impaired. Even in cases where unavoidable reality produced the pathology and where the mother bears little or no blame, she feels responsible for mitigating the difficulty. In cases of emotional disturbances the healthy mother always feels guilty. This guilt provides a stimulus for her to work towards the child's improvement even at the cost of considerable inconvenience. The availability and motivational force of a mother's guilt is one of the most important diagnostic clues to assessing whether a mother is succeeding in her adjustment as a mother and whether she is sufficiently motivated to work on the child's difficulties consistently and for a long period.

While the mother without feelings of guilt and personal responsibility is developing neither as a mother nor sufficiently motivated for the arduous work ahead, it is equally true that not all types of guilt are of positive value for the work. Various forms of unconscious guilt are very severe taskmasters to the mother's ego but are either unavailable to her as motivators for work or actually strive to undo any success, e.g., unconscious guilt which forbids the mother to function as a mother, or guilt which forces her to fail with her child. Similarly appropriate guilt and responsibility differ from feelings of narcissistic injury, though this may be difficult to distinguish. A mother may feel most concerned about her child's trouble and the part she played in its etiology but if her concern is predominantly one of hurt self-esteem it will not enable her to seek help and to work effectively, e.g., she may need to hide all or some of the child's

symptomatology or history to avoid exposing herself un-
favorably, or she may vociferously and repeatedly lament her
"sins" without changing the situation, or she may be unable
to bear improvements through the work because they would
only prove to her how much she had done wrong in the past.

Thus the important point to assess is the presence of available motivating guilt and its relative prevalence over other
forms of pathological guilt or narcissistic injury.

The feelings of narcissistic injury, however, are not altogether pathological or unhelpful to a mother. A certain measure stems in part from the mother's ties to her child—a blend
of narcissistic and object libidinal cathexes. In the course of
the phase of motherhood the child is invested with varying
degrees of narcissistic and object-libidinal ties. In general,
the younger the child, the greater is the narcissistic investment which is at its height during the pregnancy and the first
weeks of the baby's life. The importance of this for the care
of the baby is well-known. Only the extension of the mother's
narcissism on to her baby makes it possible for her to bear
the hardships of the child's round-the-clock demands and to
enjoy responding to them. As the child grows, the mother's
relationship to him changes in that he is increasingly regarded as a love object in his own right. The under-five's
physical and emotional dependency requires the mother to
keep considerable amounts of narcissistic libidinal cathexes
in her relationship with her child during these years, yet
she needs to have invested sufficient object libidinal ties in
him to be able to interact with him as with a love object
when his developing personality needs it. In her development as a mother she makes continuous adjustments in the
distribution of object and narcissistic libido in her relationship with her child. This distribution needs to be not only
age-adequately adapted to the child's growth but also needs
to be flexible enough that immediate changes can occur in
response to the child's day to day status. For example, when

the four year old becomes physically ill, when he is unusually tired, or when he is otherwise under stress the mother's cathexis of him has to readjust itself at once in favor of an increased balance of narcissistic ties so that she can meet his needs adequately on his currently regressed level.

In the mother-child relationship, both the distribution and flexibility of the mother's libidinal ties are of great importance in assessing her development as a mother. They furnish valuable motivation for her wish to seek help for her child and to work effectively toward his improvement. From her narcissistic cathexis comes the wish to help that part of herself which is invested in the child and to persist even if her efforts entail much inconvenience; his suffering is hers and in helping him she truly helps herself. From her object libidinal ties come her feelings of sympathy and empathy for him and her altruistic wish to do well by him; in helping him she helps a most beloved person.

In one sense, the intensity, balance and flexibility of libidinal cathexes determine the extent to which the mother has achieved equilibrium in her maternal development. The complexities and interdependencies of the narcissistic and libidinal ties to the child are so great that minor transitory disharmonies occur frequently during the child's early years. It is only in cases of considerable pathology, though, that the cathexes are either of themselves insufficiently strong or are rigidly maintained in an inappropriate balance, leading to extremes in either direction.

Capacity for Identification

If then we explore the nature of the mother's guilt and of her libidinal ties with her child in order to assess whether her motivation for the work is sufficiently healthy and strong, we have to look in another area for her potential to work consistently with the staff and to be able to identify with the means and aims of the work. In the long run, it is the mother's ability to make such an identification which will not only enable her to deal with the child's current problems but will best insure her ability to meet his needs in the years ahead.

In the above brief discussion of motherhood as a developmental phase it was mentioned that one of its most important aspects is for the woman to achieve a newly integrated concept of herself as a mother. This is based in part on the experiences of being mothered, the infantile fantasies of being a mother, current new aspects of identification with her own mother as a mother, real present experiences with her own child's behavior and personality, and events specifically connected with him (e.g., type of delivery, nursing experience, pattern of motility, times of illness, individual physique). In addition a mother makes new partial identifications with persons who affect her attitude to her child (friends, neighbors, other mothers, books, magazines, nurses, pediatricians and therapists and teachers). If the mother is sufficiently flexible she will be able to integrate such supplementary identifications in her total image and ideal of herself as a mother. If she has not entered the phase of maternal development she can usually use therapists, teachers, and others, only as substitute-mothers for her child, i.e., people who take over her role. If she has entered the developmental phase but it has become a sole field for the play of her earlier conflicts then she would again be unable to make the necessary integrated selective partial identifications. Instead, the work and the staff would be used as a further area for extending her neurosis. This can lead either to an inability to identify with the means and aims of the work or, by contrast, to a total unselective identification which would be employed defensively against inner conflicts and therefore could not serve the healthier purposes.

It is important to distinguish between the mother's ability to establish a "working relationship" with the therapist and teachers on the one hand, and her capacity to identify with the methods and goals of child care and treatment which the center represents.

The ability to establish and maintain a "working relationship" means that the mother attends weekly interviews regularly, that she uses these sessions essentially for a discussion of matters relating to the child, and that she treats these weekly discussions as a part of a continuous working process. Such a "working relationship" makes no suppositions as to the mother's positive or negative feelings toward the worker, her ease or difficulty in working, or the nature of her relationships in general.

The mother's capacity for identification with the principles of the work manifests itself often only after a lengthy period of work. Yet from the time of the first contact, the staff conveys emphasis on the need for a working relationship as the framework for the common task. The mother's ability to identify with the aims and means of the work does not primarily derive from her relationship to the therapist. Rather it stems from the mother's gradual experience of understanding and helping her child, and from the deep satisfaction this usually brings her.

This approach contrasts with that practiced in some other centers, which use the concept of concentrating on the establishment of a positive relationship between mother and worker, and basing the work primarily on such a relationship. To us it is not important whether the mother likes the therapist, but rather whether she is willing and able to work as part of a team toward the same goals. It has been very striking to see that many mothers were genuinely friendly with the therapist, yet were unable to make the therapist's methods and aims their own. By contrast, some mothers who maintained conflictual and difficult relationships with the therapist could very successfully identify with the principles of the work and integrate them appropriately. The latter mothers profited most in their development as mothers and could help their children best, although they taxed greatly the skill of the staff in working with them.

It should also be stressed that the capacity to identify with our approach is not to be confused with an acceptance of it. Many mothers accept the psychoanalytic orientation of the center, yet are quite unable to identify with it. Actually, acceptance of principles at the time of intake is, in our experience, more often a negative than positive prognostic sign. Other mothers have not only initial but repeated doubts and misgivings but are able to make our methods and aims their own after closer scrutiny, discussion, experience and reevaluation.

In summary, it is our diagnostic aim to select mothers who are actively in the developmental phase of motherhood even though they are experiencing difficulties in coping with its inner and outer demands. In order to estimate the relative seriousness of their difficulties compared with their underlying developmental potential we focus our attention on two areas: (1) the appropriateness and degree of motivation, as seen in the nature of the mother's guilt feelings and in the intensity, balance and flexibility of her libidinal ties to her child; (2) appropriate flexibility in her concept and ideal of motherhood as seen in her ability to establish a "working relationship" and to identify with the methods and goals of child care and treatment which the center offers.

Mothers in this group are generally not only able to work successfully toward helping their child but experience the additional gratification of maturing as mothers in the process of the work. The latter factor is not among our primary aims but becomes in time an important incentive for the mother to carry on the work and greatly benefits her children. It enables her to continue her work with the particular child in the future and to apply her new maturity to the upbringing of his siblings.

Role and Assessment of the Father

It is a very positive prognostic indication when the father shows those characteristics which were discussed as essential for the work, i.e., having entered the developmental phase of fatherhood, having a measure of the appropriate motivation and necessary flexibility in his concept and ideal of himself as a father. While these characteristics need not be present to the same degree or in all areas, it is important that the father also be able to support the mother's efforts in her work. This sounds simple but actually implies quite a mature relationship to his wife as the mother of their children. This contrasts sharply with a relationship that only accepts her as a wife or one that leads to competition for the maternal role, or to sibling rivalry with his own children.

The father with few difficulties as a father and with the capacity to support his wife plays an important part. Primarily this shows in his emotional and sometimes physical help in backing and encouraging the mother—a quiet but vital role. He contributes further in his educational and emotional paternal relationship with his children, and by sharing his valuable observations of his child with his wife, and periodically, with the therapist and teachers. In three areas he participates in the work itself: (1) by adjusting his handling of the child so as to best support the mother's work, (2) by discussing with the therapist specific areas of his relationship with his child, (3) by supplementing the mother's role in occasional instances where she may find it too difficult, temporarily or permanently (e.g., discussing some subjects with the child, or taking the child for medical treatments). Such instances of involving the father in the care of the child require special preparation of the child and cooperation from both parents.

Since the physical and emotional care of the very young child is largely the mother's task, the father is not expected to involve himself intimately. He keeps in touch through the mother and through occasional interviews with the therapist. These interviews may be for the father alone or jointly with the mother. They occur at about monthly intervals, except when specific aspects concerning the father are to be discussed. Then either the father or the mother or therapist may initiate a few additional interviews.

In every case, however, at least initial contact is established with the father and minimal contact maintained. This not only enables the center to assess the father and help him maintain his support for the work, but also aids in spotting those instances where a mother's difficulties are erroneously attributed by her to the father and therefore escape understanding.

Experience has shown that some mothers can work successfully in spite of one or another area of considerable difficulty in the father, e.g., little or no support from the father, rigidity of concept of paternal role, little ability to function as a father, rivalry over the mother with the children. Other mothers find this much more difficult; it sets limitations to their work apart from directly affecting the children's development. There are, however, cases where the father is seriously lacking in all the essential attributes and where the mother's work irritates his conflicts to such an extent that his difficulties manifestly increase or lead him to active opposition to her efforts. In these instances even a mother with great potential cannot work fruitfully.

Among the group of children treated via the parents who were studied in this follow-up project, the fathers did not appear to affect basically the children's progress, either positively or negatively. A number of fathers did not wish to cooperate with the mother's work and several others suffered from personality difficulties which, against their will, precluded helpful cooperation. Yet the summary study showed that children with both types of fathers either improved or failed to do so, depending on their mother's work with them and the nature of their own disturbances. This may be due to the relatively minor degree of paternal uncooperativeness or disturbance in this selected group—the fathers, after all, did not actively stop the work. In several cases fathers were unusually helpful in not only supporting the mother's work and improving specific areas of their relationship with their children, but also in supplementing the mother's role in certain instances. Some children improved, some did not. The figures did not indicate a trend in either direction and the individual summaries did not attribute the main responsibility to the fathers.

III. TECHNIQUE OF WORKING WITH THE MOTHER

Initial Stage

The intake procedure provides considerable material for assessing the mother in her maternal role. The reasons for referral, the child's symptomatology and personal history, the visit to the nursery school, all are equally useful in assessing the child's personality and the mother's functioning as a parent. With experience, it has been increasingly possible to recognize initially mothers who have failed to enter the developmental phase of parenthood and who may therefore be unwilling or unable to work actively with their child in our setting. In some instances it has even been possible to diagnose mothers for whom motherhood has become an extension of their previously established conflicts. But these cases are few. The admissions committee has been wary of making definite judgments about a mother's capacities. The reason lies partly in lack of knowledge, but also partly in the all important fact that the current status of a mother does not necessarily provide clues as to her potential for change. Based on initial observations, it has often not been surprising to see a mother fail to develop. Time and again, however, we have seen the opposite—namely a mother's ability, with help, to make a significant developmental step into the phase of parenthood.

Usually, only when a mother becomes active in the program, consults with the therapist and teachers and gains and applies insights and attempts to work with her child does it become possible to gauge her current strengths and weaknesses as a mother and to assess her flexibility and potential for development. For this reason the assessment of the mother cannot be complete at intake nor could a longer period of mere observation furnish the necessary data. Only during the work itself do the most crucial factors reveal themselves.

Each phase of the work brings out different aspects of understanding the mother. The ultimately most important factor—the mother's ability to integrate and identify with the Center's means and aims, generally cannot be assessed until the final phase of work. The mother's ability to "grow" with her child, to utilize the developmental energy of motherhood to deal with the internal and external stresses brought about by the changing pattern of the child's needs and personality, often can be assessed best during the middle phase of work. But the initial stage of the work provides the staff with most data, both in quantity and in quality. The initial stage requires not only the therapist's understanding of the data but also her active contribution in laying the foundations of "the working relationship" with the mother and in planning the work. The duration of the initial stage, then, is circumscribed by content rather than a specific period of time.

During the first sessions with the therapist the mother usually adds a wealth of details to those gained at intake. The therapist's task is to use these data to gain some understanding of the child, of the mother-child relationship and of the mother, both as mother and as person. But beyond that the therapist has to evaluate the significance of the material in relation to the mother's current situation and her child's enrollment in the school. The mother usually took this step after a series of hardships and disappointments that aroused unhappiness, guilt, shame and uncertainty about her past and future adequacy as a mother. The decision to ask for help represents a most trying and anxious period and a very critical point in maternal development. This is exacerbated by the fact that she is embarking on a program about which she knows very little and has no previous experience and, thus, can arouse emotional and intellectual misconceptions.

Under such stressful circumstances there is an unusually good opportunity to become acquainted with the mother's attitude about herself and with her characterological defenses. This knowledge helps the therapist to adjust the content, form and timing of her contribution to requirements of the individual case. It is equally important, however, to bear in mind that the mother's initial behavior neither indicates her usual level of functioning nor enables her to participate in a "working relationship." The therapist therefore tries to assist the mother in partly regaining her equilibrium so that she can begin to work with her child. How readily a mother comes to grips with her predicament and how much time or help she needs varies greatly, according to her personality and to her specific development as a mother. The mother who can consciously face up to and struggle with her difficult situation is at a great advantage. But even such a mother seldom will describe her inner trials and tribulations to a strange therapist and only a few mothers allude to them briefly in early interviews. Inevitably, most mothers convey their feelings by other verbal contents or in their attitudes to the therapist, to the teachers, to their own child and his problems, to the behavior of the other children and so on. Many mothers' anxiety is seen especially in their preconceptions about the work and their part in it: they fear the therapist may criticize them and know all the answers or the teachers may take over the child's loyalty. Other mothers ward off such feelings by critically interrogating the therapist or teachers or by unduly admiring them. Depending on the intensity of the mother's anxiety and the nature of her defense mechanisms, the variety of responses to the situation is limitless.

The therapist's task is easiest when the mother gives some recognizable indication of her distress, for this enables the therapist to offer verbal understanding and sympathy. Thus the therapist helps the mother to appreciate the real difficulties of the situation and to come to terms with them. Indirectly the therapist emphasizes her respect for the mother and her difficult job and begins to establish herself as an understanding and realistic assistant. Only careful observation of the mother's overall response to such initial remarks or conversations enables the therapist to gauge whether or how they helped.

Simultaneously, the therapist tries to understand what the mother expects of the weekly consultations. At opportune times, she begins to give the mother a realistic understanding of the program. Although some aspects may be disillusioning or difficult for the mother, the discussions help to focus her thinking on realistic and practical tasks in the immediate future instead of the previous uncertainties and misconceptions. In particular the therapist stresses the very active part the mother herself must take in observing and understanding her child, the limitations of the therapist's help and the numerous difficulties and setbacks that characterize the course of the work. Again one of the most important aspects of such a talk is the mother's reaction to it. Often this throws more light on the mother's personality than any preceding data.

The therapist's understanding and appreciation of the mother's difficult situation and her realistic presentation of the work may reduce the mother's stress but they do not necessarily clear the way toward a "working relationship." The mother's guilt, healthy though it is, underlies and intensifies her anxiety. In many respects it is responsible for the difficult current situation, and it continues to be a barrier as long as it is unmentioned by the mother and unappreciated by the therapist. Even those mothers whose guilt is largely conscious and within healthy limits find it hard to believe they can succeed in the work unless they have been able to share this feeling with the therapist. This is even more important with mothers who are not so aware of their guilt and/or whose guilt is unusually severe and complicated. The therapist therefore observes especially carefully the direct and indirect manifestations of the mother's guilt. She watches for opportunities to pick up this topic with the mother—to express empathy with a mother's guilt, stress it as an essential aspect of her feelings and support the mother's decision to put matters right by helping her child through this work. Among the cases in this study were several in which the mothers' discussion of guilt became a positive turning point in their work. These mothers were unable to participate in the program fully, until they could express their guilt. Thus they apparently freed their capacities and their subsequent work was very successful.

These topics are not expected to be taken up in any particular order and form and one does not expect them to be "settled" in the initial stage. But a sufficient start should be made to enable the mother to begin work with the child actively and with some realistic appreciation of her task. A few mothers cope with this early stage remarkably easily, but for many it is quite difficult and often extends over a long period. Experience suggests that a mother can best utilize her weekly consultations and work best with her child when she has, at least to some degree, been able to master her distress and guilt and has been able to accept the therapist's realistic understanding and expectation that she can help her child.

A mother seldom reaches this point before she has to cope with another major phase in her relationship to her child—his actual entry into nursery school and consequent separation from her. This is in part due to the fact that children are accepted with a view to nursery attendance, which is an integral part of the program. It also stems from the mother's own expectation, for the child's readiness for school is often closely linked with her decision to seek help. Even when the mother sees the therapist for several months before the child enters the school, upset over enrollment and upset over separation are inevitably connected. Nor is this necessarily a disadvantage. Appropriately, the child himself and the mother-child relationship should be at a stage where nursery school attendance represents a developmental step which can be mastered with adequate educational and emotional handling. In this sense the child's entry affords valuable opportunity to observe the ways in which a mother and child cope with an important phase of development and to help them with it. The nature of the mother-child interaction, their degree of verbal and nonverbal communication, their attitude to feelings of sadness, anger and anxiety, the mother's educational measures and the child's response to them, all these and more stand out in sharp relief. Equally valuable is the chance for the mother to gain an insight into her child's feelings and often to appreciate the intensity of his need and love for her. When one observes how the mother utilizes such an insight in her dealing with her child—and how soon she does or how long she does not understand his response—then one can begin to assess her as a mother at work.

For our mothers and children, however, entry into nursery school represents not only a developmental task. The school is also the place where their attitudes about the child's problems are focused, even when separation anxiety is not one of the main difficulties. Mostly their attitudes are very different. The mother may, for instance, primarily fear what an impression her child will make on the adults and how he will compare with the other children. The child may mainly fear that he is being sent to school as a punishment for "badness." It is often an intricate and highly individual process for the mother to manage her own feelings, understand the child's, eventually help him to recognize his "badness" as troubles or worries and explain how they will work on them together with the aid of the school.

In helping the mother with the child's separation period and with his realistic understanding of his difficulties, one usually finds many natural starting points for approaching the child's problems. As in child analysis, one generally proceeds from observation to interpretation of the child's defense mechanisms, from defense and anxiety to conflict, from present conflict to genetic origins. Many mothers are not only excellent observers but find the avenue to the child's conflicts via his defenses quite spontaneously. In planning the work, however, the therapist has to consider not only the disturbance of the child, but also the mother's strengths and weaknesses, the status of the "working relationship," the educational setting in the home and the mother's wishes—the areas of difficulty that currently most concern her. Usually the initial topics are spontaneously agreed upon. Sometimes it is helpful to explain to a mother why a certain approach might prove more advantageous, so that she may consider it.

This outline of the initial stage of work, as well as what appears in the later sections, is not intended as an exhaustive description nor as a prescription. It merely provides some basic guidelines. The potential success lies in the skill of the therapist and above all in his analytic training which is such a prerequisite for this work. This training enables the therapist to empathize fully with the mother's personality, to adjust all discussions accordingly, to avoid mobilizing the mother's anxiety unduly, and yet to keep the mother in a position of authority in the work. It need hardly be stressed that success depends not only on what is said, but also on how and when it is said, what is omitted and what is conveyed in the therapist's attitude. Only under such circumstances can a mother continue to develop and concentrate her energies on actively helping her child.

Middle Stage

Even after the initial major hurdles are overcome, the course of the work is characterized by repeated interferences and setbacks. This is because the early difficulties reappear at times of stress and often are joined by further problems. These stem partly from upheavals in the child's pattern of development and from the nature of his difficulties. They are also partly the result of the mother's reactions to these processes in her child, to her relationship with the therapist, and to any other concerns which may arise in her daily life.

Under optimum circumstances a mother's job is extremely demanding. Living with a disturbed child is infinitely harder, and the mother's work in our program adds much stress and strain. So one must expect a wide range of personal reactions stimulated by the mother's current experiences and realistically justified. However, a mother's reactions sometimes grossly exceed the usual extent, or are not based on reality. Such responses may be due to longstanding characterological conflicts or to current maladjustments in the phase of maternal development. They become interferences when they encroach upon the mother's work with her child.

The difficulty does not necessarily become an interference as long as the mother is aware of it, struggles with it and can share her knowledge with the therapist. But the situation is different when a mother either is not aware of the difficulty (e.g., a pathological interaction with her child) or is unable to communicate it to the therapist directly (e.g., events which have influenced the child in the past or present). The therapist then receives disguised indications of maternal stress. Since the therapist does not treat the mother as a patient, he or she can never help a mother to resolve her difficulties by means of interpretation of unconscious contents. Nor does he attempt to do so. It is a great advantage of this work that a mother's energies are not diverted into personal psychotherapeutic introspection which could cause temporary "neglect" of the child's emotional needs. The therapist tries to deal with a mother's reactions by prevention or, if necessary, by drawing the mother's attention to the manifestations of an interference. The mother may then discuss and sometimes resolve it, or overcome the difficulty through her own conscious effort or work out a plan for containing it so that it does not seriously affect her work with her child, or seek psychiatric help for herself while continuing to work with the therapist in regard to her child.

Here is an attempt to discuss in greater detail how interferences may be dealt with in the main areas in which they occur: (a) the mother's responses to and interactions with the child, (b) her reactions to the relationship with the therapist, and (c) extraneous concerns in the mother's daily life.

1. Prevention of Interferences

(a) *Interaction with the child.* A mother is intimately familiar with her child's individual behavior, but she usually lacks general knowledge of the varied manifestations and patterns of emotional development. She also is not trained in the technique of therapy and the child's responses to it. She cannot evaluate these at the time or within the total framework of his disturbance. The mother learns much of this only as she applies it to her child. This, to her, is often a hazardous journey full of painful upsets and new adjustments. The therapist assists by making sure, as far as possi-

ble, that the mother feels in active control of the work. As
much as possible the therapist allows the mother to go at
her own pace in observing her child, gaining insights about
him, and applying the insights. The mother is encouraged
not to make educational changes or to give interpretations
unless she feels fully confident about them and has been
able to anticipate, usually with the therapist's aid, the child's
probable reactions and how to deal with them. When the
therapist contributes, he takes great care not to mobilize
the mother's anxiety unduly. When he offers general understanding or suggests educational procedures, he does so in
terms of examples learned from other mothers, rather than
in authoritative or theoretical terms. When he points out a
child's defense or conflict he paves the way gradually and
stresses the infantile nature of the manifestation, so remote
and often unacceptable to the adult. When he draws a
mother's attention to an area that has gone unnoticed by her,
he proceeds in a way that the mother can maintain her
inner balance while absorbing the new insight into her
child and her reaction to it; some mothers, for instance,
can accept such a confrontation better after they have
made a positive accomplishment in another area. Above
all the therapist encourages the mother to voice her disappointments and frustrations with the work or child, her
misgivings about or disapproval of educational and therapeutic methods or her difficulty in approaching certain topics.
When a mother finds it especially difficult to express such
thoughts, either habitually or in specific situations, the
therapist may humorously contrast the mother's unusual
stoicism with what his own reaction would be in the mother's
position, or how other mothers usually respond.

(b) *Relationship with the therapist.* In the course of the
consultations the mother's relationship to the therapist inevitably encompasses elements other than the working relationship. In part these are responses to the therapist's personal

and professional qualities; in part they are due to the mother's characterological patterns of relating (e.g., sado-masochistic, infantile, dependent) and in part they stem from the mother's attitude to the very special position of the therapist, i.e., the person from whom she requests help with her child (e.g., subservience, competition, fear of criticism). Last, but not least, the mother's relationship to the therapist contains transference reactions, i.e., aspects of the mother's infantile object relationships. (Such reactions differ from the transference neurosis which develops only in the context of a psychoanalytic treatment.)

Although all these elements are present in the mother's relationship to the therapist, their effect and manifestations vary in individual cases. Quite often they contribute positively to both the relationship and the work. At other times they become the source of an interference. To a considerable extent the therapist prevents these elements of the relationship from interfering by outlining, at the start, the concept of a working relationship the common aim of which is help for the child and by establishing herself as an assistant to the mother in her own efforts. At all times the therapist attempts to adjust her discussions and behavior to the mother's personality so that difficulties of interaction are minimized. In addition to limiting his contacts with the mother to the professional setting, the therapist does not initiate discussion of topics unrelated to the work and does not actively enter into discussions dealing with the parents' personal life (marital relationship, business, special interests, personal problems present or past). He tries to represent his role realistically by correcting a mother's overestimation of it or by encouraging her to bring to the therapist's attention his mistakes or shortcomings.

(c) *Extraneous concerns.* Current concerns in daily life— illness, loss of job, housing difficulties—become interferences if the mother chooses not to tell the therapist about them. When the mother discusses such a difficulty, the therapist listens sympathetically. The next steps depend on the individual mother and her specific distress, and are taken with a view to helping her to resume work with the child as soon as possible. Sometimes this means letting the mother talk about her concern repeatedly or even bringing up the subject later in order to give her an opportunity to talk about it (e.g., during a phase of acute illness in the family). In other instances it is more helpful to attempt to limit the discussions tactfully and to bring her back to the topic of the child. In situations in which the child himself or his siblings are concerned—e.g., if hospitalization of the child or sibling is necessary, or a suitable school has to be found— the therapist may offer her active help. It should be remembered that the therapist helps the mother, to some extent, in the upbringing of all the children in the family, especially the younger ones. If a sibling's problems require too much time, or if direct help is indicated, the therapist may assist in a psychiatric referral.

2. *Discussion of Interferences*

Many mothers show their reactions in a disguised form. Some may have difficulty in keeping appointments; others may be consistently unable to observe, discuss or handle certain areas of behavior; they may accept advice superficially or apply it in such a way as to prove it wrong; they may use the knowledge they have gained to express hostility toward the child or to augment a sadomasochistic struggle; some may deny that the child is improving or attribute it to coincidental factors; they may insist on discussing topics unrelated to the child; they may show exaggerated interest in the person of the therapist, or try to befriend him beyond the professional relationships. Since even a mother's verbal expressions on relevant topics may represent displacements and therefore cannot always be taken at face value, all these manifestations of difficulty are important as signs of an interference but they do not reveal its underlying cause. For instance, a mother may appear unduly concerned about a child's illness in order to ward off her anxiety about his phallic problems or she may not discuss a subject with her child because she feels, perhaps rightly, that the therapist made a mistaken inference in connection with it.

At first the therapist makes a mental note of the nature of the interference and looks for real events which may have precipitated it. If the therapist can relate it to a specific situation—he finds an opportunity to discuss it with the mother. But if the discussion does not alleviate the interference, either because it was not caused by the event or because the discussion was not fruitful, the therapist has to draw the mother's attention directly to the interference and to its effect on her work with the child. In doing so he tries to engage the healthy maternal aspects of the mother-child relationship to deal with its weaknesses.

(a) *Interaction with the child.* When the mother's difficulty manifests itself in relation to the child, the therapist's or teachers' tactfully pointing out the interference gradually makes her aware of it. Mothers then deal differently with the problem. Most struggle with the difficulty and, despite their own resistance, eventually gain sufficient insight into the child's conflict to help him by interpretation and handling. In our case studies there were 16 in which a marked interference was superseded by a significant positive turning point in the work when the mothers "overcame" their difficulty for the sake of the child. Among them were problems of aggression, penis envy, castration fear, separation fear, need for educational control of the child, and effect on the child of specific realities in past and present.[3] Another nine mothers used their new awareness of a difficulty to look into them-

[3] The genuine wish to help their children and the great satisfaction experienced in doing so motivated the successful efforts of these mothers.

selves and to utilize the results of their introspection. Some
spontaneously recalled conflicts from their own childhood
and could, on this basis, either empathize with the child or
dissociate their own conflicts from those of the child (for
example, one mother had difficulty handling her child's
oedipal phase because of guilt over her own parents' divorce
early in her life). Some became conscious of a fantasy which
they could correct in the light of reality (one mother, for
instance, feared that her child would be orphaned). Some
used the new awareness of currently sharing the child's feeling to understand and help him (e.g., one mother could empathize with her child's separation fear when she could allow
herself to experience sadness on leaving her child). The therapist does not assist the mother in this self-searching but
when the mother reports it he brings the focus back on the
child. He stresses how these realizations can help the mother
understand her child or how the child's current situation
differs from the mother's feelings or experiences.

These two groups of cases are cited because the interference was so great as to bring the work to a virtual stand-
still and jeopardize seriously the child's chances of improvement. To a lesser extent, most mothers help their children
in spite of their emotional hardship and they also repeatedly,
though to a less striking degree, utilize the child's feelings
to gain insight into themselves. These are but extensions of
the normal processes occurring in the phase of maternal
development.

Some mothers find they cannot sufficiently overcome a
particular unhelpful reaction to some aspect of the child's
feelings or behavior. This awareness, however, often enables
them to limit overt manifestations of it. They sometimes
further improve the situation by telling their child realistically about the problem so that he will not feel responsible for it, can more readily dissociate himself from it and can,
in some instances, learn not to provoke it.

(b) *Relationship to the therapist.* While interferences due to the mother's reaction to the child are quite frequent, they are rarely due to the mother's relationship with the therapist. (For exceptions see part V of this chapter.) But there are instances where a therapist has to bring to the mother's notice a persistent interference and its effect on her work with her child, such as excessive interest in the therapist as a person, attempts at sadomasochistic interplays. The therapist appeals to the mother to return to the confines of the working relationship for the sake of helping her child. The mother's difficulty is not questioned, nor are unconscious meanings interpreted, so that introspection in this area is discouraged.

(c) *Extraneous concerns.* One finds not infrequently that a mother's interference in the work is due to a mother's current extraneous concern, a worry that has preoccupied the mother but that she has been unable or unwilling to share with the therapist. How helpful it will be for the mother to discuss her trouble depends both on the mother and on the nature of the difficulty. Surprisingly, among the cases in this study no insurmountable interference was ever noted due to a concern of daily life although these families experienced their share of hardships via illness, death, loss of or changes in fathers' jobs and incomes. The mothers seemed to derive enough relief from telling the worry to a sympathetic listener to enable them to resume their work even when the therapist could not actually help to change the difficult reality, e.g., paternal desertion, grandparent's psychotic breakdown. In one respect the therapist always offers help; to assist the mother in ways of discussing or handling the concern with the child. Several mothers felt that the gratification they derived from helping the child and from being sympathetically understood by the therapist and teachers helped them to cope better with other hardships. (The situation is different when the tragic reality concerns the mother's own emotional or physical health. See parts V and VI of this chapter.)

It is very likely that the same mothers could not as successfully overcome or contain their various difficulties in other
life situations, nor even in regard to children other than their
own. Only the developing maternal aspects of their personalities make these adjustments possible, by realigning other elements in the mother's changing ideals and relationship to
her child.

Final Stage

Like the initial stage, the last stage of the work deals with
a major developmental step in the child and in the mother-
child relationship. In this instance it is the resolution of
the oedipal conflict and beginning of latency. Coincidental,
but intimately related, is the mother's and child's separation
from the center.

In the earlier years of the center's existence, children left
the school around five and a half years of age, their birth date
determining entry into public school kindergarten. Quite
often, therefore, the last stage was precipitated by the public
school registration in the beginning of the calendar year or
by the planning of prekindergarten activities at the nursery
school, or by some similar reminder of the forthcoming
separation. In many cases this coincided with the child's internal readiness, his increasing ability to sublimate and to
enjoy relationships outside the family, and evidence of new
ego and superego identifications. But other children were
still at the height of their oedipus complex, so that the final
stage dealt much more with preparing mother and child for
the next developmental phase while the work continued to
focus on the current emotional conflicts. Under these conditions the separation from the school did not altogether coincide with a developmental step, and thus was more stressful
for the mothers and children.

In most centers the help to mother and child is discontinued when the child stops attending. By contrast in our

center mothers always could, and often did, continue fairly regular consultations with the therapist during the months immediately following the child's departure from the nursery school. Yet the child's attendance in public school made it difficult to follow and assist with the child's further development during this crucial phase. This was one reason we added a kindergarten class. Since then it has been possible to keep for an additional year children whose oedipal phase extends over a longer period, whose difficulties require further work via the mother, with whom it seems especially indicated to give optimum help during the period of superego internalization, and for whom the special educational advantages of our kindergarten are particularly helpful at this stage (e.g., children who have had difficulty in the areas of learning and sublimation or instinctual control).

Mothers have, for the most part, been quite ready to avail themselves of the kindergarten, welcoming the chance to follow the child's new development closely and to adjust to it with the additional understanding gained by their own observations and discussions with the teachers and therapist. During the kindergarten year the frequency of the consultations is usually reduced to biweekly or longer intervals after the initial period of adjustment—arrangements are made individually, in keeping with the changing nature of the child and mother-child relationship. The separation aspect still figures prominently, and care must be taken to pave the way for later contacts, but the resolution of the mother's and child's close relationship to the center comes more naturally.

For the therapist, work on the child's feelings around his separation from the center also is most instructive. It affords an opportunity to assess and consolidate the child's gains in being able to experience and express painful feelings and in using appropriate mechanisms to anticipate and master reality situations. It is also an occasion for working through earlier conflicts which are related to separation, change and growing up, such as early traumatic separations, birth of sibling, fear of competition. During this period the therapist tries to share with the mother an objective assessment of the child's strengths and weaknesses. He stresses that the services of the center, ranging from consultations with the therapist to analytic treatment, will always be available.

For the mother, usually more than for the child, it is a sad experience to give up the intimate relationship with her young child. Many mothers are aware of their distress and longing and can master it in themselves and discuss it with the therapist. The recognition of their own feelings enables them to see the child's withdrawal and preference for other relationships as a desirable step in development rather than as a rejection. At the time of the child's entry into nursery school they learned to substitute the earlier bodily closeness for the differently rewarding relationship expressed largely in closeness of feelings. This experience helps them now to adjust to the child's new need for neutral interests and activities as he is about to enter public school. They begin to enjoy the new shared experiences and the more mature objective discussions with the child, to understand and respect his struggles with his new harsh superego and to evaluate his behavior accordingly. The better mother and child can cope with the transition into the next phase and the separation from the center, the easier is it for the mother to plan realistically for future contacts in terms of follow-up visits or in terms of seeking further help if necessary.

In addition the final stage is, above all, the time at which the mother's ability to develop with her child and to identify with the means and aims of the work can be assessed. During the first years of our work we were wary of the possible disadvantages of the mothers' long-term regular contact with the therapist and of her unusually intimate work with and understanding of her child. Some questions we asked ourselves were: Would mothers become too dependent on the therapist? Would their relationship to him become too intense? Would mothers find the special closeness with their child too gratifying and have difficulty helping the child to reach and enjoy latency? Would the child become too attached to the mother and find it difficult to resolve his oedipal ties with her?

These misgivings were not borne out. We found that the work helped mothers and children to take the developmental step into the latency period and to make the necessary changes in their relationship to one another. Follow-up studies have shown that achievements have been maintained with a high degree of consistency and have been succeeded, age-appropriately, by pubertal development in the child and maternal adjustment to it—often in spite of considerable stress.

It seemed to us that this was only in part due to the child's receiving help in overcoming his early disturbance which paved the way for his further healthy development. The follow-up studies confirmed the impression, gained already during the work, that in part the later harmonious development of the mother-child relationship stemmed from the gains the mothers had made. Through her work a mother's capacity for maternal development is always supported, and sometimes freed in certain areas. The pleasure derived from helping her child also often facilitates her ability to identify with the center's principles of child-rearing and to integrate them into her ideals of and functioning as a mother. If she can achieve this she has not only learned to cope with her current relationship with her child but is better able to help him, and adjust to him, in his later development. This type of partial identification, in contrast to temporary acceptance or dependency, can usually only take place after a long-term contact and meaningful experience with the work. It is heralded by instances of the mother applying principles of understanding or approach to new material and to different reality circumstances, or by her utilizing her knowledge in the care of her other children, or by her ability to continue her work with her child during vacations. During the last stage of the work the mother herself frequently becomes aware, or can be helped to become aware, of her ability to manage new phases and situations. This helps her to antici- pate the period after the termination of regular interviews.

IV. THE ROLE OF THE NURSERY SCHOOL IN THE WORK
WITH THE MOTHER

The great advantages of the nursery school's participation in the work with the mother are most evident to those of us who have treated young children via their parents in other settings, such as child guidance clinics, or who have had the experience of working with mothers for prolonged periods prior to the child's entry into the school (E. Furman, 1964). There are two main areas in which the contribution of the nursery school cannot be overestimated, i.e., the areas of observation and education. An attempt is made below to discuss briefly these two areas as well as to consider some additional factors.

Observation

A. Katan (1959) has already discussed the value of the nursery school setting as a diagnostic tool. There is little doubt that the initial direct observations of the child in the school and of his interaction with his mother add consid- erably to the overall understanding of his personality and specific pathology. I shall not enlarge on the topic of diag- nostic observation but rather focus on the fact that the observational advantage extends beyond the diagnostic stage. Throughout the years of work, day by day, it reflects the pattern of the child's development, the changing nature of his conflicts, and his means of coping with them.

One may be tempted to think primarily of the obvious usefulness of these observations for the therapist in enabling him at all times to obtain a total picture of the child and to pinpoint the mother's changing areas of strength and weakness. This is important but by no means the main value. Of greater worth is the availability of the nursery school observations to the mother herself. It was mentioned earlier (in part III of this chapter) that the teachers bring their observations not only to the therapist but to the mother, in such a way that she can, in most instances, accept them as a positive help in her work with her child and can, again often with the specific encouragement of the teachers, utilize them in her interviews with the therapist. These newly observed areas may include some which, due to the mother's "blind spots," had gone previously unnoticed by her, but they may also include many which the mother could not make herself, such as detailed observations of the child's functioning in her absence, his reactions to the school experiences—relationship with peers and teachers, acceptance of rules, ability to utilize educational materials and activities. In this way the mother's understanding benefits from the school observations.

There is also the opportunity for the mother to make direct observations herself. A mother can often understand her child in a different way when she is temporarily freed of the responsibility of caring for him, when she sees him in the different setting of the school, or when she can observe his reactions to the teachers' educational approach. For example, one mother had been blind to her little boy's severe fears until, in the nursery school, she repeatedly observed how her son singled out for sadistic attacks certain girls with "defects," e.g., one girl had a pronounced speech impairment, another had just lost a tooth. When the teachers stopped his behavior, explaining that it was against the rules and not helpful either to him or to his victim, he became visibly afraid. The mother could now see her boy's anxiety and gain insight into the defensive nature of his aggression.

If the child attended another good nursery school the mother might also be tactfully informed of behavior she had not known about and she might also be allowed to visit and observe. It would be difficult, however, even for a skilled group of teachers to know how or what to observe in such detail, when to impart it to the mother so as to best help her in her work with the child, and how to adjust their handling of the child's difficulties according to his needs at any given time. Teachers can only be this intimately in tune with the child, the mother, and her work, when they have had special training and when they work in close cooperation with the therapist as members of a team.

The nursery school observations are always valuable, whether the aim of the treatment is to work with, and free, the child's whole personality development or to focus on the alleviation of circumscribed symptoms. The school observations are particularly necessary in the following cases: (1) children whose pathology involves areas of ego-functioning (in contrast to isolated symptoms); (2) children whose disturbance is largely rooted in experiences that occurred during separation from the mother (with these children the nursery school often becomes the setting in which derivatives of the original reactions are displayed, whereas the home serves as a protection against a possible repetition of earlier incidents, e.g., a boy who had been repeatedly frightened by a sadistic family friend without the mother's knowledge); (3) children whose difficulties in general manifest themselves mostly when they are separated from their mothers, such as fear of loss of control, difficulties in peer relations, castration anxiety, separation fear; (4) children who have a tendency to displace conflicts from the home to other settings; (5) children whose mothers have prominent "blind spots" and are unable to observe some areas of the child's behavior.

Education

The area of education is at least as important as that of observation as far as the nursery school is concerned. As a factor in the mother's work with her child it is probably unequalled in importance. We were aware from the start that a mother's weakness as an educator often contributes considerably to her young child's disturbance and that, even when the under-five's conflicts originate primarily from other sources, therapeutic measures can only succeed if the child's ego is helped by adequate educational measures. For th's reason, helping the parents as educators has always been among the main aims of our work. Follow-up studies have highlighted the importance of this approach. The mothers' abilities as educators were assessed at the beginning and the end of the periods of work with her and compared to the children's initial diagnostic categories and to their subsequent course of development as reflected in the diagnoses at the times of leaving the nursery school and of follow-up. Education was subdivided into three main areas, namely (1) education of drives (libidinal and aggressive), (2) support of sublimations, and (3) handling of reality situations. These three areas do not cover the whole educational task but were chosen to represent it here, partly because they were most frequently mentioned by the therapists in individual case summaries, and partly for the purpose of organizing the data. We learned that, at the beginning of work with the center, almost all mothers were inadequate as educators of drives, and the majority also were unable to help the children in dealing with reality situations, but more than half the mothers were effective in encouraging and supporting sublimatory activities. The most impressive finding was that the mothers' ability to become effective educators was the factor which correlated most closely with the children's improvement. Of the educational areas listed, drive education appeared by far the most important in this context, whereas support for sublimations was the least important, and dealing with reality ranked midway. (For detailed description of the method of assessment and study as well as for relevant tables see Appendix.)

While the therapist needs to be as familiar with child analytic treatment as with education in order to assist the mother in her task, the nursery school shoulders a considerable part of the educational aspect of the work. It supports the therapist's approach in word and deed. Frequently a mother is dubious about the advisability or practicality of an educational measure that she has discussed with the therapist. Whether her reluctance is due to ignorance or resistance, it is usually helpful to her thinking to find that the teachers support such a measure, have actually carried it out in many instances, and can discuss in detail their experience with it. The nursery school provides a model of educational practices for the mother. Many mothers closely observe the school's educational methods (serving food, helping with dressing, handling children's questions, dealing with their response to frustrations, encouraging them to express feelings in words instead of actions). They then either spontaneously apply these observations themselves or bring them up for discussion with the therapist. Often they decide on a new measure or approach and then gain further assurance by observing it in practical application in the nursery school. The school also directly helps the mother by making sure that her increasingly appropriate methods are continued during the child's school day. This insures the consistency necessary for the child's progress. We have found this most essential in helping the child in verbalization of feelings and in the basic education of drives (toilet-training, uncontrolled aggressive behavior, etc.). In these areas the mother's role with the child extends to the teacher. In other areas the nursery school has the main educational opportunity and therefore significantly supplements the mother's role, e.g., helping the child with problems in peer relations, teaching special skills and sublimatory activities. The value of such assistance to the mother depends not only on the educational methods and standards of the nursery school. The day-to-day cooperation with the mother makes it possible to adapt the school's handling to the changing needs of the child and in turn enables her to include the child's school experiences in her work with him. Last but not least, the nursery school helps the mother by advising her in educational matters which do not directly enter into her work with the therapist or where the teachers' knowledge enables them to make a more appropriate recommendation, such as management of birthday parties, home visits with peers, suitable toys and play materials, choice of books, TV programs, movies.

Support of the Mother in Times of Stress

The nursery school also plays an important part in supporting or relieving the mother at times of stress. Many children are disturbed in such a way that they cannot attend an ordinary nursery school. Many have tried and failed. It is the mothers of these children who most need respite from the interpersonal tensions with their children in order to view their situation more calmly and to apply themselves to working on it. The nursery school provides this relief in a manner helpful to both mother and child. Even when the mother's stress is not so great initially, later periods may come when the work with the child becomes very difficult either because his behavior or his newly recognized pathology become intolerable for the mother. At such times it is not only the teachers' support which enables a mother to continue her work but also the mere fact that the child attends the nursery school and is usually well settled in it. The mother's consideration of the child's beneficial school experience sometimes makes it possible for her to overcome her distress or reluctance, and to carry on her work for a much longer period and into wider and deeper areas. In other instances difficult reality circumstances in the family add greatly to a mother's heavy burden and threaten her ability to persevere. Again it is most helpful to the mother to count on the sympathy and support of the teachers as well as that of the therapist. Mothers and therapists have noted this advantage repeatedly in cases of stressful realities of a long-standing nature, such as paternal desertion, or in short-term crises, such as hospitalization of the child or his sibling.

Disadvantages of the Nursery School

At the same time, there are possible disadvantages of the nursery school for the mother. It affords her a ready opportunity for such defensive maneuvers as splitting of attitudes between therapist and teachers and displacement or "spilling" of material from consultations with the therapist to discussions with the teachers. There are always some mothers who show such propensities. Teachers and therapists are aware of this and can do much to prevent it from interfering—the teachers may limit their discussions to certain subjects and direct the mother to the therapist, the latter in turn taking into consideration equally the mother's behavior in the consultations and in the nursery school. In practice a mother's inability to work effectively with the team tends to be a reflection of her disturbance in her relationship with her child rather than having its roots in the set-up of our program. Also, a mother who tends to split, displace or "spill" would probably do so even without the nursery school, choosing perhaps neighbors, relatives or physicians. In such cases it is a great advantage when the mother turns to our nursery school whose teachers can and do support the mother's work with the therapist.

For the role of the nursery school in helping the child see also Chapters 2, 4 and 8.

V. LIMITING FACTORS IN THE MOTHER

At the very start of our program we surmised that some mothers would be incapable of working with their young children and that others would be limited in their ability. We therefore made it our task to investigate this area in each case in order to pinpoint the relevant factors in the mother's personality and to assess when, and to what extent, they interfered with her work. An earlier paper (E. Furman, 1957) summarized our tentative conclusions in this respect. The subsequent years, and especially our inquiry into this subject in the context of this follow-up study, shed further light on the nature of limiting factors in mothers and made it necessary to revise some of our earlier impressions.

As the basis for investigation the research committee used that section of the therapists' individual case summaries which dealt specifically with the mother's limitations. The reviewing therapist, aided when necessary by the therapist who originally handled the case, assessed in each instance the nature of the limitations, the extent to which they interfered, whether the mother was able to overcome such limitations wholly or partially, and what effect this had on the child. The role of each limiting factor was assessed by comparing its effect and course in all the cases in which it operated, by relating it to other factors, and by correlating it with the child's improvement, or lack of improvement, as evidenced by his diagnostic status at the end of his treatment via the mother and follow-up (see Appendix for details and tables). The results of this inquiry led us to the following conclusions.

"Unsuitable" Mothers

Our earlier impressions were confirmed in one respect: certain personality disorders preclude a mother's effective cooperation and cannot be overcome or contained by her during the course of the work. Such disturbances are those which prevent a mother from entering the developmental phase of parenthood or which make parenthood a mere extension of the mother's pathology (see also part II). Among the former are instances recognized earlier (psychosis, borderline states, consistent inability to assume maternal responsibility for the care of the child); among the latter are serious neuroses and character disorders which fully encompass the mother-child relationships leaving no room for healthy development. Among our studied cases there were, for example, a mother with a severe obsessional neurosis, one with a psychopathic character disorder, and one with an incapacitating psychosomatic disease.

In cases in which a mother's parental development was seriously impaired, the work with her was geared towards different goals (see part VI).

In addition to the pathologies listed above there were two groups of mothers whose difficulties relate closely to this category. Our experience with them deserves special mention.

(a) Three mothers could assume maternal responsibility but could not mother their children consistently. In two cases this was due to the mothers' overall personality difficulties and could not be affected. Both mothers could do some work with their children, but both children were diagnosed as neurotic already during their stay at the nursery school. In the third case the mother's difficulty stemmed from a particular meaning the child had for her—the child represented a partner in one of her early object relationships. During the work the mother came to realize this and could thereafter consistently mother her child and work effectively with him. The child improved markedly and maintained his good adjustment into adolescence.

(b) In the treatment-via-the-parent group there were no mothers with serious depressions during the child's earliest years or during the time of the child's nursery school attendance. (There were several such cases in direct psychoanalytic treatment.) In seven mothers underlying depressive tendencies were recognized, but these did not grossly handicap the mothers' ability to help their children, except in two cases where the mothers' disturbance was exacerbated during the work by events not directly connected with the child. In these two cases ability to help the children became much more limited and this had a detrimental effect on the children's progress. Of the other five mothers, four had serious depressions in later years (three required hospitalization) but this apparently did not affect the development of their children who by then were already in their latency years.

Mothers with Limited Ability

It was already known earlier that even when there was no overall serious disturbance in the mother, certain aspects of the mother-child relationship could interfere with her work with the child. Our recent studies have enabled us to describe a greater variety of such aspects and to assess better their significance as well as amenability to change in individual cases.

1. Difficulties with Direct or Indirect Drive Manifestations

Among the treatment-via-the-mother cases in this study the most frequently encountered limiting factor was a mother's pathological attitude to drive expression in herself and/or in the child. Several mothers had unusual difficulty in dealing with *aggression;* they were unable to tolerate their own and/or child's aggression on all or some levels, or were unable to control aggression adequately. A number of mothers had unusual difficulty with *libidinal drives on all levels;* these were unable to recognize the child's libidinal behavior, or were unable to tolerate the necessary minimum of libidinal satisfaction in the child, or were unable to frustrate adequately the child's libidinal needs.

Even more mothers had unusual difficulty on specific levels

of the child's libidinal development. A particularly prominent group were mothers who had *anal-sadistic difficulties*
which showed in the continuation of an intense sado-masochistic relationship with the child, coupled in some instances
with a perpetuation of the child's dependency on the mother
in the area of elimination. Another group of mothers had
special difficulties on the *phallic level* which manifested themselves in relation to their sons, for example, by acceptance of
passive behavior patterns and intolerance of masculine phallic strivings, or by denial of the boys' castration fear and a
need to expose them to threatening situations. In relation to
their girls the mother's phallic difficulties were expressed, for
instance, by denial of penis-envy, by an inability to understand the child's defenses in this area, or by failing to empathize with the girl's feelings. Difficulties in the *oedipal
phase* were found least often. They showed in a mother's inability to tolerate the positive or negative aspects of the
oedipus complex, or in failing to handle the child realistically
because of undue sympathy with his conflicts.

In all these subgroups some mothers could, during the
course of the work, change their attitude in relation to the
child, some could do so partially, and others could not do so
at all. It appeared that more mothers could effectively overcome their difficulties with aggression than those in the libidinal areas, but in no subgroup did all mothers change. It was
also found that some mothers who initially had difficulty
with both drives and/or on several levels of development
were able to overcome, or contain, their limitations effectively
in regard to the child, while other mothers could not modify
their difficulty with one drive on a single level.

2. Cases of Mother and Child Sharing Important
Conflicts or Prominent Defenses

In a considerable number of cases mother and child used
prominently the same defense mechanisms or suffered from

identical symptoms, or the child had a problem which his mother had suffered from in her childhood. Several mothers shared their children's severe separation anxiety, one mother and child suffered from a fear of death, another mother and child had severe fears of bodily injury which the mother warded off with phobic mechanisms while the child used predominantly counterphobic measures. We had several cases of children suffering from psychosomatic, or physical, or functional disorders whose mothers had suffered from identical difficulties in their childhood. A number of mothers shared their children's prominent defenses against sadness, or anger, or narcissistic hurt. We had originally thought that such a constellation would preclude a mother's successful work. Our studies now indicate that as many mothers can, as cannot, overcome or contain this handicap, and several others are able to modify it, often sufficiently to help their children in this area.

This limiting factor, like the previous one, does not, by virtue of its mere existence, preclude a mother from working successfully with her child. Rather, its ultimate significance depends on the psychological framework in which it operates in the mother.

3. *Disturbances in the Libidinal Cathexis of the Child*

Into this group fall cases in which the mother relates to her child primarily on a narcissistic basis. The child, or his difficulties, represent a part of herself, either loved or hated. One such mother was unable to frustrate her child, gratifying herself by gratifying him and remaining unaware of the effect of her handling on the child's personality. Several mothers experienced the child's problem as a personal defect. Some dealt with this by denying the child's difficulties, others by punishing the child severely in order to terminate the child's disturbed behavior and thereby to remove the "blemish."

They could not empathize with the child's suffering or genuinely wish to help him.

Also in this group are cases where the mother does relate to the child with an adequate amount of object-libidinal cathexis, but the child is not a love-object in his own right. Rather, the child represents primarily a partner in an earlier object relationship. In two cases the mothers believed their children to be mentally damaged as their own sisters had been. With one mother this led her to expect that the child could not be helped effectively and only needed to be protected in the face of reality. With the other mother this resulted in an inability to mother her child consistently. In still another case the mother saw in the child the husband who had deserted her. She loved and hated in the child the qualities which represented her husband but she could not handle her boy according to his own personality needs.

This limiting factor, too, proved amenable to change in as many cases as not. It was striking, though, that generally mothers either were able to overcome this difficulty wholly or not at all. Only one case showed partial success.

4. Gross Educational Inconsistency

Although we had in theory and practice always stressed the importance of the mother's role as educator, we were still impressed to find that gross educational inconsistency ranked among the mothers' major limiting factors and that this factor was relatively much less amenable to change than any of the other prominent factors—probably because in our cases the limitation was the product of serious maternal disturbances. Sandler, Daunton, and Schnurmann (1957) describe similar experiences.

The term "educational inconsistency" implies that a mother is unable to adhere to any chosen measures for furthering the child's ego development and lending age-adequate support to the child's ego in dealing with internal and external demands. The inconsistency applies not only to the handling of different areas, such as overgratification of oral needs coupled with premature expectations in toilet training, but also the erratic changes in the handling of the same area, such as letting the child hit his younger sibling one day, but punishing him for the same behavior the following day.

Among the mothers with this limiting factor, about half could not change, half changed partially, and only one was able to alter her educational approach fundamentally.

5. *Pathological Guilt*

A number of mothers could not help their children because of their pathological guilt in relation to the child or his difficulties. One case was that of an adopted child where the mother's unrealistic guilt about the adoption resulted in her conviction that she did not deserve a well child. In two cases the mothers' unconscious guilt made it impossible for them to tolerate an improvement in their children. In two other cases the mothers felt unduly guilty over their handling of events in the child's past. In one such case this preoccupied the mother to the extent of not being able to manage the present; in the other it led to the mother's denial of the event and of those difficulties in the child which were related to it.

Our records show an even distribution between mothers who could and could not overcome this handicap.

6. *Inability to Integrate Means and Aims of Educational and Therapeutic Principles*

As was mentioned above, mothers vary considerably in the extent to which they identify with our approach and in the time it takes them to do so. On the whole those mothers integrate it best who have two or even three years of continuous contact with us or who go through the working process a second time with a younger sibling of the first child.

However, a few mothers work quite successfully with their

children as long as they maintain continuous contact with the center. After contact is terminated they largely exclude their newly gained knowledge or insight from their mothering. The cause seems to lie in the mother's dependence, for various reasons, on the personal contact with the staff. In cases of this kind the mothers could work effectively until their children began to enter the latency period. The subsequent relative loss of the mothers' insight therefore did not affect the children too adversely. (A case of maternal difficulty, similar in its manifestations, was described by D. T. Burlingham [1951]. In that instance, however, the mother's inability to identify lastingly with the worker's approach appeared to stem from different factors in the mother's personality. Also, the child was in a younger age-group.)

Very different, but also belonging to this category, are mothers who are able to work with their children effectively only as long as the child's prominent difficulties require their help. We have compared such mothers to "medicine takers" because they use the center's approach as one would use a medicine: even if bitter at times, it is taken conscientiously as long as the acute illness persists; once health is seemingly restored, the medication is discontinued. Both types of mothers described here are able to help their children quite well with their current difficulties. Their limitation, however, may affect their handling of the child's development in the future. In the very few cases of this kind our follow-up studies are not conclusive.

Discussion

All the aspects described represent limiting factors which in some, even if not all cases, jeopardize a mother's ability to help her child. Our studies have shown a close correlation between a mother's overcoming such a limitation and her child's improvement and, vice versa, that when mothers could not modify their difficulty their children's disturbances tended to remain unchanged or crystallized into neuroses. This does not imply a simple causal connection. Many other factors enter into the making of a child's health and pathology and, in their turn, affect the mother's capacity to overcome her side of the difficulty. Also, some children are able to utilize even limited help, others are not. In this context only the maternal aspect of the limitation is considered. We are aware that an overall study of the significance of limiting factors would have to include consideration of corresponding factors in the child's personality.

In the majority of the cases studied, a mother's limiting factor did not operate in isolation but was interacting with several other limiting factors. Several mothers could overcome some limitations better than others: Marie's mother succeeded in altering her severe sadomasochistic interaction with her little girl but remained handicapped by the predominance of narcissistic elements in her relationship to Marie; Gretchen's mother overcame the marked limitation of sharing her daughter's problems in two prominent areas, yet the mother's difficulties with conflicts on the phallic level interfered with her ability to help Gretchen in this area. Some mothers could successfully modify a combination of factors: Ben's mother was successful in overcoming her extreme narcissistic involvement coupled with pathological guilt, a considerable overall difficulty with aggression, both in herself and in Ben, and an intense sadomasochistic relationship. Others remained unable to contain one single important factor; Bertha's mother was warm, insightful and therapeutically competent with her daughter but had difficulty in maintaining a consistent educational approach. No one aspect, or combination of aspects, however, could be pinpointed which definitely precluded a mother from working with her child. For this reason the initial diagnosis of limiting factors has come to be regarded as a potential danger sign rather than a basis for not attempting to work with the mother. Our question has mainly centered on recognizing the psychological framework in which the difficulties manifest themselves and which are indirectly responsible for impeding the mother's work in some instances and enabling her to effect a change in others.

Some examples of mothers with a prominent sadomasochistic relationship with their children may serve to illustrate situations in which this factor can and cannot be overcome and may also show our approach to the problem.

Case 1

For Frank's mother, sadomasochistic relationships were a characterological form of adjustment. Her difficulty in this respect focused primarily on her young boy, but it included also all her love objects and even persons with whom she had only superficial contacts. Her sadomasochistic relationship to her son had started in his earliest babyhood and been acted out on all levels of his development. Their interactions led to gross instances of mutual bodily and mental maltreatment. When the mother gained some insight into her part of the pathological interplay and its effect on her child, she was still largely unable to contain her reactions. It became increasingly evident that her sadomasochistic attitude was a part of her major personality disturbance that had distorted her maternal development so that there were hardly any elements of healthy cathexis in her relationship to her child. Both mother and child started direct analytic treatment.

Case 2

Ben's mother also maintained all-round sadomasochistic relationships. This showed much less in her handling of her children's oral phase than in the anal and phallic stages. Although she frequently lost her temper both verbally and physically and carried on many arguments for long periods, she was never cruel or heartless. On the contrary, she was capable of considerable warmth. When she eventually realized the impact of her sadomasochism on her boy, she responded with a sense of humor that implied her capacity for insight: "You seem to think it would be better never to fight. And where would be all our fun in life?" She found that her sadomasochistic behavior with her child was intensified when it served as a defense against her narcissistic hurt and guilt over his problems. She was able to contain her difficulty in relation to her boy (it persisted in her relationships with adults). She found new "fun in life" in the rewarding and more mature relationship with her son as he, too, began to progress. In spite of all the severe stress this family had to endure in later years, the mother-child relationship did not regress to the sadomasochistic level.

Case 3

Eleanor's mother enjoyed mature relationships with her husband and other adults. She also reported a satisfactory relationship with her little girl during the first almost two years. At the time of referral, however, when the child was about three years old, mother and child were locked in an intense sadomasochistic interplay around the little girl's toilet training. The mother gained understanding of her part in the struggle. She was able to contain her difficulty enough to learn that the soiling and wetting were the child's attempts at coping with early phallic anxieties, stimulated in part by an operative procedure. The mother could empathize with her daughter in the area of phallic concerns, could work with her successfully and establish a close age-adequate relationship. When this mother coped with her sadomasochistic interplay with her child, she reported her similar early struggles with her own mother which had affected their relationship to this day. When the mother had overcome her difficulty with her little girl, she spontaneously reported a like improvement in her relationship with her own mother.

The above illustrations show that for the purposes of this work it is important to assess the context in which the sadomasochistic relationship operates. It may be but one expression of a basic disturbance in maternal development (as with Frank's mother). It may be a part of the mother's personality structure which invades her mothering but can be contained with the help of maternal ideals and appropriate maternal feelings for the child. Or, the sadomasochistic interaction may have developed within the framework of the mother-child relationship during the child's anal-sadistic phase, partly stimulated by the child's behavior and partly responded to on the basis of the mother's reactivated early conflicts in this area. This last situation is the most hopeful in many, if not all, instances. The clinical picture of the sadomasochistic relationship in such cases can nevertheless be very severe and, if it has continued for a considerable time, can lead both to a serious disturbance in the child and to an arrest in the mother's capacity for further maternal development.

These cases also show some of the clinical features which might help in assessing the nature of this limiting factor initially or early during the work. E.g., are all of the mother's relationships sadomasochistic? If it occurs only with the child, when did it begin? Does it show in physical or verbal interactions? How episodic or continuous is it? How gratifying is the relationship to the mother? Could she enjoy another more mature relationship? Does she experience conflict over her difficulty? Does she have insight into her part in the struggle?

The described cases illustrate only some of the many individual constellations in which sadomasochism operates as a limiting factor. With each of the other listed factors individual examples would likewise reveal the great variety of psychological settings in which they manifest themselves.

With experience we have become somewhat more skilled in detecting the existence of a limiting factor, in assessing its significance, in helping some mothers to modify it, and in gearing the work toward different goals in instances where the mother was unable to overcome her limitation and therefore could not help her child sufficiently (see part VI of this chapter).

VI. SPECIAL APPLICATIONS OF THE WORK WITH THE MOTHER— PREPARATION FOR THE CHILD'S TREATMENT

Many children in our nursery school suffered from disturbances which were not accessible to treatment via the mother. Direct psychoanalytic treatment was indicated for all children whose pathology was diagnosed as categories IV and V and for some of the cases in category VI. Further, psychotherapy three times weekly was required for a few children who with all but one exception were diagnosed as category III. In these latter cases the mothers' limiting factors had prevented them from helping their children with specific aspects of their difficulties. (For description of diagnostic categories see Chapter 5, for figures on direct treatment see Chapter 8.)

In the majority of these cases, regardless of diagnostic category, there was a period of work with the mother, the aims of which differed to some extent from the cases of treatment-via-the-mother described previously. Chapter 8 contains a detailed description of some of our experiences with those cases. No attempt is made here to duplicate these data, but rather to show how this work, like the treatment via the mother, derives from our understanding of the early mother-child relationship.

The Parents' Role in the Direct Treatment of Under-Fives

Whatever the age of the child, it is always hard for parents to accept a treatment recommendation for him and to persevere in giving his analysis the necessary practical and emotional support. In attempting to treat under-fives, however, these difficulties are considerably magnified. Experience seems to show that parents are particularly reluctant to consider analytic treatment for very young children. At the same time, with the youngest age group the success of the treatment and the child's subsequent development depend on effective parental cooperation more than with any other age group. Not only is the child's regular and continued attendance completely dependent on the parents, but their appropriate education of the child and their ability to meet the changing needs of his developing ego decide to a considerable extent how far the analytic material is burdened by the child's reactions to current pathogenic interferences and how far the child can derive lasting benefit from the analytic work.

Although these difficulties pertain also to the analysis of older children, there is a marked difference in degree. The latency child can usually take over some part of the practical responsibilities involved in attending sessions, and his more mature and structured personality can more easily cope with inadequacies in his parents' current educational handling.

It has been our aim to understand better the significant role the parents play, especially the mother, in facilitating or impeding the direct treatment of under-fives. On this basis we have tried to find ways of assessing a mother's capacity for sustained cooperation and means of helping her in this respect.

The Impact of Direct Treatment on the Early Mother-Child Relationship

It is well known that a child's neurosis or other severe emotional disturbance forms a barrier to the natural understanding between mother and child and impedes the harmonious development of the mother-child relationship. Psychoanalytic treatment of the child not only frees the child for healthy maturation but also reestablishes the age-adequate avenues of communication between him and his mother. Yet, when this is initially explained to a mother of an under-five, she does not usually welcome therapeutic help for her child.

This is quite understandable when one considers the meaning of the direct treatment of her young child from the point of view of the mother. To her the child's pathology is not an extraneous barrier impeding her relationship with him. She views it, at least partly, as the unfortunate outcome of her relationship with him and as such it represents to her a failure on her part. In treating her child herself the mother can actively improve this situation, recover her maternal self-esteem and continue her development as a mother. When it is suggested that a therapist, i.e., an outsider to the mother-child relationship, treat the child, the mother often interprets this as a confirmation of her presumed inadequacy. The therapist tends to be seen as the more capable mother with whom the child may establish a better and closer relationship. The months and years which precede the child's improvement may, for the mother, represent a gap in closeness with her child which she fears she may not be able to bridge. The therapeutic intervention is therefore frequently regarded as a threat to the continuing development of the mother-child relationship and even as an obstacle to the mother's further maternal development.

A mother's feeling in this respect is not altogether unjustified. Although the child's treatment aims at restoring the health of the mother-child relationship, the analysis does initially interfere with it. It introduces a third person into a natural twosome. This has inevitable repercussions both on the child (often in terms of a loyalty conflict) and on the mother (in terms of her maternal development) and is not in accordance with a normal developmental step. All other early age-adequate transfers of relationship, such as to teachers or relatives, do not contain confidential aspects from which the mother is excluded.

In cases where the mother's maternal development has reached a level of considerable healthy stability, she may overcome the feelings described above sufficiently to insure her active cooperation in the child's treatment. However, with mothers who have experienced difficulties in their maternal development, such reactions cannot be coped with as readily. Especially when the mother is unaware of her conflicting feelings, they are apt to manifest themselves in lack of initial or later support for the analysis. They may also adversely affect the mother's handling of the child during the course of the treatment.

Thus, a foremost aim of the work is to assess whether, in an individual mother, the described feelings are particularly intense and whether they interfere with the mother's capacity for initial and continued support of the child's treatment. In many cases it is possible to help mothers to clarify these feelings for themselves and to overcome them sufficiently. Only then can the mother concentrate on the task of preparing the child for his treatment.

In some cases it becomes clear that the mother cannot cope with her feelings and therefore either cannot accept the treatment recommended for the child at this time or cannot give the analysis her necessary support. In such instances one may merely aim at ensuring continued contact with the mother so that an analysis for the child can take place at a later date.

Sometimes, the mothers who most readily wish for their child's treatment are the most disturbed in terms of maternal functioning—e.g., one mother who was incapable of consistent mothering rather welcomed the suggestion for the child's analysis because she viewed the therapist as a substitute-mother who would relieve her of her job. Although in such a case the child's analysis is not likely to be interrupted, its chances of helping the child during his prelatency years are greatly reduced.

The Mother's Contribution to Direct Treatment

By merely starting and continuing the therapy a mother does not give enough support to the analysis of her under-five child. For the mother, in turn, it is not enough to be aware of her conflicting feelings about her child's treatment and to resign herself to being a relative outsider. She needs to be an active party in helping him, in order to experience the continuous development of her relationship with him. It therefore has to be stressed with the mother that as educator she retains her close and exclusive relationship with her child, and also takes an important role in the child's treatment to a significant extent. The analysis has a chance of benefiting the young child only when the educational environment created by the parents helps him to meet age-adequate internal and external demands. Later, when during the course of the treatment the child's psychological equilibrium changes, the daily educational measures need to be adapted to these changes to further the child's ego development and to enable him to utilize and stabilize the gains of his analytic work.

During the period of work with the mother which precedes the child's treatment the mother is helped to understand the importance of her educational role and to become a better educator. Many mothers achieve considerable success in this area. As a result their relationship with their child usually improves, the neurotic aspects of the child's personality become more clearly delineated in the mother's understanding of him, and the way is paved for the child's fuller utilization of his treatment. At this time the mother also establishes a working relationship with the therapist which carries over into her regular contacts with him during the course of the child's analysis. (For additional aims of this work prior to and during the child's treatment, see Chapter 8.)

By encouraging the mother's active participation as the educator in the child's treatment, her difficult situation is

somewhat alleviated and the child and his treatment gain the
necessary benefits of her work. The principle of having regular contacts with the mother during her young child's treatment is applied in many centers and by many child analysts.
Our work differs in only two respects: (a) a period of work
with the mother often also precedes the child's treatment, (b)
the therapist who treats the child also works with the mother
in order to enable the mother to cooperate as intimately as
possible with the child's analysis (D. T. Burlingham [1951]
and E. Buxbaum [1954] discuss this subject in greater detail).
There is one parallel to such cooperation by the mother in
her young child's specialized treatment: when the child has a
bodily sickness. With most childhood diseases the mother is
her child's nurse. She adapts her maternal function of bodily
care for her child to his special needs in cooperation with the
child's physician. Even in instances when the child has to be
hospitalized, enlightened pediatricians have increasingly encouraged mothers to nurse their young children themselves.
Many mothers are found to be very capable in this capacity
and find satisfaction in their work in spite of its strain. The
advantages to the child are considerable and the doctor's task
is at least indirectly eased through the patient's greater emotional well-being.

In some cases one finds that a mother is incapable of providing the minimum of educational help for her child. In
such instances—often they are the same ones found to be incapable of supporting the treatment emotionally—one again
aims at continued contact with the mother so that the child
may be treated when he is older. If possible and indicated,
the mother may be helped to gain insight into her own disturbance so that she may decide to seek psychiatric help for
herself. Several mothers entered psychoanalytic treatment or
psychiatric therapy. They did so not in order to help their
children but because their work with their children gave
them insight into their own difficulties which they then

wished to understand and resolve. Whenever a mother was in treatment during the years of her child's nursery school attendance, she continued her work with her child with the help of the usual weekly consultations with the nursery school therapist.

In cases where the child's treatment may materialize only in later years, we have, for the most part, kept the children in the nursery school for the usual full period. This was based on the twofold assumption that (a) this was the best way of continuing regular contact with the mothers and paving the way for the necessary follow-up and (b) the educational environment of the nursery school might help to support the development of those aspects of the child's personality which were not affected by his pathology. The follow-up studies on these cases indicate that individual children profited in very different areas and there are as yet no discernible general trends (see also Chapter 5).

4. Case Reports

ROBERT A. FURMAN, M.D.,
EDWARD J. SCHIFF, M.D., J. BENKENDORF,
and ERNA FURMAN

Treatment of the child under five years of age by way of his parents has many different aspects: the therapist's work with the mother, the teacher's role with the child and with the mother, the interaction of the therapeutic and educational aspects, as well as the insights and understandings the program makes possible. It is impossible in a single case report to adequately describe all these different aspects and their inter-relationships.

We intend, therefore, to present a number of case reports, fully cognizant that each may emphasize, according to the case, one aspect in preference to others. We hope that a series of reports will more fully convey the total picture of treatment via the mother within the therapeutic nursery school.

The first case perhaps emphasizes the actual work with the mother while the second and third strike a balance between that done by the mother and that done by the teachers in assisting her. The fourth case report emphasizes the insights made available for research purposes from the unfolding of the treatment, omitting some details of the work done with the mother.

CASE 1: SALLY[1]

Sally was three years, eight months when her mother began work with me, although the mother had first initiated contact

1 Reported by Robert A. Furman, M.D.

with the school six months earlier. She was self-referred, knowing of our school because she lived only a few blocks away.

The presenting problems were a severe sleep disturbance and bedwetting. Sally could not go to sleep unless everyone in the house was in bed and asleep. She would wake frequently during the night, have trouble going back to sleep, and would wake her mother to tell her so. She was at the time sharing a bed with her mother. Her bedwetting occurred five or six nights of the week. This, like the sleep problem, had been going on for a year. Both started when the parents separated, the father having left the home.

In addition, we observed that Sally had a speech difficulty, which the mother did not mention. Later we also became aware of the tremendous difficulty Sally had with her aggression which was strikingly turned upon herself.

Sally had a brother, age 11, a sister, age eight, a younger brother, age two. Shortly after the birth of the brother, the father had a character change. He began to gamble and drink and had a mistress who lived about a block from the home. The family had gotten progressively in debt. The dependable reliable head of the household changed to a very erratic unreliable one. This led to verbal fights with the mother and then to the father's leaving, before Sally came to us. When the father moved out, Sally replaced him in the bed with the mother.

The family lived in a very close-knit neighborhood. The mother's brother and his family lived in the second floor of their duplex and the maternal grandmother shared the family's first-floor suite. The father's mother lived in an adjacent house, which was on the same lot, and the father's mistress was just down the street.

It would be wise at the outset to summarize Sally's psychological status when we started to work. These observations were made during her first two months in school and are presented in accord with Miss Freud's Developmental Profile (1963).

On the instinctual side her level of libidinal development revealed that she was in contact with oedipal feelings. She had very excited play with a little boy called George who was her boy friend. George was a very thin disguise for her older brother, whose name also was George, and served as a substitute, we felt, for her father. But there was evidence of difficulty with her phallic concerns. She had a preference for slacks, which we thought was not culturally determined, and had great difficulty wearing anything else. Although the mother's taste was excellent, somehow if she got a dress on Sally, by the time she got to school she appeared a most unattractive looking little girl. Nothing feminine would be communicated. Her appearance evidenced the low self-esteem she felt as she failed to convey any feeling of pride or pleasure in herself. Her object relations seemed age-appropriate with her peers, but not with her mother, and it was here that her anxieties forced her into a controlling sadomasochistic level of relating. Her mastery of aggression did not seem age-appropriate, since the only expression that we could observe at school was the sudden impulse to hit teachers, as well as her mother. What was initially only a suggestion of the aggression turned against the self later came into focus quite clearly.

On the ego side, she had an IQ of 124, with no impairment of memory, motility, reality testing. She had impairment in speaking, eating and bladder control. Her main defenses were denial and passive into active. These are best demonstrated, we think, in her beginning school. She acted as if she wasn't being left by her mother at school, and, by running abruptly away from mother, acted as if she were doing the leaving instead. At the end of the day, when the mother came to get her, she would let mother wait, reversing the situation of her having waited all day for the mother to come to her. She used reversal of affect with excited giggling, which came frequently when she felt sad. It was in the areas of eating and sleeping that her difficulties interfered most with her functioning. She was able to manage rules and regulations age-appropriately in the absence of her mother and the teachers.

In her lines of development, there were contrasts. The relationship with her mother was primarily on the anal-sadistic level, that with her peers was age-appropriate. Eating was a fighting ground at home and at school, both about food to be eaten and the manners to be used. She had no bladder control at night. She did seem age-appropriate in her management of her body, except for the feeling with which it was done and for what later emerged as her aggression turned against herself. She was age-appropriate in her companionship with her peers. She played with them, not beside them. She used toys well and was age-appropriate in the transition from body to toy.

Genetically there were pathological fixation points in the oral area, in her speech and eating troubles, and in the anal area, in her relationship to her mother and her mastery of aggression, plus a potential pathological fixation point in the phallic area as evidenced by her wetting and apparent rejection of femininity. Economically, her frustration tolerance, sublimation potential seemed age-adequate. Her ways of coping with anxiety seemed inadequate, resulting in the symptoms already described. Progressive factors were evident in many areas, in marked contrast with the other areas where forward movement had been arrested. The overall picture was one of uneven development.

A summary of the two years' work with the mother, and the work with Sally through the mother, can be divided into five periods: (1) the preparation for and the actual starting of school; (2) start of school until the first spring and the control of Sally's wetting; (3) the first spring until the first summer vacation and the partial resolution of the sleep-separation problem; (4) the second year's work, which was devoted to Sally's oedipal and phallic problems and culminated in her entering latency; (5) the six months after Sally had entered latency and while in kindergarten.

The initial contacts with the mother revealed an utter chaos, with the mother quite overwhelmed. Debts were mounting; there was no reliable income and, when we were starting to work, Sally's younger brother had two hospitalizations for respiratory illnesses. These pressures culminated in the mother's developing dermatitis on her hands, which went just above her wrists—a glove distribution on both sides. In December, about two months after we had started work, she decided that she would go to work and put off Sally's starting school until, as she put it, the father was squared away. I said I thought she had really been waiting for me to square things away since October. She replied with a great deal of feeling that she had been waiting not only since October but since the preceding spring when she made the first contact. After expressing her anger about this, she then decided to work it out, have Sally start school and postpone her getting a job. But when her dermatitis got worse, she impulsively took Sally to the family doctor about her speech and had a so-called tongue tie clipped.

When Sally was about to begin school, the mother brought what she thought Sally's feeling would be: Sally would feel unwanted, hence sad and angry. I told her I was aware that mothers, when their children started in nursery school, often would get a feeling of being a bit unwanted. She then said that the teachers might take over Sally, and what a loss it would be for her. She seemed greatly relieved when I explained that the teachers as well as myself were all there to help her, not to replace her, and that all effort would be funneled through her. This was a bit of a euphemism that later became true.

After the explanation, the mother told me that she was afraid Sally was crazy. I did not realize at the time that she was, in fact, telling me about her husband. We talked of Sally's difficulties, the difference between a child who is upset and someone who is "crazy."

Relieved of her anxiety, she reported that the grandmother had been suspicious of us before, but now liked us.

The first insight that we utilized was primarily mine: "Little Miss Turn Around." Little Miss Turn Around served to cover Sally's defenses against separation feelings, in which she turned everything around—not only situations but also feelings. The mother methodically went along with me discussing Little Miss Turn Around with Sally. The first time I really felt the mother was beginning to work was when she humorously described an episode that happened at her home.

It was at nighttime, Sally's time to go to bed—in fact, it was long past bedtime. Sally was on her way to the apartment upstairs to see her aunt and uncle. The mother merely shook her head and said sympathetically, "It's so hard to go to bed." Sally looked at her mother and said, "Yes, Mommy, I know exactly how you feel." At this point I thought the mother had a feelingful grasp of what Little Miss Turn Around was all about. And this was when I felt the mother really began to be able to use her feeling in understanding Sally. The mother then herself made an observation about the turn-around, noting that the excited hyperactivity was used to ward off Sally's sadness.

Of the second period, until the spring and control of the wetting, I will hit only the high spots. The first observation made by the mother about the wetting was confirmed by a teacher. Sally would inevitably wet on the day or night after the father had visited. Then she recounted a vital bit of history about Sally's wetting. It first occurred on a night shortly after the separation. The father, taking Sally out for a walk, had taken her to where he was then living with his mistress down the street. Although we had established that when Sally couldn't have feelings about the father's visits, it looked as if then she wet, the mother was very feelingless in presenting this to Sally and told her it was the contacts with the father that made Sally wet. "You wet because of your father" was the phrase she used. This was striking because we had previously agreed to first point out to Sally her lack of feeling about father's visits and then to make the connection between the wetting and this lack of feelings.

The mother was surprised after she realized how she had presented it to Sally. At this point, she agreed that her feelings interfered, which made it impossible for her to deal with Sally's difficulties as she wished. On this basis we discussed her feelings about her husband. And only then it became clear to me that the father had had a paranoid episode. His departure was not merely, as she had initially presented it to me, her abandonment in favor of the mistress. The father went through a severe character change with many paranoid features. Once the mother saw this as an illness and not just a rejection of her, she was able for the first time to take active steps through her attorney to get her husband to pay for the maintenance of the family on a regular basis and to limit his visits to prescribed times.

The father was once picked up by the court for not making his payment. Jailed overnight, he had a tremendous outburst against being with Negroes and Jews. From that time, out of fear of jail, he has been making his payments regularly to the family.

From our standpoint the episode was very helpful. When the mother was certain that her husband was ill, she was able to give vent to her anger. One day she said with great feeling. "If I could just get my hands on him." She soon saw the connection of the statement with her hands and her dermatitis. Shortly after, her hands began to clear.

Then she began to be more sympathetic with Sally in their

talks about Sally's feelings toward the father. She helped Sally
with her feelings of sadness, but seemed dubious about my
thought that Sally's wetting had something to do with crying. She finally came around to my side when for the first
time Sally had a succession of dry nights—about three or
four dry nights in a row—and cried in her sleep each night.
The mother was firmly convinced that the tears came instead
of the wetting. When she brought this out to Sally—the connection of the wetting and the crying—then Sally could begin
to have her sad feelings, although she still had some trouble
crying. Crying came freely to her and the wetting truly under
control when Sally could admit to her mother her fear that if
she started to cry, she would be so sad she could never stop
crying.

The mother was now able to get the home in control, rules
enforced. Late in spring she herself went to work. We hated
to have her leave the small boy at home, but the family
needed her income drastically. The mother had a difficult
time going to work; most of all she hated being the wage
earner, her husband's role, and leaving her small children at
home with her mother, who would then take over her role.
Quite naturally, it was a very difficult situation.

Through the two periods, my major goal had been to help
the mother regain control through understanding of the
very difficult reality problem. I had presented it to the mother
that we were working primarily on Sally's wetting, and this
had been our focus in the sessions. But in the instances when
the mother couldn't work with Sally, we learned we had to
look into her feelings that might be interfering.

In the third period, from late spring until summer, we
focused on the sleep problem. The sleep problem wasn't
really very difficult in its resolution. The mother soon said
it was very clear that Sally was staying up late at night to
make sure everyone was in bed and asleep, so that no one
else would leave as the father had. She discussed this with

Sally. Sally did express her fears that her mother might leave, as her father had. Mother told her that she would not, would never leave, as father had. There would be no more leavings. But the separation fears of mother and child took a while to work through and were particularly acute with the coming of summer vacation. The mother responded a bit by losing some of the control that she had gained. She even let the father come and baby-sit a couple of nights for her, which she recognized was not a wise thing to do. The mother herself felt unwanted during the summer and when she could cry about this, she realized that when she felt unwanted, then she felt she couldn't control. She saw that our leaving her for the summer was recalling feelings that she had had when her husband's sickness, in effect, had taken him from her. Then she got back in control for the summer and was amazed how well she managed. During summer vacation, she finally made the move to get Sally out of her bed. She gave the bedroom to Sally and her sister and slept on a lounge chair in the living room.

Most observations at this point had been made in the nursery school, brought to the mother by the teachers, then confirmed at home by the mother and reported to me from there. On the interpretations, the teachers would wait until I discussed them with the mother and she had initiated them at home. But the working through of interpretations was mostly a part of the work of the nursery school, since the mother often could not do it.

Sally's return to school the following fall goes into the fourth section of the work. Her symptoms, except for her speech, were now very much better both controlled externally and internally and her developmental difficulties began to unfold. These were, at this stage, managed by the mother.

Sally returned to school looking much more feminine, but she had an anxiety which she verbalized at school—an anxiety that she might die. We tried to work with this at school, but couldn't understand it. Here, Sally helped us out very much. She showed a table symptom, literally spilling things at the table in school, which she did not do at home. The mother picked up laughingly that Sally was literally and figuratively spilling at school things that belonged at home. We saw then that the death anxiety belonged home and should be sent home. On this basis, with the mother now ready to work, we changed policy and had all problems referred home and did very little interpretive work at school.

Sally could tell her mother her anxiety about dying. When mother was with her she worried mother would leave, and when mother was away, she worried mother would leave soon after she had rejoined her. One time she said, "Are you going out? I wish my Daddy was here." The mother immediately saw Sally feared retaliation for her oedipal jealousy and her wish to lose her mother, and ably handled it by pointing out to Sally she knew sometimes little girls wished mommy would go away and maybe even stay away. But then they got so worried that they felt someone should punish them and later got worried they themselves would die.

Sally feelingfully worked through some of this aggression toward her mother, but only after further work on the aggression toward her father for having left. All this was difficult for her. There were times when she was obviously angry at her mother and had trouble expressing this. During this period she turned her aggression very much against herself at school. It took the forms of accident proneness and hair cutting. Slowly we realized two reasons why Sally had such a hard time directing her anger to her mother. She felt that her mother's omnipotent anger had sent father away since she remembered most clearly the mother's yelling at the father. It was hard for her to accept and understand that mother's yelling was a response to father's illness and not the cause of it. Underneath this, Sally was sure that the mother yelled at the father because Sally so provoked her mother and made her angry. Therefore it really was all Sally's fault. She made mother very angry, so mother sent father away. She felt so guilty about her own anger and felt that her mother's anger was so powerful that she had difficulty in directing aggression to her mother.

Once this was clear, the aggression came forth much more easily. At home when she was angry, she would do little annoying things to provoke punishment from her mother. This came so often that the mother came to understand it quite well. She worked it through with a story of the little girl who wanted punishment for being angry at someone she loved very much. The mother told her this story a number of times. Late one night when she had just put Sally in bed and didn't tell her the story again, Sally asked for the story. She said, "Mommy, tell me the story of the sad angry little girl, who had such a bad conscience, who is so afraid of arguments."

Two other aspects now came to the fore. The first followed the work with the mother about the aggression and concerned what Sally told the mother was her great sad secret. It took a month before she could confide this to her mother. Her great sad secret was that George, whom she was so fond of at school, and Dr. Furman, loved others and not her. The mother handled this very nicely. She interpreted nothing but simply reassured Sally that, yes, it did seem to be that way and that it was hard for her. But if she waited and grew up—it would be hard, it would be a long wait—but if she could wait until she grew up, then she would have a man to herself. After this, Sally blossomed so much in her relationships that a number of people in the home community spontaneously commented on it.

The second aspect concerned bringing sexual information to Sally. The teachers told the mother that Sally manifested signs of her need for this information. We remember trying time after time to get the mother to approach the problem, but it was a place where she had great difficulty. Finally, one day the mother came in with new glasses she had just purchased, and said to me, "Now, I think I can see what you're talking about." She then discussed the proper information with Sally.

The following fall begins the fifth period. Sally was to be in kindergarten until she started first grade in January. She returned to school very much a latency child. She was more relaxed, more free with her peers and even began to enjoy learning in a way we hadn't quite anticipated.

During this period there were a number of events with which she had to cope: her brother's starting in nursery school; her acquisition of glasses and, finally, her leaving the school. Each event aroused old problems for Sally. Her brother's arrival at school revived his arrival at home—his birth, and the start of the father's illness; the glasses made her feel different and bad and aroused in her the phallic aggression that she felt had been at the root of her father's leaving; the leaving from school revived her separation difficulties. We could see transient difficulties appear in school, primarily in the disruption of her good level of functioning. The trouble was resolved by referring it home and explaining it and talking about it with the mother.

Once during the term, her old symptom, wetting, occurred again. Towards the end of the year, the mother of a nursery school child suddenly died. Her brother was, of course, in the same nursery school group. After hearing about the death, Sally asked her mother only one question: Who would take care of the child? She listened without any questions of her own, while the mother gave a very poor religious explanation to the brother in response to his questions about death. The mother suspected she hadn't done very well with the questions so she asked the children to let her think and said she would talk with them again later, because it was an important topic. This was a way of stalling, which we had often discussed. She saw me three days later, and we reviewed her talk. She went back and discussed death again with the children, this time giving them a realistic explanation. Sally again had no questions, but she wet each night in succession during the three days after the first news, until the mother came back with the realistic explanation about death. Sally hardly asked any questions but the realistic discussion apparently was enough to help Sally control her wetting. Since then, she has never wet her bed two nights in a row, and she wet perhaps only once or twice in the following year.

After Sally left kindergarten, the mother was functioning well when she was in weekly contact with me, but not as well when the span was longer than a week or two, such as over the summer holidays. She failed to control the father's erratic visiting, failed to intercept his hollow promises to the children, although she knew they would never be kept. Sally had to deal with this on her own and dealt with it even for her younger brother. The mother heard her tell him once when he complained about daddy and his promises, not to count on anything father promised because you just never knew if he could keep his promise. She added that it makes you angry but that's the way it is.

When she left school to start first grade, we detected no sign of pathology except for her speech, which persisted indistinctly, although improved. We were especially pleased to see her able to be angry verbally in a constructive way. She seemed to get angry only when it was appropriate, and could be effectively verbally angry when her rights had been impinged upon.

Now just a brief summary of the follow-up evaluation a year later. We believe there are a couple of points of interest. What we did in the follow-up was to obtain a report from the school. A social worker went out and got this detailed report. (It took her a full half day there, interviewing teachers, reviewing records.) Sally's report was significant, we think, because she had two different teachers by the end of the year. And they were very different, both in personalities and in their way of operating the class. Yet both of them had uniformly excellent reports for Sally. She was scholastically at the top of her class, making straight A's, had good relationships with both the teachers and the boys and girls in her class. One teacher commented that Sally tended to avoid the out-of-control children, that she had two close girl friends and was the girl in the class most frequently the object of the little boys' attention, and their notes.

The mother reported in the follow-up visit with me and Sally confirmed, when I saw her, the absence of symptoms at home and Sally's pleasure in helping mother and cleaning the house. She was eager and anxious to baby-sit for her aunt's family upstairs as her older sister had often done. She could remember little about our school when she saw me, had forgotten all about George who had been such an important boy friend. When I asked her about this she told me about being teased by the current boy friend named Ricky. She had told mother one of her current fantasies. It went, "Sometimes I think to myself about being a princess, and I make up stories about it." When she saw me she didn't directly tell me the princess fantasy, but she began to draw a picture of a princess and I asked her about princesses. The princesses she told me about seemed so appropriate for an early-latency girl. The princess first of all has a crown. Second, a princess has a castle, where both her mother and father live. For Sally the importance of the latter is obvious.

Her speech was still poor in many ways. For example, there was no "h" in "shirt"—which came out "sirt." It is a lazy type of babyish speech but she is consistently understandable.

I was pleased in the follow-up with the mother's report referrable to Sally's aggression. The mother said, "She won't

look for an argument, but she won't back away from protecting herself." I was not prepared for one thing that happened as a reaction to Sally's return visit to see me. That
night she walked in her sleep for the first and only time in
her life, and she walked in her pajamas, out of her bedroom
out of the apartment, down the stairs, and was headed down
the street following the path that she took whenever she came
to nursery school and kindergarten, also the path that led
past the home of the father's mistress. The mother woke her
—caught up with her on the street. Sally was unaware of
what had happened and had no explanation for it. I saw
the mother just this past week almost another year later and
Sally continues, as far as we can tell, completely asympto-
matic in every way and doing very well in school.

CASE 2: JILL[2]

Jill was three years, 11 months when she was referred
to the Hanna Perkins Nursery School. A small, attractive,
brown-eyed girl, she seemed excessively shy and sad. She was
well coordinated, and her physical health had been excellent.

The immediate reason for the referral was Jill's reaction
in the first nursery school she attended. She had been unduly
frightened by the behavior of some out-of-control boys on
the school bus and at school. Because of her fear she finally
refused to go to school.

Jill and her 22-month-old younger sister were children
whose parents had each been married previously. The father
was a highly successful businessman in his late 30's. He had
an eight-year-old daughter who visited the home frequently,
but whose relationship to the family was not explained fully.
The father seemed a very narcissistic man and quite seductive
with his daughters.

The mother was in her early 30's, had a nine-year-old son

---

[2] Reported by Edward J. Schiff, M.D.

by her first marriage, who had been in psychotherapy for two years because of a learning problem. This boy was extremely disturbed, very often out of control, sexually precocious, exhibitionistic, frighteningly aggressive and without adequate controls by either parent.

When she entered nursery school, Jill had two sets of grandparents who had disturbances that exerted a direct influence on her. Both sets of grandparents tended to be overly affectionate, fondled and kissed excessively, pinched buttocks and cheeks.

The mother's pregnancy with Jill was uncomplicated, and Jill was born at term. All early developmental signposts were within normal limits. She sat up independently at the appropriate time, was weaned without difficulty, walked and talked at the appropriate age. In the early phases of her development there seemed to be neither excessive stimulation nor deprivation.

The toilet-training period was traumatic in a number of ways. Training was initiated in her 18th month without much success. The mother was then five months pregnant, but there was little forcing and apparently no undue strain in the mother-child relationship. The sister was born when Jill was 22 months of age. Jill had not been well prepared by the mother for this event. She did not ask any questions, and very few explanations were given for the birth, the separation from the mother or the arrival of the strange nurse in the home.

In addition, the nurse apparently tried to train Jill forcibly by having her sit on the toilet for long periods of time. The facts were unclear, but the mother suspected that Jill was also spanked at this time. Upon the mother's return from the hospital, the nurse was discharged and training was postponed for approximately six months. Jill was afterwards quickly and easily trained. Note that when the mother returned home from the hospital, she came without Jill's sister; an exchange transfusion was required, and the baby had to remain in the hospital for two weeks. Very little about this was explained to Jill.

The economic situation in the family was good, and the children had always had their own rooms. Because of the lack of supervision, however, the mother's nine-year-old son was able to exhibit to Jill and get her to touch his penis and excited her in many other ways. The boy's behavior proved to be an important factor in Jill's development.

Although the mother knew of the sexual excitations, her response alternated between complete denial and great distress accompanied by furious rages at her son. But she could not consistently protect Jill from the boy's repeated seductions nor from Jill's own internal excitement which caused her to provoke the boy's attacks. She would, for example, undress in front of the boy with the door of her room open, despite the mother's repeated warnings. Also, when the parents went out in the evening, inadequate sitters were often left in charge, causing repetitions of the seductions.

In the beginning of the work with the mother, it was thought that she had many strengths: her warmth toward her children, her love of the girls' femininity and her pleasure in Jill's accomplishments. Moreover, her own verbal facility enabled Jill to become a very verbal child. Most of the mother's weaknesses were a result of her defenses, particularly her denial of Jill's repeated seductions and their effect. Another problem was her inability to prepare Jill for difficult or potentially traumatic events. She found it hard to be consistent. She would sometimes keep a close watch over her son, sometimes unconsciously permit exciting games and seductions.

At first the mother appeared to be quite narcissistic: more interested in herself, her clothing and material possessions than in her children. This seeming narcissism was later understood to be a defense against her own anxiety and feelings of inadequacy.

The father, too, showed undue denial of the implications of his stepson's sexual activity toward his daughter. He shared with his wife a tendency to intellectualize and interpret instinctual material inappropriately. Their inappropriate explanations, instead of affording relief, excited and confused Jill.

The mother was in psychotherapy herself, but this seemed only to increase her own difficulties. Instead of helping her overcome her conflicts, the treatment tended to strengthen her crippling defenses and to promote acting out, especially in regard to her children.

Early in the work with the mother, it was learned that the boy had been repeatedly seduced by his own father from at least age three, when the mother was divorced, until age six, when the stepfather was able to secure custody of the child and adopt him. This information was disclosed in the boy's psychotherapy.

Early Assessment

Jill was in the phallic level of development and had many questions about sexual differences. There was a contamination of phallic interests by anal material, with much excitement about B.M.s and B.M. activity. Jill would frequently draw attention to her anal area. Prior to beginning nursery school, she had a mild anal fissure, which the mother treated by applying an ointment. Jill derived great pleasure from the mother's attention and many times tried to get her to repeat the anal stimulation. Jill's object relationships were both sadomasochistic and exhibitionistic. With her mother she was often involved in a sadomasochistic struggle; with her stepbrother, highly exhibitionistic.

Jill's ego apparatus was intact and all ego functions were age-appropriate. I noted early on that she used certain defenses. One was reaction formation, as shown in her excessive cleanliness, neatness and orderliness. Another was passive-to-active. Jill had been the object of considerable exhibitionism, now she herself tended to exhibit to her stepbrother. Projection was also often used; she felt that boys wished to attack her and through projection she avoided her aggressive and sexual feelings toward boys. This defense interfered with her relationships with other children, especially boys, and made separation from her mother difficult. Jill's excessive use of another defense, denial, interfered with her understanding of sexual differences. In her play with other children, her strong reaction formation was an inhibitory factor. It inhibited her use of play materials that reminded her of dirt; she could not play with clay or sand or paints.

Jill's conflict was primarily an internal one. Her anxiety and fear, which were at least partially a result of the repeated seductions and frightening experiences with the stepbrother, were carried over into other situations and other relationships. Examples were her fear while riding on the bus, her anxiety about separations from her mother and her fear of excited boys. Her frustration tolerance was low, especially in regard to libidinal impulses which threatened to overwhelm her when not protected by her mother's presence. There was little evidence of neutralized energy available, and there was an inhibition in creative play.

Work with the Mother

Jill attended the nursery school for a year and a quarter, during which time many things were worked through via the mother. The mother's success lay in her warmth and perceptiveness, as well as in her capacity to identify with the aims of the therapeutic work and the goals of the school.

Because of Jill's referral—her anxiety about separation from the mother and about being with boys—an attempt was made to define her relationship with her stepbrother.

The stepbrother's exhibiting to her had at least a two-year history at the time of the referral. Jill apparently had been enjoying his exhibitionism and turned passive into active by exhibiting both to him and to her younger sister, just as the boy himself had turned passive into active by exhibiting to Jill. The mother denied her son's exhibitionism which had been forcibly brought to her attention by his therapist. It soon became evident that her denial was an attempt to protect herself from an overwhelming guilt.

Her son's exhibitionism was only one of several reality events which the mother denied. Another was the impact of the birth of a sibling on Jill, then 22 months old. When she began to discuss these events with me, her feelings of guilt and lack of self-esteem came to the fore.

The mother spoke of her apprehension that she could do nothing right for her children. She admitted that she wanted her husband to take over so that she could avoid feeling inadequate; she was very angry with him for putting community interests before his family. Gradually she came to understand that by effectively denying various reality events and their significance, she protected herself against an overwhelming guilt—for everything she had allowed her son to witness, for her first marriage to a very severely disturbed man and for her daughter's seductions.

This early work with the mother had the effect of bringing her many feelings of sadness and lowered self-esteem into the discussions. In addition, it had an important implication for future work. The mother now began to recognize that by facing her own feelings in regard to Jill she would be freeing herself to be available to help Jill work through her feelings, both current and past ones.

With further discussions, the mother gradually recognized that she had always been afraid of the intensity of her own feelings. Slowly she came to understand that strong, unpleasant, and disturbing as her guilty feelings were, the associated events were in the past, and by facing her feelings about Jill she would help Jill cope with her own.

A significant step was her recognizing that her denial had not really protected her from her guilt but had actually been destructive, in that it allowed many events that interfered with Jill's progress in development. This helped the mother realize that her careful observations and active work offered Jill a protection she had not had before.

The mother's first active work was to provide adequate supervision in the home. This was difficult in view of her anxiety that she might fail, plus her anger over literally having to police the children at all times, which limited her freedom. To her surprise, the price of her limited freedom was well worth the relief of her guilt. With this relief she was more able to discuss her anxiety about herself as a mother and her current handling of Jill. Also she could examine more closely some things she was doing and their effect upon Jill.

One was her practice of washing Jill's genitalia in the bath. She now recognized that Jill was quite able to do this herself. Recently Jill had put a bobby pin in her anus. This incident, which occurred when she was sexually excited, was aimed to secure attention to her anus. The mother, now aware of Jill's motive, talked with her about her wish to be stimulated anally by the use of creams and ointments for minor anal inflammations. Jill acknowledged her pleasure in the anal attention and asked many questions about her anus and vagina and their functions.

The incident helped the mother consider other areas of Jill's life. She thought of the grandfather's behavior with the children; he kissed too much and pinched buttocks. The mother had allowed this behavior in deference to her father's mild depression and sensitive feelings. There proved to be several ways of coping with her father. One was to unobtrusively protect the children by handling visits differently; another was to discuss with Jill her behavior with her grandfather (teasing, excitement, laughter and chasing games).

It was an important discovery for the mother to understand that she was not a helpless little girl but an active mother protecting her children against undue excitement. Her newly found activeness, in both words and actions, afforded her further relief.

She soon discovered another area where her guilt had interfered, this time in relation to reality. Jill had often asked questions about family relationships, which the mother tended to evade. After discussing the reasons for her evasion (her guilt in relation to her first husband), the mother was slowly able to untangle for Jill her own earlier marriage and her father's earlier marriage and which children came from which union.

After the mother's denial and feelings of guilt had been worked through to some extent, a second major obstacle had to be dealt with: her tendency to intellectualize everything. She flooded Jill with interpretations of instinctual material, both sexual and aggressive, much too early and in a very confusing way. This stopped any verbal expression of feeling on Jill's part.

The mother recognized she did this primarily to overcome her own anxiety and feelings of guilt. She rationalized that if she gave detailed explanations, Jill would feel more protected when she entered puberty. The mother now understood that instead of enlarging Jill's horizons, her explanations effectively prevented Jill from expressing her feelings. Realizing all this, she was able to help her husband control the same tendency. Now, instead of giving Jill intellectual explanations why she liked to play exciting games with her sister and her stepbrother, the mother simply stopped the games firmly, pointed out to Jill how excited

she was and explained that these were feelings Jill should
discuss with her mother.

The mother's tendency to use intellectual explanations to
avoid feelings was strikingly illustrated by a particular event.
If it had happened earlier, the mother would undoubtedly
have overlooked some of Jill's anxieties and sexual curiosi-
ties. A boy, the brother's friend, was to have an operation.
Jill brought some questions to her mother, which the mother
began to answer factually. (The boy had an undescended
testicle.) This time, however, before launching into a long
intellectual discussion, she caught herself and gave a very
simple explanation; she then asked Jill what her thoughts
and questions were.

Jill wondered whether the boy was going to be made into
a girl; if this was possible, whether she could be made into
a boy. This was a fortunate example because it demonstrated convincingly to the mother the many other questions
Jill must have had previously, which had been shut off.
As the mother listened to Jill, she recognized that Jill's angry
feelings about being a girl changed to an accusation that the
mother loved only babies (Jill's sister). Jill then began to
baby-talk, and the mother interpreted her wish to be a baby.
Although this interpretation was indeed correct, it became
apparent in subsequent discussions with the mother that
Jill, shut off too quickly, had withdrawn. The mother saw
that she often interpreted too quickly because she wanted
to reassure and protect Jill from feelings of anxiety, which
she later realized were her own. Suppose she had no answer?
She was afraid of making another error, hence more guilt.

The next task was focused on helping Jill with her feelings
of excitement and the anxiety associated with these. Jill
told her mother about a sitter, an adolescent girl from next
door, exhibiting to her by going to the toilet in front of Jill.
Jill asked questions about vaginas, pubic hair, urination.
Although the mother was distressed for having allowed this

to happen, it did not prevent her being appropriately active. She made sure that when the bathroom was occupied, the door was closed. She also discussed the subject with the sitter, in a nonpunitive way and explained to her why she cannot continue sitting with her children. She then discussed the entire episode with Jill so that Jill herself would not feel guilty.

Jill's fears and occasional wetting at school were discussed in the context of her feeling that to be away from her mother was to be unprotected (from libidinal impulses). It took considerable time for both the mother and the teachers to help Jill understand that the teachers, too, could protect her.

The mother gained further understanding of Jill's excited feelings when we discussed an incident in which Jill complained that her vagina hurt. The mother told her that all little girls have excited feelings, that these are private feelings, but that Jill had a special worry about them because of her stepbrother's out-of-control behavior. Jill stopped complaining about vaginal pain and instead demonstrated to her mother her wish to be a boy by trying to urinate standing up. The mother then explained to Jill her wish to be a boy, later adding that Jill must feel that if she had a penis she would never have been so frightened and overwhelmed by her stepbrother, and would have had something to show, as he did.

As summer vacation approached, both Jill and her mother began to dread the closing of school. The mother was afraid she could not manage without the school, and Jill was afraid she could not manage without the protection afforded by the teachers (against her libidinal impulses). In particular, the mother was concerned about handling her own sad separation feelings and whether she could remain firm without the help of the continued discussions. When she understood her own separation feelings, she was able to discuss Jill's feelings more effectively with her.

One of Jill's feelings on the separation was anger. Her observation that a teacher was pregnant brought her angry feelings toward her sister into focus. It reminded her of the time when her mother left for the hospital without much explanation and returned without the baby Jill expected. Jill now wondered whether her mother was going to have another baby. The mother helped her see the feelings she had at the time, about which she had so few words, and explained their connection with Jill's angry feelings about the current separation. The mother also helped her see that her feelings about the baby did not cause the sister's sick blood that had to be replaced, and that Jill's present anger could not cause a recurrence of the younger sister's former condition.

The discussion with Jill revived the mother's feelings about the younger child's neonatal erythroblastic disease. She remembered she had feared the baby would be defective, and the blood problem had confirmed this for her. As a result she had been depressed and in many ways unavailable to Jill for a number of months following the birth of the younger sister—the time of the seductions by the stepbrother.

Jill's anxiety about leaving school was demonstrated to her mother when Jill became frightened on a picnic. She fantasied that there were Indians in the trees (who could hurt her), that a policeman might arrest her, that she might die. The mother thought Jill was trying to say that if she were unprotected by the school and the teachers, something might happen to her; she could be exhibited to or herself exhibit, especially in the summer when the stepbrother was around more often.

After this discussion the mother assured Jill she would protect her in every possible way from the stepbrother, as well as from her own wishes and fears about getting out of control.

Jill then told her mother she felt sad about leaving school for the summer. The mother was able to help her with this feeling since she had previously recognized that she herself was sad and apprehensive about the summer vacation. The mother's feelings came into focus when she said how difficult it was to be a mother of three children whom she had to supervise constantly, in addition to sensing their feelings. Her recognition of her own angry feelings toward the school helped her to cope remarkably well during the summer.

After vacation, Jill's passive-to-active mechanism changed. She asked her father frequently about his penis, handling by words the feelings she formerly handled by actions (showing and looking). She asked her mother about breasts or milk for babies and would then tease her father with the same questions when alone with him. She did this partly because she was Jill, partly because the mother gave her inadequate answers and partly because the father enjoyed Jill's bringing these questions to him.

After some thought, the mother suggested to the father that he tell Jill she could discuss these things with her mother. The father responded positively (although not without some annoyance) and told Jill he knew how excited she felt but that it would be preferable for her to discuss her feelings with her mother rather than with him. Accordingly, Jill had no choice but to bring her feelings to her mother. The mother explained to Jill that by not wearing a bathrobe she was exciting her stepbrother's curiosity and interest. She reminded her that all girls her age had excited feelings, but that Jill also had special feelings of excitement because of her experience with the stepbrother.

A further opportunity to help Jill with her excited feelings occurred in the bath. She asked her mother to wash her genitals and the mother refused, whereupon Jill got angry and vomited. The mother then explained to her how frightened she must be of her out-of-control excited feelings. Jill confirmed this by telling her mother that the teacher at the nursery school read a teacher's book during naptime and so could not see what the children were doing.

Many other sexual questions were brought to the mother by Jill. Still stimulated by the teacher's pregnancy, she continued to ask about babies. The mother handled these questions quite realistically, as Jill expressed angry feelings to her mother about being a girl. She now expressed her wish to be old enough to have a baby herself.

Jill became concerned about her body when her mother developed a breast tumor. The mother expressed her own overwhelming anxiety about the tumor in our discussions. She was afraid she had a malignancy and that she would lose her breast (a highly cathected part of her body) and wondered how to discuss all this with Jill. But after expressing these feelings in one of our sessions, she was able to reassure Jill (as she had been reassured by the surgeon) that she would not lose her breast.

Jill showed her concern in a number of ways. She got very angry with her mother, a reflection of her anxiety that something might happen to her mother. Later this feeling was turned upon herself as she identified with a girl in the nursery school who had a defective eye and worried about this girl. When Jill developed a small sty on her eye, she related it to the other child's eye, then to her mother's breast tumor and finally to her feeling of being defective because she was a girl. She was able to discuss all this with her mother, which proved very helpful to the mother and her work with Jill.

A positive benefit for the mother in her work with Jill was her increasing pleasure in Jill's original and creative work. As both the creative work and the mother's interest in it developed, the reaction formation noted earlier seemed to be less intense and less inhibiting.

The following is a summary of the work with the mother.

At the beginning, the mother appeared withdrawn and distant, with a marked tendency toward intellectualization. As the work progressed, she emerged as an extremely warm, friendly and insightful person, not without many inner conflicts, to be sure, but well able to give of herself to her family. She changed markedly over the period of a year and a quarter, primarily because she was able to express her own feelings, which in turn became the route to a more effective understanding of Jill's feelings. This better understanding on the part of the mother encouraged Jill to express her feelings, which the mother could then interpret for her at the various levels that were appropriate. The mother's pleasure in Jill as she progressed in development was obvious to everyone. Her ability to help her daughter despite considerable anxiety in relation to some family problems was a great credit to her.

Role of the Nursery School

The therapeutic work done by the mother directly with Jill was supplemented by the nursery school, which played a most important role in Jill's development and in the mastery of her problems. The teachers had been informed by the mother about Jill's seduction by her stepbrother and her fear of boys at the first nursery school and were therefore prepared for Jill's reaction to other children. Initially she was assigned a special teacher, who was available to help her whenever she was particularly worried about the other children or was bothered by her separation feelings. The teachers, by knowing the reason for Jill's anxiety about boys and her difficulty in being with a group of boys or girls (her constant fear of attack, as well as her fear of provoking attack because of her own excitement), were able to help her express some of her feelings of anger, sadness and anxiety at appropriate times. As Jill gradually became able to tell the teachers about these feelings, she was afforded a protection against both her aggressive and her sexual wishes.

The role of the teachers especially early in the work, was quite essential. Initially, the mother's defenses, especially her intellectualization and denial, interfered with her effectiveness in helping Jill verbalize her feelings; thus Jill felt unprotected. As the work progressed, the teachers, by their example of preparing Jill for various events, were most helpful in educating the mother, hence in educating Jill. At the beginning of her nursery school attendance, Jill used the teachers as objects of need-fulfillment, in much the same way as she had used her mother. Later she came to regard the teachers as people in the outer world with whom relationships could be formed rather than as mother substitutes.

Equally as important as the relationship between the teachers and Jill was the strong relationship that the mother formed with the teachers, with whom she identified. Her self-esteem as an effective mother was a by-product of the teacher's interest in both herself and Jill. As a result she was able to express her warmth and love for Jill in an atmosphere of reassurance and acceptance.

Work with the Father

The father has been mentioned only briefly at the beginning of this report. During the year and a quarter of therapeutic work with Jill he was most cooperative. Despite his own internal difficulties, he was able to be quite feelingful and warm toward his children and to support his wife's involvement in the school and her work with their daughter. During this time the father was seen monthly. Toward the end of this period he suffered some business reversals, which caused him to withdraw and to become depressed. Although this depression had a considerable effect upon his wife and children, it did not interfere with Jill's continued progress and development.

Assessment after 15 Months of Treatment via the Mother

When Jill left the nursery school she was five years old and was firmly in the phallic oedipal phase of development. For a year and a quarter there had been a gradual shift from an interest in B.M.s to a greater interest in sexual differences, with much less confusion about these differences. She now had more exact knowledge about sex and birth and was full of questions and fantasies about growing up, marriage, brides and babies. Her fondest wish was to become a bride, and she talked about this frequently.

Jill's relationship with other children went through several phases. At first she allowed herself limited group play with girls, but not with boys. Gradually, however, she became more a part of the entire group. With boys she was often both excited and fearful. Then came a period of several months when she regressed to playing with only a few children, clinging to the teacher and appearing very sad. This behavior always coincided with separations from the school for vacations, as well as with the father's mild depression and the mother's reaction to this.

Despite the periods of temporary regression toward the end of the nursery school year, Jill was able to relate more fully both to children and to teachers than she had previously. She became an active member of the group, although still retaining some reserve about participating completely in all group activities.

Over the year her expression of aggression changed. She became freer to express anger openly and was much more appropriate in showing anger toward her sister and her mother. With other children her anger became quite verbal, an expression which had not been possible earlier. She now stood up for her rights, had much less anxiety and was able to say what she thought.

Jill's defensive structure also changed during this period.

This was one of the most important points in her continuing development. There were changes in the defenses already mentioned, including reaction formation, passive-to-active, projection and denial.

Her reaction formation remained as a defense but was much less intense than formerly. Its major manifestation was in her mild anxiety when toys and clothes were not in place at home. Jill could now tolerate being dirty, having her clothing torn, and she was able to share, whereas a year previously this would have been impossible. The passive-to-active defense (used earlier to provoke attacks by her step-brother) lessened markedly. Projection and denial were very much less in evidence. Another prominent defense mechanism, which earlier had been habitual, was now used only in specific situations. This was a regression to clinging behavior, withdrawal and sadness. With separations, Jill would still appear sad and lonely. Jealousy and rivalry with her sister and changes in the mother's or the father's mood would also at times result in clinging behavior.

When Jill left the nursery school she was very much in the oedipal phase of development. Her mother continued to discuss her oedipal fantasies with her as Jill brought her questions more and more openly.

Jill's conflict was primarily an internal one. There may have been the beginning of some neurotic conflict (as evidenced by a remaining reaction formation, a fear of separation and a tendency still to express sexual excitement openly), but because she *was* in the phallic oedipal phase of development it was thought too early to assess the degree of neurotic conflict.

Jill still had a lowered tolerance to frustration, and it was still difficult for her to cope with libidinal impulses as a result of overstimulation from the environment. Nonetheless there was more control of these impulses than formerly.

Jill's sublimation potential widened markedly in the year

and a quarter of therapeutic work. She made many gains in her ability to play creatively and to do original work with various playschool materials. She began to learn to read and say her numbers and showed obvious pleasure in the mastery of these tasks. There was evidence of sublimation in her continuing and expanding interest in clothing, colors, textures and designs.

Follow-up

Five years after Jill left the therapeutic nursery school a follow-up study was done.

The follow-up process included several interviews with the mother, an interview with Jill and a visit by the social worker who was assisting in the study to the public school that Jill attended. Jill was now in the fourth grade. There was an opportunity for an interview with both the third-grade and the fourth-grade teacher. Some shyness in Jill was noted by the third-grade teacher; very little by the fourth-grade teacher, who considered Jill bright, alert, outgoing and a leader among the children. Her grades were quite good.

The mother reported that Jill was very busy with many outside activities, including Girl Scouts, piano lessons, dancing and extra classes in religious instruction. In all these pursuits she was successful. Areas of mild difficulty were noted by the mother especially in Jill's intense competitiveness and occasional jealousy in relation to her younger sister, who was rapidly catching up in physical size. Jill's small physical stature was a source of concern to Jill. The previous summer she had attended a day camp, where she had excelled in various group activities.

In the interview I had with Jill she appeared slightly shy. She remembered the nursery school and the teachers. She was able to talk about her stepbrother and admit her relief that he was away at boarding school, where he had been for three years. She spoke of family activities with considerable warmth and interest and could be really spontaneous when talking about school and her outside activities.

Both the history and the interviews showed Jill to be a child firmly in latency, the gains of the treatment via the mother apparently well maintained.

CASE 3: MARTIN[3]

By the time Martin enrolled at our school at four years, three months, he had endured three unsatisfactory nursery school experiences.

Because he was an only child, lacking companionship of other children, his mother had taken him to join a neighborhood nursery group when he was almost three. The teacher disciplined the children by giving them a good shaking and talking to them loudly. The first instance this happened to Martin, he got so upset that he would not return to the group.

Martin stayed home until the family moved and then entered another nursery school at age three years, three months. The parents were not expected to visit, but when Martin complained, after some months, that he spent much of the time being put into a corner, the mother did investigate the situation. She found the nursery school overcrowded and understaffed and removed Martin. She could not establish why Martin had been excluded so frequently.

Martin was then returned to the original nursery group (though not the same teacher) and now there was no uncertainty why he could not remain with the group. Within one month he was asked to leave since several mothers had threatened to withdraw their children because of his constant unprovoked attacks.

Around the time of this exclusion, six months before Martin came to us, the parents noticed a definite change in the child. Although he had always been a very active and deter-

[3] Reported by Joanne Benkendorf.

mined boy, he had been manageable at home and friendly with outsiders. This time he began to make seemingly unprovoked physical and verbal attacks on people. Previously he had responded to strangers on the bus or street with a friendly hello, now he told them he did not like them, they should go away. Martin would be upset by visitors, grab their possessions, such as pens and umbrellas, although the parents were excluded from his attacks, both physical and verbal. In addition to his aggressive behavior Martin had bouts of hyperactivity, occasional nightmares and at times wet his bed. He had some specific eating problems, centered mainly on the appearance and origin of foods. He was afraid of the wind and of handicapped people.

Martin was a well built, good-looking boy, with strikingly mobile facial expressions. He could have the most winning affectionate smile, as well as a complete distortion of his features.

Martin's parents impressed everyone with their concern about their son and their devotion to him. Both tried to keep their home life as harmonious and peaceful as possible. This seemed centered around their child and his demands and both parents showed an unusual tolerance. Martin was included whenever possible, often being the only child in a group of adults.

The father, a soft-spoken, gentle person, was able to largely overlook what he called "ugly" events in Martin's life. He had unending patience and "things have to go very far until he will call them terrible."

His mother could maintain this only up to a point, when she would resort to spanking with a hairbrush. These were quite infrequent occurrences, and she always felt very guilty afterwards. After some weeks of nursery school Martin was glad to report that his mother's brush would only be used for her hair from now on.

The mother experienced considerable difficulties conceiving Martin, and continued to have a hard time during her pregnancy and delivery. Yet she wanted to plan for another child soon after the baby was born. However, the father contracted TB some weeks before Martin's birth and when Martin was five weeks old the father was hospitalized for eight months.

This was a very distressing time for the mother who visited her husband daily at the hospital. She breastfed the baby throughout and he accepted the once-daily bottle while she was absent very well.

When Martin was nine months old the father returned from the hospital. It was felt that Martin resented his presence for the first week, but the father took care of the child a good deal and after a short time their relationship was established. One of his lungs remained collapsed and he continued to receive weekly treatments. No explanation had been given to Martin and his concern about germs at a later stage showed his preoccupation with his father's illness.

According to the mother, "up to 14 months, Martin was a doll." He was healthy, ate and slept well. Gradually he gave up the bottle, except for one at night which he kept until he was two years, six months. Three important developmental steps occurred at 14 months: Martin began to feed himself, he started toilet training and he began to walk. He became a very active and determined toddler.

Self-feeding and toilet training presented no particular problems. Martin showed an early discrimination in his choice of foods and disliked their being mixed up. Although of changeable nature, Martin had retained some difficulties in this area. He was toilet-trained at two years, taking a very active part in this accomplishment. Except for the occasional bedwetting, he maintained bladder and bowel control.

All his life Martin had lived in an apartment, mostly on

an upper floor, which may have put more than the usual restrictions on his freedom of movement. Once he was upright he never walked but ran, and showed an insatiable need for large motoractivity. He became an incurable climber. The parents installed climbing equipment in his bedroom but Martin found it very hard to restrict himself to it and had to be watched constantly. He moved about very quickly and it was difficult to keep up with him and protect him from getting hurt. This lasted well into his third year and whoever took care of Martin was constantly concerned about his physical safety. It played a major part in making Martin's first separation from his parents such an upsetting and significant event.

When Martin was two years, six months, the parents took a weekend trip and Martin stayed with his paternal grandparents in a nearby city. The grandmother could not adjust to his active behavior and speed, hovered over him anxiously and was convinced something would happen to him while in her care. She warned him constantly that he would "break his neck or legs, knock off his head." This conviction never seemed to leave her and when at five years Martin broke a bone in his foot jumping from a fire escape, her comment was, "I have always said he will grow up with one leg." The weekend stay went very badly and Martin reacted with increased activity to grandmother's alarming warnings. They were both much relieved when the parents took over.

Martin said his first words when he was a year; about six months after, he could carry on a conversation. Essentially there has always been good verbal communication between Martin and his parents. His health has always been good and he had no unusual medical experiences.

When Martin was tested he managed his age level with self-confidence and enjoyed the 100% success; however, the first failure at the next age level made him give up completely. Hence his IQ of 117 was not as much a true estimate as an indication of his low frustration tolerance, his abrupt giving up when effort and persistence were required and when it meant possible failure.

Martin was four years, three months when he started our nursery school and stayed with us for 18 months. Throughout his stay he proved a continuous challenge to the teaching staff. His behavior demanded great skill, patience and understanding on their behalf so that they could extend all possible help to Martin without neglecting the group and the individual needs of the other children.

When the mother started to work with me, she was not only deeply concerned about Martin's problems, but was also quite puzzled by them and the kind of behavior they produced, all the more since the severe instances occurred in her absence.

Asked to give examples of Martin's aggressions, the mother told of a foreign-born, elderly man who lived across the hall, was very fond of Martin and the family and frequently invited the boy to his apartment. The mother noticed that recently Martin had raised his arms defensively when the man entered their apartment. Martin was sent home occasionally from a visit because of bad behavior, though the mother did not seem to know what exactly happened. However the mother did know that the neighbor was constantly "teasing and joking" with the boy. He would tell him, "I have taken off your nose," and pretend to put it into his pocket; he would threaten to "bite off your ears," "hide your bellybutton." Furthermore he delighted in telling the most gruesome stories. On one of his visits, Martin was naughty and the man, whose name incidentally is almost identical to Martin's, was going to call the police to put Martin in jail. Jail was pictured as a place where one is exposed to sadistic attacks by the police and to rats and poison.

The mother considered Martin an utterly fearless child (apart from his fear of the wind and handicapped people).

He had never minded seeing the doctor nor going to the barber, the mother often leaving him there to get his hair cut on his own. She gave a lively demonstration of how she had actually to instill some fear of heights into him. When he had climbed so freely on their third-floor open porch, the mother had taken one of his plastic cars and forcefully thrown it on the cement where it smashed to pieces. She told him, "In this way all your little bones will be broken should you fall off the porch."

Anyone who met Martin in the nursery setting could not help but be impressed by the intensity of his anxiety. In relation to the teachers or any adult present, Martin felt very distrusting; he had to continuously test their ability to protect him. Past experiences led him to expect danger in the absence of his mother and he was compelled to assure himself of his safety in school, in spite of all verbal assurances and, of course, repeated proof. Will the teachers protect him from hurting others and the resulting actual or feared attacks? What means will the teachers use to control him and the other children? When a girl was temporarily excluded from the lunch table, Martin asked anxiously, "Will you call the police?" He thought teachers would stop the children from hurting him "with whips and straps." Finally he announced, "I do not need a teacher to protect me, I can do it myself, I will bring a gun tomorrow."

His relationship with the other children was also full of dangers. He soon singled out those who had poor control of their aggression and proceeded to attack them. For instance, since biting seemed to threaten him most, the boy in the group with the known biting problem became the target of Martin's attacks—including biting—without evident provocation. When he singled out two girls for his verbal and physical attacks, it was his way of showing the concern their "defect" aroused (one was somewhat handicapped in her movements, both had difficulties with speech).

In spite of his strenuous efforts Martin was unable to ward off his anxiety. His persistent identification with the aggressor, turning passive into active and projecting his aggression onto the people in his environment, proved inadequate. It also brought him into constant conflict with his environment, which he had to control at all cost. He was most unhappy not to be liked by the group, yet his need to be feared by them and to put them in as unprotected a position as he was exposed to, took precedent. When frightened, Martin would dramatically change, accurately mimicking the facial expressions and behavior of his frightening neighbor, presenting the children with dire threats.

From the start the teachers somehow conveyed to Martin that they were aware of his fears. He was told, for instance, "Some children fight when they are angry and some when they are afraid."

Martin's ability to concentrate on any sustained activity was severely curtailed; he was exceedingly restless and darted from one thing to the next. He was unable to share, wait, take turns, play fair, listen to or follow rules. It was quite impossible for him to stay put. Activities like music and fingerpainting proved so exciting that they had to be postponed for some months.

Martin's most urgent problem—his overwhelming fears, particularly of castration and the ways he dealt with it— was in no way apparent to the mother. Initial attempts to make her understand that Martin had overwhelming fears met with disbelief. It was primarily her confidence in our work that made her promptly follow my recommendations to reduce Martin's contact with the neighbor to an absolute minimum and then, only in her presence. In fact she felt bad depriving those "kind people," whose grown-up children and their families had moved away, of Martin's company.

During the initial weeks, Martin's mother spent most of the days watching him at school (unseen by Martin) and for the first time saw the full range of his behavior and how it was handled by the teachers. Their early recognition of Martin's difficulties as based on fears, which Martin confirmed at every instance, was invaluable in convincing the mother that the boy was afraid. She was deeply impressed by what she had observed. During one lunch time, for instance, an upset Martin changed his appearance completely. He hunched up his shoulders, walked like an old man, distorted his features and, in a teasing voice, threatened the children around him. The mother was shocked to see Martin behave like their tormenting neighbor, both in appearance and action.

When the mother returned for her work with me following a week's observation of Martin, she had for the first time accepted his fears. She wondered how she could have missed noticing it and said, "But he never *says* he is afraid." This proved a good starting point to explain that Martin needed to hide the nature and extent of his fears from himself and consequently from others. Shocked to see Martin look and act like the neighbor, she began to recognize his "jet-propelled," aggressive behavior occurred when he was worried. These defenses and expressions of anxiety she explained to Martin.

For Martin, the separation from his mother at nursery school had special connotations. The mother felt openly sad and aware of her reluctance to let him stay the who'e day and she could readily help him with his feelings of sadness. It was much more difficult and painful for her to recognize and deal with all the anxiety arousing aspects and experiences linked to separations, and the resulting anger for being left poorly protected. For the mother it meant reviewing past and present separations and their significance for her child. Fortunately she could face and tolerate her ensu-

ing feelings of having failed her child and welcomed the
opportunity to make up for past mistakes. Work on the
separations proved complex, lengthy and repetitive, and we
had to keep working it through until Martin left the nursery
for public school.

As soon as the mother was able to tell Martin of her sincere regret for all the scary things that happened to him in
her absence and promised to protect him from such experiences, a vital change occurred in their relationship. For
the first time, Martin could reveal his worries in words. He
was so relieved that he flooded his mother with reports of his
fears. This was not surprising to the teachers who had seen
Martin's grateful response to their knowing that he was
afraid.

While struggling with the imposed passivity of naptime,
he would ask, "Could I be a mummy? I might want to." He
was curious about the sex of his toy monkey and thought
it was a boy because he wore a hat. Simultaneously, he expressed his dislike of girls, "Did their wee wee get hurt?"
His attacks were concentrated on girls, threatening to bite off
their noses or taking a precious belonging, such as a candy
or toy, from their locker.

This proved one of many occasions when Martin was a
step ahead of his mother. Whereas earlier in his childhood
she had to hurry to keep up with him physically, she now
had to catch up with his emotional needs. These periods,
which fortunately never lasted long, needed careful coordination between nursery school, therapist and parent. Martin
was told that it was best to take his questions to his mother
who was learning to understand and help him with such
worries.

At home, Martin responded well to the mother's continued
work on his defenses. She recognized herself that Martin's
acute dislikes, i.e., girls, masked his being afraid of them.
In this connection she recalled that on a visit some time ago

Martin met a very forceful girl, who undressed herself, bit him quite badly and locked him in a toy chest by sitting on its lid. This, too, the mother now thoughtfully discussed with Martin.

The mother needed a great deal of help to cope with the sexual questions raised by her child. Although her pace of progress at first did not match Martin's urgent needs, she soon trusted herself enough to deal with his sexual curiosity and castration fears with increasing security and sympathy.

The bathroom rule was changed so that everyone had privacy and Martin who previously had not shown any verbal interest in his or other people's bodies, did so freely. The mother was able to clear up much confusion about pregnancy and conception, which up to this time had been explained as the function of "mother nature." When he asked about sexual differences, the trend of his questions concerned harm and damage to parts of the body.

His fear of the wind was resolved when he was given the answer to his question, "But could not the wind blow *it* off?" His fear of handicapped people was overcome about this time, too.

Both at home and school Martin was extremely upset by physical pain and for a brief time could not bear to look nor touch the painful spot. Once when he bumped his head, he kept asking the mother anxiously, "Have I knocked it off?" He was greatly relieved when the mother placed his hand onto his head. On her own, the mother saw the grandmothers' prophesies reflected in this fear and worked on this. I agreed and asked how Martin felt about touching himself, since he seemed to need his mother's reassurance and permission to touch his bumped head. The mother quickly assured me he never handled himself unless he was sore and everytime she observed him she expected him to be sore and supplied vasoline. These observations led us to discuss at first how children generally felt about touching themselves

and in light of this, consider Martin's specific fears and conflicts. Again, the mother needed "her time" to assimilate this
piece of work, in order to deal with it effectively, which she
did with good results.

The mother's work with Martin was reflected in the noticeable progress Martin showed after about six months at school,
though I hasten to add, it still left him one of the most difficult children in the group. In spite of his incompletely resolved fears, he was better able to control himself. His "vacation" from music and from creative media such as paints
and clay was over; he now enjoyed both and participated
well. His attention span increased and he could be observed
working hard and for a long period at the workbench with
good results. Martin's activities became constructive whereas
before they had been solely used as vehicles for his fantasies.
Whatever he undertook was done with great intensity, accompanied by much physical activity; when others sat, Martin stood and moved around. The most difficult features of
his behavior at school was still his unpredictability and his
persistent need for outside control. Consequently it was regarded as a triumph for Martin to settle a dispute with a
"feared" peer by leaving the scene and reporting, "I was
in trouble, I walked away." From home the mother reported
that Martin was able to meet new children and even adults
without the usual verbal and physical attacks.

At this point an event occurred which showed how the
mother failed to recognize anxiety-arousing situations for
what they were and, when she did, took an unduly long time
to relieve them. In the course of a routine check-up the pediatrician told Martin he had large tonsils, which had to come
out. Martin overheard that he would have to go to the hospital. Arrangements were suggested to see a nose and throat
specialist about a tonsilectomy.

My suspicions rose when this mother who usually was such
a conscientious reporter had not mentioned the visit to the

pediatrician halfway through our next meeting. Being asked, all the details emerged including the fact that Martin did not suffer unduly from nose, throat or ear infections. After some discussion the mother readily understood the inadvisability of such an operation at this time, was most willing to discuss it with the doctor and arrange for a hopefully lengthy postponement. This the mother accomplished quite promptly and was relieved to tell me the good news the following week. Nothing had been said to Martin. It was clear that the mother expected Martin to take the initiative in mentioning and questioning this frightening event, but since both employed the same mechanism in avoiding painful subjects, neither could introduce the matter. The mother offered several rationalizations, such as her wish for the father to be present when Martin was told, that he had worked late most of the week and admitted a general inability "to find the right time."

It took two incidents to convince the mother that Martin needed to be told immediately that his tonsils would not be removed. Reports received from school were most disturbing. Martin changed abruptly, was very much out of control and reverted to his former threats and actual physical attacks. The mother also "neglected" to report that Martin had a nightmare that week—the first since our contact—and that he wet the bed. He cried out, "Don't take my tonsils away." Not only did the mother at this point find the time, but she also found the right way to handle it with Martin—by honestly telling him of her sincere regret about not telling him about the postponement, that mothers, too, find it hard to talk about worrying things. They both must watch out to do better in the future.

During the following weeks, Martin's mother watched closely for signs of fearfulness in the child, still relying too much on his ability to say "I am afraid." When taken to the barber, for instance, Martin acted as nonchalantly as usual, cooperating fully. But the night before, he wet the bed and explained to his mother in the morning, "I must have had a bad dream or a big worry." Another instance concerned Martin's granted wish to shower with his father. Again he was very nonchalant about it with no questions, yet he again wet the bed. Up to this point the mother had been very tolerant about the bedwetting, which was not too frequent, and had never questioned it herself. Martin introduced "a bad dream or big worry" as possible causes. By paying close attention to both, the mother was able to work with Martin on the bedwetting, linking it to situations which aroused intense castration anxiety. The nightmares and wetting subsided except for isolated instances, such as spending the night at the grandmother's home, though in the presence of the parents, but sharing a bed with his aunt; fracturing a bone in his foot and the final separation from nursery school.

In view of the mother's difficulties in initiating painful and anxiety-arousing discussions with the child, it was most encouraging to see her deal with the terminal illness and death of her brother some months later. She phoned me at once, not waiting for her regular appointment: "This time I want to be a step ahead of Martin and not delay it like the tonsillectomy." Nevertheless, it was painful for her to talk about this event; she could not even tell her husband until he noticed her upset and questioned her. The next day, when still "no opportunity" arose to tell Martin, the father's support and encouragement enabled her to start talking to Martin about it.

Earlier when Martin's goldfish died, he had been told they were "resting." After this explanation had been corrected by the mother, Martin's ability to rest improved. Martin did not want his mother to attend the uncle's funeral. Since it took place in another city we thought this was due to his separation problems. Although the separation played an important part, his main concern was that his mother would "catch" the uncle's illness. At the same time he became very germ conscious, watched his food, dishes and eating utensils and feared he might be given bad or poisonous food. He would not trust the mushrooms the mother once served for a meal. At some stage of the father's illness protective measures were taken to minimize contagion; for instance, special care had been taken about dishes. The parents were now well able to give Martin realistic explanations about the father's illness in the past and the weekly treatments he currently received. For this separation the mother took great care to see that Martin was well protected from unnecessary upsets. She would have preferred the support and company of her husband, but decided against it, since he was the only person she could leave Martin with safely. She further anticipated that the father was very likely to visit his mother in her absence, asked him to be watchful and under no circumstances to leave the child there.

As indicated earlier, the work on separations continued all along. Several events at the nursery and at home helped to uncover and deal with various aspects of this difficulty culminating in the final leaving from school which revived once more the total problem. Martin's reaction to the first vacation from the nursery was to ask anxiously, "Is there no school for me because I was naughty?" Everytime a teacher left Martin felt he had driven her away with his anger and naughtiness. To combat this anxiety, he tried to control his environment by actively preventing such a separation. Nothing was spared to prove his need for protection from this teacher, showing how exposed and endangered such a separation would leave him. In turn he attacked the teacher for leaving or would try and bribe her into staying. He tested out the remaining staff to make sure they were able to protect him, and approached the new teacher in the same way. Also he tried actively to bring about his dismissal from school, to forestall being left behind, by repeating behavior for which he had been sent away from his former nursery.

Both school and home worked closely together in helping Martin to verbalize his conflicting feelings and thereby master them. While the school handled his present behavior, letting him know of their awareness that some very upsetting separations in the past caused all this, the work with the mother linked these past experiences with present behavior.

The opportunity presented itself to carry this out when Martin reacted violently to hearing that the parents of one of his friends at nursery, a boy his age, were both in the hospital and their grandmother was taking care of the children. A Thanksgiving visit to the grandparents was coming up shortly and Martin pleaded with his mother not to leave him there again, asking why the parents had not taken him along on their weekend trip. Unable to trust the mother's promise, he had to make quite sure he would not be asked to stay by misbehaving shortly before it was time to leave for home. While sitting on the grandmother's lap, at her request, he suddenly got off and kicked her leg. Later on he no longer had to misbehave on each visit, but remained uneasy and was relieved when the time came to go home.

There was another very important aspect of Martin's feeling unprotected in his mother's absence, which had not been discussed so far. It provided the basis for the work of the final year. So far we had dealt with the dangers that had threatened Martin from without, when separated from his mother, and the feelings they aroused. With these anxieties no longer so intense, they could be tolerated and managed by Martin. The dangers from within, which at the age of almost five years, threatened Martin in quite an overwhelming way, were his lack of independent control over his impulses, particularly his aggression. Furthermore, he showed no shame and remorse about his actions, felt sorry and guilty only if his mother knew and disapproved. His ego controls and superego functioning had remained the responsibility of his mother, who at present served as his conscience.

Our joint aim was to help Martin gain reliably independent control over his drives, to make their direct primitive release ego alien and provide all possible incentives for neutralization and sublimation. These achievements were to be reinforced by helping him establish an independently functioning, well internalized superego.

Both mother and school were carefully prepared for weeks and months of slow moving, arduous and at times discouraging work, while Martin caught up with vital developmental steps he missed at the appropriate time.

Martin's mother was not at all unaware how the child regarded her as his "emotional crutch" and gained sufficient insight to understand how this affected her part of the relationship. It helped greatly for the mother to disclose that for some time she had tried to start another pregnancy and in spite of medical attention had been unsuccessful. At a point when the mother had to reconcile herself to the fact that Martin might remain an only child, she was expected to make some very basic changes in their relationship, which ultimately were to enable Martin to function more independently and age-appropriately. One could fully sympathize with the demands the task ahead made of her. She was expected to give up something important to her, accept being needed less and altogether in a different way. Fortunately, Martin's mother could derive support from her genuine and unfailing wish to do the best for her child and could also take pride and pleasure in his achievements and progress. In addition she had the full support of the father, the therapist and the nursery.

Although both school and home had to coordinate their educational approach very closely, for a time Martin's tie to his mother was still on the level where he would do things for her sake and in her presence only and was unable to accept teachers as substitute educators. The parents educational standards and expectations were well below that of his age level, particularly in the area of drives. They showed unusual acceptance and submission to Martin's instinctual demands. We found that all educational changes and innovations had to be initiated by the mother and once accomplished with her Martin could then transfer his gains to school, where he could be helped to maintain them more securely. At first Martin would only respond to or attempt to meet the demands of his favorite teachers.

We discovered a special pattern in the relationship between Martin and his mother, who was visibly upset and worried over his behavior. Martin would have what he called a "bad" day at school. This could consist of, provoking, disrupting, destroying someone's work or occasionally biting or otherwise hurting a child. He would request the teachers to tell his mother all about it. At home he confessed all the wrong things he had done, would watch the mother's face closely, wanting to know, "Are you ashamed of me?" The mother felt deeply ashamed. Martin said he was sorry. Long sympathetic talks ensued, which ended in the mother cheering up a sorry Martin who would repeat his behavior the next day.

Until now, Martin relied exclusively on the watchfulness of his environment, his mother at home and the teachers at school who were to report everything faithfully to her. Efforts were made to guide Martin towards growing self-observation and to experience the feeling of responsibility for his actions. It was decided that all reporting to his mother had to be taken on by Martin who began to feel ashamed to give a "bad" report. When he concluded such reports with a searching look at her face and the question, "Are you ashamed, how do you feel?" the mother now responded, "But I did not do this," or "I wonder how you feel," or

"I wonder how Tommy feels whom you bit this morning?" He tried to get the mother's and teachers' attention by using his fears and what he learned about them as permission and justification for his acting out: "I bit Tommy because I was afraid." When this was no longer acceptable to home and school, it gradually became unacceptable to Martin. For the first time he began to show concern for his victims, asked to phone a child he hurt, after school, or make appropriate amends for something damaged. In replacing a "stolen" caramel from a girl's locker, he explained "I should not have taken the caramel, I did not really enjoy it." While taking his bath, Martin could be heard telling himself, "I am just not going to bite anybody. I must not bite or hit. It's terrible to bite people. Mother is right, I have got to manage." Once the bus jerked while Martin and his mother were on it, as a result a lady sitting next to Martin moved very close. Martin whispered to his mother, "I don't like this lady to sit next to me, but I am going to behave."

While struggling to tolerate feeling "bad" for his own sake and his own actions, Martin tried to seek relief in getting instant punishment from the teachers. Yet many times he hung his head and was sad when he managed poorly. The group had responded to Martin's increasing self-control and his obvious concern over his behavior, and he began having some friends, which pleased him enormously. However, the uncertainty of his controls and the still not too infrequent "incidents" made Martin a very unreliable friend and often brought rejection from the group. This proved of vital importance to Martin. He was found sitting by himself in a corner, crying quietly, "Nobody loves me, nobody wants to play with me." One morning he presented the group with a little speech where he told them he was "sorry for all the bad behavior on those other days," telling them how much he wanted to be their friend. Martin began to trust himself to mix more freely and on his own with the children

in the neighborhood, though the mother found it quite difficult not to keep watching him from the window.

Gradually one could observe a growing awareness of his
behavior and its effect on others and a closer union between
his conscience and his actions.

While helping Martin in his struggle to set up acceptable
standards for himself, and particularly in helping him give
up the unfortunate identification with the disturbed neighbor, one became more aware of a strange discrepancy in the
mother. Of seemingly very adequate standards for herself,
she could in no way judge and realistically appreciate the
grossly overt sadistic behavior of this neighbor towards Martin and for the longest time continued to admire and credit
him with loving attention and affection.

Since the father did not share this attitude, he could be of
considerable help to Martin who by this time gave many
indications of moving into the oedipal phase. It was felt at
this point, that the father needed to take a more active role
in Martin's education, especially in the area of discipline,
age-appropriate demands and expectations, in order to
strengthen Martin's identification and conscience formation,
which so far had largely depended on the mother.

With growing evidence of conflicts becoming more internalized, defenses more age-appropriate and the phallic level
less threatened by regression, Martin could make the move
into the oedipal phase with its accompanying conflicts.

At school one could see Martin's attempts to displace his
conflicts from home. All of a sudden he was in constant
trouble with the boy who had his father's name. He tried to
attract the teacher's attention and keep them from being
with another child. Gradually the shift back to home was accomplished by the teachers making him aware of the displacement and the home being ready to receive and deal
with this new step in development. Martin began to show
more openly his jealousy and rivalry with the father. Once

he asked the father to let him try on his wedding ring. This the father refused with the explanation that even without the ring he was still the mother's husband, that he understood how Martin felt, but he would have to wait until he was bigger to find his own sweetheart. Martin began to show concern over the father's safety and well being. On the beach he worried when the father swam a distance from shore. Once when the father was out at night in a storm, he had to stay up and await his return. Martin tried to separate the parents and the mother began to realize how very rarely the parents spent time on their own. With some encouragement the mother planned some outings at night which did not include the child. Martin handled these occasions very well, telling of his disapproval and then retreating into his room to keep busy. Proud as she was, the mother was also very hurt by his self-sufficiency and independence. For the future she would have to prepare herself to anticipate, tolerate and even encourage further steps in this direction.

During this period, Martin had two "accidents," both resulting in fractured bones. After a brief visit to the circus, for which he was well prepared and allowed to leave whenever he wanted to, he fell off a fence pretending to be the wild animal trainer. He cracked his collarbone. Later he wanted to keep up with some older boys who played superman and jumped from a fire escape breaking a bone in his foot. This seemed a very dangerous denial of his oedipal castration fears. For Martin, dangers were not allowed to exist; he had to prove himself invincible.

While struggling with his emerging oedipal feelings, life presented Martin with an additional new "danger" situation, namely the prospect of leaving the nursery for public school. This was to coincide with a move into a new home and a new neighborhood in a distant part of the city. For some time, Martin had been able to handle separations quite well. He had generally learned to "prepare himself" for anxiety arousing situations, i.e., he would ask the doctor to explain the whole procedure before letting him put his foot in a cast, or he would have the mother prepare him before being left in someone else's care; he admitted he was anxious and worried. The separation from the nursery revived in full force the whole separation problem, but this time centered around the school. It brought back the separation-castration equation, some nightmares, and bedwetting. At the nursery he refused to participate in any activities aimed to prepare the children for kindergarten. He constantly demonstrated his being unfit to be sent to public school, telling the teachers if he was bad enough he would not have to leave; school just would not accept him. He tried to extract a promise from his mother that he could return to the nursery "if I don't like it at school." To prevent the move, Martin became unmanageable while taken to look at houses. He worried about their new neighbors: "I may not like them." The mother helped Martin understand his reaction to leaving the nursery was linked to the way he felt in the past when left with his grandmother or the neighbor, but the mother was firm and told Martin that he could and would have to manage, since he had no alternative.

Martin lived near a school, though not the one he was to attend. He would watch the children rush out of school, and ask some how they liked school and what they did there. It was apparent that gradually the working through of his fears and anger with the mother's help plus firm educational measures both at home and at school enabled Martin once again to cope more realistically and age-appropriately with the separation.

Martin began to ask the teachers questions and wanted to be shown and taught how things were done in kindergarten, instead of refusing to listen. Before, when he could not be "the best" he ended up being "the worst." Now he could accept being a "medium boy." His behavior and relationships at nursery school once more improved and progressed. He showed better all-around control without working hard at it, perseverance on learning new skills, a widening scope of interests and knowledge and pleasure and pride in his achievements.

During the final weeks of our work, the mother was prepared for the coming steps in Martin's development, considering not only the accompanying conflicts and stresses, but also the progress to be expected. The mother felt the separation from the nursery and her work with the therapist very keenly, and as she had done before, could help Martin very nicely with his sadness.

On the last day at the nursery Martin brought gifts for the teachers. With tears in his eyes he told them how sad he felt, regretting that he had not been nicer to them during his stay.

On the basis of his age, Martin was placed in first grade in his new school. After two months, the mother was given a very good report as to his adjustment there. He was regarded as very bright, stood out in the group by his positive contributions (not by any bad behavior). He did get restless at times, but could control it. At home he presented no particular problems.

Martin left the nursery at a point when after delayed and interfered-with libidinal, ego and superego development he had progressed to age-appropriate levels in these areas. It was hoped he would be spared further traumatic experiences to safeguard his newly won gains and stabilize his future development.

Follow-up Evaluation

Nine years later we resumed contact with the family for a follow-up evaluation. Martin was almost 15 years old. The year before the family moved to a nearby city, where Martin had just completed his second year at junior high school.

Since Martin was reluctant to be seen, the mother came by herself and gave a very insightful and honest report about the intervening years. She looked remarkably well and attractive. Both parents led a far less "Martin-centered" life.

On the whole the family has done well, considering that there had been some deaths and illnesses among relatives; two years earlier the father had an automobile accident from which he recovered completely and recently the mother had been ill. Martin coped well with these events; he was concerned and helpful with both parents and able to assume added responsibilities at these times.

The mother stressed that the move was of great advantage to everyone. She was particularly pleased with Martin's present school which she regarded as excellent both academically and in relation to the children who attend. Martin had gone to summer school where he had caught up with work and during the past year had managed to improve his grades. This also coincided with his growing independence from his parents as school work had remained the one area where he still depended on the mother's judgment and expectations. Recently he had shown concern about his future. He showed interest in car design, would like to go to a technical college and realized that unless his grades kept improving his chances were limited.

In describing Martin, the mother gave a picture of a boy moving into adolescence. Most striking to anyone who had known Martin during his early years were his sense of responsibility and reliable self-management. His actions no longer brought him into conflict with his environment nor did he seek punishment by self-injury or provocative behavior.

Martin today spends a good deal of time independently away from home. If his mother is out on his return from school, he can plan his own time in the apartment, report his whereabouts and come home on time. The mother feels completely relaxed and assured about his varied activities. He handles his weekly allowance sensibly; and on his own initiative he once negotiated for himself a caddie job at a golf course. Also, he supplements his allowance with grass-cutting and other odd jobs. Martin has a tremendous investment in athletic activities. He is rather small for his age, not very husky and with little aptitude for sports, yet he strives to succeed by sheer hard work.

He is part of a group of boys who share his interests, also has some contact with girls though mainly in school or other group settings.

At home he is rebellious and stubborn with both parents, yet responsible and independent. When at home he spends a good deal of time in his room keeping busy and will retreat there when in disagreement with his parents. He prefers to seek the advice of outside authorities, rather than the parent's, whose decisions he accepts readily. For instance, he consulted the barber about shaving his upper lip and insisted the football coach make the final decision about his trying out for the team.

In his relationship to his mother, Martin still seems to be slightly ahead. He objects to being called by the childhood abbreviation of his name, wanting the mother to use it correctly. This she finds impossible and too formal and has worked out the following compromise: outside the family she refers to him as "son." The mother also continues to call him "shrimp," to which he objects. She has promised she will only call him this as long as he is smaller than she, which means the shrimp period is practically at an end. The mother feels Martin lacks a sense of humor and has been trying to develop this with him by a sort of "friendly teasing" as opposed to the "unhealthy teasing" of their former neighbor.

Martin and his father enjoy spending time together; they share interests in music, literature and sketching.

Throughout, both parents have given full support to Martin's growth and continuing development and have shared with him their pride and pleasure in his achievements.

CASE 4: JANIE[4]

Janie was not referred. She came to my attention as the reputedly happy and uncomplicated little sister of Susan when the latter entered our nursery school. At that time Janie was barely seventeen months old, a pretty cherub-faced toddler, with blue eyes and blond curls, bodily active and mentally alert. Susan was three years and a half, Janie's senior by two years.

Developments Prior to Entry into Nursery School[5]

Only several weeks before I began work with the mother regarding Susan, the family had vacationed in A. While there the parents left the sisters in the care of a nurse for a couple of days. During their absence, Janie, Susan and their older boy cousin, Pierre, played in the yard alone. Somehow Janie got into the deep end of the swimming pool while the older children were in another part of the garden. The nurse, who could not swim, found Janie drowning and jumped in after her. After a few minutes a family of friends arrived by chance and rescued Janie and the nurse. The latter was still conscious but Janie was not. The friends revived her with the help of artificial respiration and then rushed her to the hospital for a check-up, which showed her to be in satisfactory condition. That night the nurse called the parents and they returned the next morning. The incident was not particularly discussed and Janie appar-

4 Reported by Erna Furman.

5 Janie's development and the work with her mother prior to Janie's entry into the Hanna Perkins Nursery School were reported in greater detail in "Observations on a Toddler's Near-Fatal Accident" (E. Furman, 1964). *Bulletin Philadelphia Assn. Psa.,* Vol. 14, No. 3.

ently showed no reaction. She continued to love the water, both in bath and in the pool and seemed unperturbed.

When Janie was 19 months old her parents again left the children for a few days, this time with their beloved maid. In contrast to Susan, Janie was unconcerned about the forthcoming separation. On the first night without the parents, however, she jumped out of her crib. Susan woke and rushed to help Janie. In telling her mother about this after her return, Susan linked Janie's jump from the crib with her fall into the pool. Though quite verbal as a rule, Janie did not say anything but developed a sleep disturbance. Before falling asleep she would thrash and jump about and would call her mother to retrieve her "cotton" (a comforter) which she had thrown out of the crib. During the night, too, she would wake up with the same insistent request. The mother told Janie that she was saying bye-bye to the cotton like mommy had said bye-bye to her and that it must have made Janie sad and angry that she could not have mommy back when she wanted her. She also encouraged Janie to express her anger appropriately during the day. Janie's sleep difficulty subsided with this interpretation but, throughout the following year, Janie kept her tendency to show upset over even very short separations at night rather than during the day. In all other areas, however, Janie's development progressed evenly. By the age of two years she achieved bowel and bladder control except for occasional incidents of wetting.

Exactly a year after the pool accident, when Janie was two years, four months old, the family vacationed by the seaside. There Janie saw nude little boys on the beach and asked about the sexual differences. During the summer, but more so after the family's return home, Janie developed an acute separation fear from the mother and a serious sleep disturbance. She could not fall asleep, woke frequently during the night and cried and thrashed wildly in her sleep.

Up to this point the mother had kept me informed of

Janie's progress in an informal way in connection with her work with me in regard to Susan. Our regular weekly interviews started in an effort to help Janie with her difficulties.

The first clue to our understanding came from Janie's preoccupation with her "broken" possessions. In talking about this in relation to the sexual difference, she said one day, "But I was broken, I was broken in the pool." This was the first reference in over a year to her near-drowning. Until this time Janie had given no indication of recalling the incident and had casually absented herself whenever mother and Susan discussed it. Within a few days Janie likened falling asleep to falling into the pool and Janie's mother wondered whether the wild thrashing around during her sleep was a reenactment of Janie's attempts to stay above water. During the many following mother-child talks Janie recalled with strong affect her loneliness and anger in A. She had wished to bring mommy back by going to the deep end of the pool because this had always made mommy drop everything and rush to her. Janie was unimpressed by the mother's sincere apologies and repeated bitterly, "But you did not come," thereby expressing her feelings of being deeply shattered, disappointed and angry at mother's failure to protect her.

Very gradually Janie mastered the reality facts of her accident, learned that she could now protect herself better in many situations, accepted safety rules and began to trust her mother's promise not to leave her in an unsafe situation. At the same time Janie's behavior showed how difficult it was for her to cope with her anger at her mother. Screaming and occasional biting had been Janie's extreme expressions of anger and were now supplanted by fears of noises and of insects biting. Janie's aggression on another level could be understood from her increasing concern with *The Wizard of Oz*. Janie wondered over and over, "How did Dorothy kill the witch by putting water on her?" With enough clues from Janie, mother could eventually tell her that she really was so angry at mommy now, and at the time when mommy had left her in A., that she had wanted to put a lot of water on mommy, had wanted to throw her into the pool. Janie agreed wholeheartedly, adding, "But you didn't come to pull me out." Verbalization did not seem to help Janie's inner controls. Mother then became aware that Janie was extremely guilty over her occasional wetting "accidents," which the mother had treated in a most lenient manner. One time while mother was on the phone, which obviously irked Janie, she told her father that the water that killed the witch was like urine on the floor. Mother now understood Janie's guilt and took up with her how angry Janie's urinating was and how she used it to express her continued wish to flood and kill mother. Janie's wetting accidents ceased.

When she was three years old Janie's phallic interests began to show, also, the influence on them of her pool experience. For the first time she distorted her accident saying, "I think I walked down the steps into the pool because I didn't want to wet my curls." Her difficulty in falling asleep returned and she complained to her mother of her trouble with "itching." Although now the danger stemmed from Janie's own excitement she felt she needed mother's presence to keep herself safe. The mother discussed this with Janie and reassured her about her masturbation.

When Janie was three years, four months, Janie again vacationed near Pierre's family, which provided many opportunities for mother and child to talk over Janie's early experience. Janie, who had never lost her love of the water, learned to swim and dive that summer and was proud that she now really knew how to be safe in the water.

By this time Janie had repeatedly recalled the traumatic event with affect, had worked through some aspects of the conflicts connected with it, and had progressed adequately in her instinctual and ego development. Her pool experience, however, had already shown its impact on Janie's handling of her castration fear and masturbatory conflict. It seemed likely that the same would hold true for the new developmental stresses that lay ahead for her, e.g., adjustment to nursery school and kindergarten, the height of the phallic and oedipal conflicts. It thus seemed indicated that the mother receive assistance in helping Janie during these years so that the trauma could be mastered further and, hopefully, prevented from leaving its imprint on new experiences. These considerations made it commendable for Janie to attend our nursery school and to continue the work with her mother.

Introductory Remarks

In the following pages an attempt will be made to sketch some aspects of Janie's development and the work with her mother during the years of Janie's stay at the Hanna Perkins School. In tracing the vicissitudes of Janie's phallic-oedipal stage and the beginnings of latency, emphasis was placed on the recurring theme of her early trauma and its interaction with the different parts of her maturing personality. In describing the work, stress was laid on the close cooperation between mother, therapist and teachers. Janie never showed gross behavior or learning disturbance at school, yet some aspects of her difficulties manifested themselves only in the school setting. The teachers' detailed observations of Janie proved essential for the mother's and therapist's understanding of Janie's conflicts.

Inevitably, many other areas of interest in this case had to be omitted. In particular this report does not detail the therapist's work with the mother, the nature of the obstacles encountered in it or their handling. Several reasons account for this. First, it seemed unfeasible to do justice to every aspect of this type of work in one illustrative case presentation. Second, Janie's mother had the previous experience of working with the therapist in regard to Susan, the older daughter. It was during that work that most of the interferences arose and were overcome by the mother to a large extent. Her later work with Janie profited from this. It ran a much smoother course from the points of view of the mother's available insight, knowledge of therapeutic and educational measures and working relationship with the center's staff. (Though this is not the rule, we often find that a mother's previous experience with this work helps her greatly in applying it to her younger child.) Third, some aspects of the therapist's work with the mother needed to be omitted for reasons of discretion. Although these factors were an important part of the therapist's work, they did not materially affect the nature or understanding of Janie's difficulties.

Status at Start of Nursery School during Phallic Phase

Janie was now three and a half years old. At home she was contented and without symptoms. Her main, though not very marked, difficulty appeared to be her reluctance to separate from her mother. She had no desire for peer relations and seemed happiest at home with familiar adults.

Our observations of Janie during the first two months of nursery school revealed a picture that contrasted sharply with that of the radiant active little girl she was at home. At school most of Janie's energy was taken up in following the movements of the older boys in the group. She constantly waved "Hi" to them, begged them to let her play with them or at least to smile at her. When she was overlooked, turned down, or unable to participate in their give-and-take games, she wandered off on her own and repeatedly performed a particular trick of hanging upside down on the parallel bars. She refused the teachers' offers of comfort and help. When girls or younger boys invited her to join them, Janie would accept halfheartedly but would soon leave them without an explanation. Janie appeared preoccupied with herself and lacking in feeling for and with others. Her observations of her environment were mostly related to her own feelings, e.g., while oblivious to many normally interesting events, she would suddenly hear a child's cry from a neighboring house and become quite concerned about it.

At home Janie had been able to concentrate on and perform neutral activities most adequately, but at school she had to be coaxed to join in drawing, clay work and other creative skills. Her attention wandered. Often she would not make an effort and seemed to care little about achieving well. She took no pride in her productions. Even her excellent large muscle skills were somewhat interfered with at school by her need to test the safety rules and by attempts at bravado performances.

In her general behavior though Janie was a well-controlled child, willing and able to follow all the school routines and most responsive to the slightest criticism.

The separation from her mother proceeded gradually over several weeks. Janie was well able to express her varied feelings to her mother. Her ambivalence did not seem unusually intense but she struggled with it for a very long time. Sometimes Janie was anxious to leave her mother in order to escape home restrictions and to do "fun things" at school, e.g., a little uncontrolled bumping on the swings. At other times she was reluctant to leave home complaining that she would be lonely. During the first week or so she visited her mother freely in the waiting room spending affectionate moments or saying she wished mother would leave. Later on, when her mother already left her for longer stretches of time, Janie would greet her with pleasure or anger or rejection. On the whole she appeared able to cope with her feelings in this area though she refrained from forming a close relationship with her teacher. In striking contrast, Janie was not at all aware of her difficulties in her behavior with her peers and in her lack of interest in activities and achievements.

Early Experiences in the Context of the Phallic Phase

Increasingly Janie complained at home that the children "don't like me and don't want to play with me" and that the activities were "no fun." Observations of Janie at school and discussions with the therapist helped the mother to understand Janie's extreme feeling of inadequacy in the nursery school setting. She also recognized that, at home, Janie had been able to ward off her anxiety by using an effective defense. Friendly adults, and even her older sister, had often expressed admiration for Janie's pretty curls. Janie always managed to draw the attention of familiar and strange grownups to her hair, taking for granted their friendly word or touch. Thus Janie was using her bodily asset, coupled with her smiling charm, to secure constant proofs of love and admiration. Janie's peers at school failed to admire her good looks and were not charmed by her smile to which Janie responded by feeling unloved and inadequate.

The mother's first task was to acquaint Janie with her defenses which she did gradually at opportune moments over a considerable period of time. She pointed out to Janie that it seemed safer to her to insist, "They don't like me," than to feel "I don't like myself and I don't like them." She made her aware of relying on people to say, "Oh, what lovely curls," so that she would not have to think "I don't like some parts of myself." Janie's disinterest in creative activities was interpreted as meaning, "I'm afraid I can't draw well, so I won't even try." As Janie came closer to her painful feelings we began to learn more about the specific experiences which influenced her behavior at nursery school.

At home, Janie now played with a stuffed octopus whom she called, 'Pear.' It had been given to her by the mother of her much older cousin, Pierre. At school Janie engaged one of the willing bigger boys in a repetitive octopus game in which they excitedly pretended to grab at each other with outstretched fingers. Janie's mother was able to link these games with Janie's experiences of last summer when they had vacationed with Pierre's family. She now recalled that Pierre had been most charming with Susan and had played many exclusive games with her, but he had persistently and harshly rejected Janie's approaches making her feel very dejected. On one occasion he had even tried to lock Janie in a closet. Whenever mother had offered to play with Janie instead, Janie would reject her and soon make another futile attempt to solicit Pierre's friendship. In their talks the mother reminded Janie of last summer. She suggested Janie had thought that in coming to nursery school she was again turning down an unsatisfactory mommy and getting herself a big boy. Now she felt very sad and angry when she could not succeed in this. Janie replied by telling her mother that her "hanging-upside-down trick" had to do with falling into the pool long ago. At that time they had also vacationed in A. with Pierre's family. Pierre had then played with Susan and refused to have Janie join them. That was when Janie had wandered away and fallen into the pool. The general facts were correct. The details of the circumstances preceding Janie's accident had not been known to the mother but were now confirmed by Susan.

Later Janie added more to our understanding. She often became babyish in speech and mannerisms and complained "only boys and babies get attention." She also revealed that her great interest in diving stemmed from her fantasy that she had lost her penis when she fell into the pool and might retrieve it, or something equally precious, by diving for it. Janie's mother knew that Pierre used to exhibit himself urinating during that vacation of over two and a half years ago. Even this last summer he had been showoffish with his size, strength, and skills, although bodily privacy was strictly kept. Pierre's earlier crude exhibitionism had made a deep impression on Susan. Much to the mother's dismay it now appeared that Janie had also been exposed to the sight of Pierre's penis when she was 16 months. This may have in part accounted for the outbreak of Janie's disturbance a year later when she saw naked little boys on a beach. It was then that Janie first recalled her pool experience in words and later insisted that it had made her genitals "broken."

The mother now linked Janie's feelings in the successive experiences with Pierre, the nude little boys and the boys at nursery school and tried to clarify Janie's displacements and misconceptions. Janie seemed to confirm that she had seen Pierre's penis when she was 16 months. She spoke sadly of her wish for a penis "to do tricks (urinate like a boy) and to be pretty." Janie had had no other opportunity to see a boy urinate since both at home and at school, bathroom activities were private. When Janie later confessed her angry wish to grab or bite off a boy's penis, she could be shown that her pursuit of boys was really a wish to acquire their penis. She rejected women and girls because they had no penis to give her and because it made her feel less sad and angry when she could reject them as she had been rejected by the boys.

The gradual working through of these conflicts enabled Janie to overcome her phallic difficulties to some extent. Her symptomatic behavior subsided. She entered the oedipal phase, made marked progress in her reality testing and was better able to relate herself to her school environment. She formed a close relationship with her teacher and joined in give-and-take play with her peers. Her attention span lengthened and she began to participate more actively in sublimatory activities.

Personality Reactions during the Oedipal Phase

As Janie's oedipal feelings intensified, her earlier conflicts again interfered to the point of causing her considerable stress. For a long period Janie could allow herself only negative oedipal feelings at home. She demanded her mother's exclusive love, resented father's homecoming in the evenings and did not want to join him in the games or little outings he offered her. Her positive feelings for him evidenced themselves at school where Janie persistently sought excited and exclusive "private" play with one boy. The teachers had to stop her repeatedly. She responded with anger at their interference and blamed them for not providing her with the kind of "fun" she wanted. Her interest in the planned program waxed and waned as did the quality of her neutral productions.

The displacement of her feelings, however, did not protect her from her anxiety. Janie's unusually strong guilt feelings came to the fore, often disguised by primitive defenses of projection and turning against the self, and, characteristically for Janie, accompanied by a lowering of her self-esteem and depletion of self-love.

On one occasion Janie flirted with a girl friend's father when the latter visited his daughter at school. She succeeded in diverting his appreciative attention to herself. Immediately afterwards she played a game in which her doll had been very naughty and was spanked severely by her pretend mother. Janie, who had never been spanked, increasingly meted out strict punishment to her dolls. At home she complained that her mother was not punitive enough and accused her, "You don't love me." At nursery school she commented untruthfully, "My mommy will hit me," when she did something wrong. Even the hanging-upside-down trick was revived, accompanied occasionally by slight "accidental" self-hurts and by testing of the safety rules. Actually Janie never got hurt badly. She always seemed to make sure that her minor accidents and testing occurred within the attentive sight of an adult. Since she always succeeded in having the teachers rush to her on these occasions, her behavior was interpreted as a call for help. After some discussions with the therapist, mother talked this over with Janie. She suggested that when she fell into the pool Janie had been in danger from outside but that now the danger came from within her. She related it to Janie's angry feelings at her mother. Perhaps it was Janie who did not love mommy sometimes and was afraid that her anger might get out of control and hurt mommy. Janie confirmed this when her parents left town for a couple of days. Just before they left Janie displaced her anger onto a minor detail, had a temper tantrum and tumbled down the stairs in front of her mother. Typically she was not hurt. Addressing herself to Janie, the mother wondered whether her tumbling was a way of hurting herself so she could not hurt mommy when mommy was gone. Janie denied this but the next day said at school, "I'll hit my mommy only when she gets back."

Janie became severely self-critical whenever she failed to achieve her own high standards. At school she underestimated her capacities to the point of not wanting to try new skills. She gave up at the first slight mistake and angrily destroyed her work even when it was actually good or could have been repaired. The mother had many talks with Janie on her dislike of herself. She pointed out that Janie's repeated complaints of not being loved really reflected her not loving herself because she felt so badly about feelings that she did not even know about.

Janie strongly resisted the mother's and teachers' attempts to show her that her feelings for her special "boy friend" at school really belonged to her daddy at home. One Sunday Janie and her daddy were alone in the house. Janie had a specially nice time with him but, in an unobserved moment, marked up mother's favorite chair. She was in tears about it later and helped to wash the chair. Both parents now recognized the other aspect of Janie's instinctual fear. Janie was not only afraid of losing control of her anger at mother, she also feared becoming too excited with daddy who might not adequately restrict her. Janie's father reassured her that he would not let her be "out-of-control" and would never lose control himself. This helped Janie to tolerate and show her love for her father and her relationship with her boy friend at school changed. She could now enjoy constructive games with him and included other children in their companionship.

By now Janie had asked many questions about birth and conception but her ability to integrate the answers fluctuated. Her continuing difficulty in coping with her ambivalence and in tolerating her position of outsider to the parental relationship caused her to regress. She developed food fads, often could not eat with the family and provoked being sent away from the table by acting babyishly messy and obstreperous. Finally she confessed that some foods made her think of eating genitals. This opened up mother-child discussions on Janie's oral-aggressive wishes toward the penis and fantasies of impregnation. At another period Janie insisted that both intercourse and giving birth were painful experiences. She declared that she would not want to have a baby herself and asked many questions about how one could prevent conception. The mother could be helped to see that Janie was not primarily asking for information on contraceptives but needed to be told that children sometimes wish these exciting experiences were hurtful because then they would not have to feel so envious of the parents. Some children even wish they could prevent mommies from having babies. Janie reversed her feelings and begged her mother to have a baby for whom Janie would help care. Sometimes Janie could express her anger directly at her mother, but most of her envy and competitiveness centered on her sister Susan, with whom she loved to play.

Janie was at this time five years old. She was physically well developed and as pretty as ever, except when anxiety tensed her delicate features. At home her behavior periodically reflected her inner stress. In addition to the forementioned difficulties, Janie had occasional trouble falling asleep and would call her mother during the night. She also still needed a nightlight in her closet and clung to her "cotton" comforter in bed. At nursery school, however, she was a well adjusted and well liked member of her group. Her sublimatory activities had again taken a turn for the better and her interests included letters, numbers and checkers at which she became quite an expert. The main reasons for planning to have Janie attend our kindergarten were her precarious balance in mastering her oedipal conflicts, her tendency to severe self-criticism and lowering of self-esteem and the lability of her beginning sublimations. It was feared that these factors might jeopardize her healthy resolution of the oedipal complex and lead to the formation of a pathologically severe superego. We did not foresee the extent to which the traces of Janie's earlier experiences would be revived within the content of her oedipal phase and its resolution.

Revival of Early Experiences in the Context of the Oedipus Complex

Janie anticipated the transition into kindergarten with much trepidation. She was realistic enough to recognize her good achievements and knew that a recent intelligence test had placed her in the very superior range. She was familiar with the kindergarten from visits within the framework of our prekindergarten program. Yet she feared she would not be "up to it." The mother learned from Janie about the latter's unrealistic expectations, e.g., "Everyone will have to read right away and do hard sums." Mother's reassurance helped Janie little. She was not happy either when the mother, after discussion with me, suggested that Janie's fear stemmed from her wish to become grown-up the moment she entered kindergarten and stressed that learning, like growing up, was a slow process.

Janie handled the separation from her beloved teachers well, allowing herself to feel and express her mixed affects. This was somewhat in contrast to home where she generally still found it hard to tolerate the sadness, anger and loneliness of separations.

The first day in kindergarten appeared to go very well for Janie. That night however she had a nightmare. Her screams brought her mother to her. Janie sobbed, "I was alone in a big swimming pool with Jim." The mother could not fully waken her and by the morning Janie had forgotten the dream. Jim was one of the biggest and smartest boys in Janie's class, known to all children for his loud exhibitionistic behavior. The mother told Janie of her dream and suggested she had scary feelings about kindergarten, which they needed to understand better. Several days later, on a Sunday night, the parents were out in the evening. Just before bedtime there was a big mysterious noise, which the sitter and children finally identified as a fallen flowerpot. After the parents' return during the night, Janie woke with another dream, called her mother and was eager to tell her the details which she could well remember the next morning. In the dream Janie and mommy were in a swimming pool and a dangerous stranger was also present. Then a charge of TNT went off in front of the house. Later Janie added that she had placed the TNT there. That day Janie tripped her mother accidentally. The mother was not badly hurt but Janie felt very badly. This helped the mother to relate the incident to Janie's dream. She discussed Janie's ambivalence with her and reassured her that she would not hurt mommy badly even if she wished to and that she would learn to manage her anger better as she got older. Within another few days, after a fireworks display in which two little boys received minor injuries, Janie had a third dream: "Mommy, daddy and Janie were in the swimming pool, then they were outside their house and something happened to mommy; perhaps she went away." This was the first time that daddy appeared in the dreams and that Janie identified the pool as the familiar one used habitually by the family. In talking about the dream with Janie further, the mother interpreted Janie's angry wish to displace mother in the parental relationship and Janie's fantasy that kindergarten would instantly bring her the pleasures of being adult, that she would finally have for herself all that she had ever wanted. Following this Janie was for some time quite vocal about her "left-out" feelings and her nights became quite restless. She disturbed the parents' in the evenings with complaints of not being able to fall asleep and of her genital area hurting. She wanted warm baths to soothe the soreness. For a time the mother went along with these requests sympathizing with the child's anxiety. It did not however mitigate Janie's complaints. The mother recalled Janie's past difficulty with masturbation and reassured her that she could not hurt her body with angry and excited feelings and touching. This helped her for a while but the difficulty continued into the early fall when Janie was in kindergarten.

At first Janie was rather shy in kindergarten, kept herself aloof and showed little genuine interest in the program. At free periods she usually played alone with a block game. She felt readily rejected by her peers, particularly by her earlier boy friend who now often played with another girl. Janie concentrated hard on learning to ride a two-wheel bike and was the first in her group to succeed, thereby gaining a lot of admiration. She was elated that day and spent an unusually affectionate evening with her father. But this was followed by a bad dream about witches and more insistent complaints about pain in her genital area. The parents tried to show Janie that there was a difference between her success with the bike and success in having daddy, but Janie was not ready to restrict or give up her impulses.

During the ensuing months we saw, much to our dismay, a repetition of all of Janie's difficulties of a year ago. We did not know, of course, that this would lead to a better understanding and working through of Janie's old conflicts.

Following her old pattern Janie displaced her impulses to school. She became distractible, performed poorly and refused to try unless she was sure of immediate success. With her teachers Janie became irritated and demanding. She did not want to share and would not participate in activities unless she was the first chosen. She was passive to the teachers' effort to involve her in adequate activities, preferred to tease and chase after the boys or giggle excitedly with one of the girls. Quite often she wiggled on her chair and handled her genital area. At home, by contrast, Janie was a devoted loving daughter to her mother. She was reasonable, cooperative and enjoyed joint activities. She tried to enlist her mother's help in learning to read and write. Whenever there were situations apt to aggravate Janie's oedipal jealousy (parents going out, adult parties), Janie's reactions showed only at school in her having especially difficult days. Although it was painful for the mother to recognize that her youngest daughter's close and loving relationship with her was maintained at the cost of difficulties with outsiders, she attempted to show Janie her displacement and its unfortunate outcome for her. Finally the teachers told Janie that they would have to help her by restricting her excited behavior more firmly and by providing her with planned assignments during free play periods in order to help her control herself and better utilize her time at school. At home it was hard for the mother to adopt a firmer stand in refusing Janie's bids for night-time attention but she now began to do so and pointed out to Janie the secondary gain she derived from her sleep troubles and genital soreness. She suggested that Janie would not have to punish herself so much by feeling sore if she controlled her angry and excited feelings both at school and in bed. The firmer regimen certainly helped Janie to do better at school and her nights were much more peaceful. Instead of acting excited, however, she now appeared quite anxious, sad and lonely at school. She complained to her mother that nobody loved her and insisted that she could only learn things at home with mommy. Janie did not hold her pencil correctly and refused to accept the teacher's help with this. With her mother, however, she practiced willingly for several days. When the teacher, in a prearranged plan with the mother, insisted that Janie transfer this new skill to school, Janie said she could do so only with the pencil she had used with mommy.

For a long time, the mother tried to help Janie with her aggression toward her. She would draw Janie's attention to its absence at appropriate occasions at home, she would point out her transferring her hostility to school and sometimes toward Susan. Most of all she would sympathize with Janie's trouble with her excited angry feelings when Janie was not with mommy, like at school and at night. Janie could not allow herself to face the intensity of her aggressive masturbation fantasies. In her sessions with me, Janie's mother decided that it was futile to pursue this point. She thought Janie could not accept angry feelings because she feared they would overwhelm her. We thought that perhaps the reason for this was that Janie did not feel loved nor was loving when she was separated from her mother. We decided to approach Janie's difficulty with the lack of love in mind rather than her aggression.

Our theory was substantiated by Janie's repeated questions whether mother thought of her when she was busy during the day and her uncertainty about it. Shortly afterwards the parents planned to leave town for a couple of days. During the packing Janie brought mother her stuffed animal suggesting mother take it along to remind her of Janie's love. After the parents' return the question, "Do you love me when you are not with me?" came up again. The mother knew that Janie was not bothered by not being able to think of or remember the absent mother but rather that she experienced a feeling of being empty and "no good." After discussions with me, the mother decided to tell Janie that when mommy was busy she did not particularly think of Janie but she felt good and comfortable inside because she had Janie's love for her and her own love for Janie within her. She said it was similar to being hungry or satiated. When she has had a good breakfast she does not spend the morning thinking either about being hungry or about having eaten, she just feels comfortable inside. Mother suggested that Janie had trouble taking mother's love along this way, that's why she feels uncomfortable and unloved when she is alone. When angry and excited feelings come up she worries that she has no love from mommy or for mommy.

These interpretations were given gradually over several days with Janie listening carefully for the first time in a long while. One evening Susan asked about the difference between "dead" and "unconscious." Janie surprised her family by suddenly saying, "When I was drowning in the pool, I was not conscious." Janie's statement was such a surprise partly because the pool incident had not come up for discussion in many months, partly because neither Janie nor her parents ever referred to it in those words. Janie was very pleased with what she said, the mother reported, as though Janie was experiencing a new mastery. The mother noticed that Janie's recall of her near-drowning coincided with their recent talks about feeling "no good inside." She discussed this with me and later shared with Janie some of our discussion of it. She told her that when Janie was but 16 months old and fell into the pool during mother's absence, Janie, like other toddlers, would have had trouble feeling loved or loving when mommy was gone. She must have felt very uncomfortable because at that age children cannot keep mommy's love inside when alone and they can only love themselves when mommy is there to love them. Perhaps, she added, Janie's trouble at school and in bed was similar to her feelings from that time, that it might change if Janie knew why she felt that way and that she could now manage being alone differently because she was so much older. Although Janie did not respond in words, within a couple of days she gave up both her "cotton" comforter and the night light. She was happier and more outgoing at school. She suggested that the teachers stop giving her assignments because she now had her own good ideas for activities. She proved herself correct.

Soon Janie became very friendly with her teacher, was affectionate and called her "mommy" with a somewhat guilty giggle. At home Janie's aggression toward her mother came more into the open at appropriate times. She competed with her mother and voiced death wishes on several occasions. The teacher told Janie that she was not her mommy and that Janie should call her by her proper name. Janie readily complied but her guilt over her disloyalty showed itself in her repeatedly asking her mother, "Do you love me best?" and in bids for punishment. The mother told Janie she knew of Janie's dissatisfaction with her at times. She felt mommy had never given her the things or people Janie wanted most. Perhaps she sometimes wanted a "better" mommy. Then she felt so badly that she either worried this made mommy love somebody else better or she had to keep all her love for mommy and stay away from liking others lest she like them too much. Janie was reassured repeatedly that different people are loved differently and that daddy and teachers are loved in addition to mommy, not instead. Janie vehemently disagreed with this idea in regard to having to love daddy differently from the way mommy loved him, but it did help her to re-establish an adequate warm relationship with her teacher, hence helped her in her studies.

The Last Period of the Oedipal Phase

Janie's father had by now pointed out to Janie several times that his relationship with mother was different from his love for Janie and told her not to interfere in the parental relationship. She reacted to this furiously, berated him and often would stomp off in a temper. The father knew that for Janie anger was easier than tears on these occasions, but Janie would not let him talk to her about it. During the following weeks Janie showed signs of accepting the frustration of her oedipal wishes. She spoke of having a boy friend in the future and talked of "when I grow up" in terms of long years. But giving up was not easy for Janie. Her father's "rejection" revived her earlier experiences of phallic disappointment, particularly at the hands of bigger boys.

At home she still stormed at her father; at school she again manifested signs of feeling inadequate. Her interest slackened. When she found herself in group learning situations she was quite anxious when called upon to perform. She would become silly and showoffish and could not produce the correct answer. Her feelings were projected onto others whom she belittled and teased when they made mistakes. She had a particular difficulty with some boys. She patted them and addressed them in an excited babying manner. Janie's mother guessed that Janie's difficulty was related to her feeling that she had been rejected because she was a girl who had nothing to show off. Janie provided an opening for discussing this when she told her mother she feared the big boys at school would put her into a barrel (barrels were a part of the play yard equipment). The mother replied that Janie had acted at school as though she might wish to do just that to the boys. Janie agreed that by patting and babying the boys she was "cutting them down to size" because she was angry and afraid. Mother and child talked further about Janie's fear of not being bright enough to impress the boys just as she used to feel frustrated because she did not have a penis to show off urinating tricks. We wondered whether the specific fear of being put into the barrel related to Pierre's putting Janie into the closet and to his rejections and exhibitionism. Janie was a very active partner in this part of the work and it appeared to help her. Her father also helped by quietly sympathizing with Janie's hurt and engaging her in the companionship of neutral joint activities.

Janie now blossomed out at school. Her stress quieted down at home. She showed a new ability to tolerate her feelings and impulses. Increasingly there were signs of her latency development in her widening interests, in her preparation for public school and in new gaps in her memory. Around the time of her sixth birthday, Janie once again met Pierre while on a short vacation. The mother reminded Janie of her previous experiences with Pierre, but Janie did not evidence much feeling about him anymore, although she did want him to watch her swim the length of the deep pool. He did so and awarded her with his rather curt adolescent praise. On returning to school, Janie commented casually that Pierre had taught her to swim long ago!

Janie found it quite hard to give up her school and with it her early childhood. She could not express all of her sadness before leaving, but she spent her first weeks in her new school missing kindergarten and sadly recalling each detail. This helped her to integrate the transition, without jeopardizing her participation in her new environment.

Status at the Beginning of Latency

At age six and a half, Janie had reached dominance at the appropriate instinctual level and she maintained age-adequate relationships with her family and with adults and peers in her wider environment. Her ego functions were well developed and showed no secondary interference. Repression and rationalization, as well as reaction-formations of pity and tidiness, replaced some of her earlier defenses. Her newly integrated superego enabled her to keep up acceptable behavior but did not interfere with her enjoyment of life nor did it plague her with undue guilt. Always active in facing some of her anxieties, she extended this ability to master difficult situations.

Though not manifestly symptomatic, those who knew Janie could well see the weak links in her personality make-up. Janie appeared to feel secure with adults, but with peers, she needed their love and appreciation. When somebody belittled her, her self-esteem was readily lowered. Sometimes her growing understanding of other people's difficulties helped her overcome her reaction, but initially she was deeply hurt. Another weakness was Janie's difficulty with integration. This used to be quite prominent in the instinc-tual sphere (ambivalence, masculinity-femininity), in her long-standing trouble in mastering her early trauma and in her distractability. The latter often showed in her work, as well as in flighty, somewhat disjointed sentences which reflected the rapid jumps of her ideas. Under stress this tendency was still noticeable. Lastly, Janie's frustration tolerance of her libidinal and aggressive impulses and with neutral activities, which had always been low, now improved greatly, although it still was not among her strong points.

During the five years of work with Janie she fluctuated between coping ably with her inner stress and experiencing considerable interference in functioning. Compared with other children in our center, this was not unusual. It seemed to be characteristic of this particular developmental stage, as well as of the course of the therapeutic work. Only Janie's subsequent maturation would show whether her tendency to such fluctuations was also a significant personality factor.

Parents

Janie's parents were extremely conscientious, understanding parents who maintained warm relationships with their children and a mature one with each other. Their cooperation with our center's program was consistently excellent.

The father whom we saw every other month contributed important observations, as well as discussed minor changes in his interaction with Janie. He always kept in touch with the work and gave the mother his full support.

The mother had a marked gift for psychological insight and utilized her therapeutic skill to the utmost. There were some weaknesses that limited her work at times but they never jeopardized it. The mother found it difficult to be a firm educator in regard to aggression. She tended to be too permissive about Janie's aggressive behavior, but set rigid controls for herself. Janie's difficulty was partly due to adopting her mother's code too early without the necessary ego strength to conform to it. In this aspect the mother improved greatly. Further, it was hard for the mother to interest herself and her children in the typical presublimatory activities of under-fives. Highly intelligent and cultured herself, she was more at ease with the sublimations of older children. Janie's fluctuating enthusiasm for creative activities was related to this difference between home and school expectations. Lastly, the mother, like Janie, set strict moral standards for herself and often felt guilty and underestimated herself. The mother was aware of this difficulty, had been able to alter her ideals in some respects and had discussed this with Janie to forestall or modify a possible identification.

5. Diagnosis

ELIZABETH DAUNTON

I. REVIEW OF THE LITERATURE

In the diagnostic assessment of the children in the study, the research group chose the factor of progression or regression in development as the initial focus. The use of this criterion was first proposed by Anna Freud (1945). She showed that the criteria appropriate to the assessment of mental health and disturbance in adult life, the capacity to lead a normal love and sex life, and the capacity to work, are not applicable to children. By contrast, "Childhood is a process *sui generis,* a series of developmental stages, in which each manifestation has its importance as a transition, not a final result." Anna Freud continues that "diagnostically the factor of central importance in childhood is the child's ability to develop, not to remain fixated at some stage of development, before the maturation process has been completed."

Anna Freud (1962) outlined the diagnostician's task as follows: "To ascertain where a given child stands on the developmental scale, whether his position is age-adequate, retarded or precocious and in what respect, to what extent the observable internal and external circumstances and existent symptoms are interfering with the possibilities of future growth." She indicated that to make such an assessment "a comprehensive metapsychological picture of the child (i.e., one containing structural, dynamic, economic, genetic and adaptive data) is necessary," and outlined the Developmental

Profile, which provides these data. Part C of Section V of the profile is concerned with the development of the total personality. Here the combined action of drive and ego development is studied in "The Lines of Development and Mastery of Tasks." Anna Freud (1963) charted a number of significant lines of development. She also showed how these lines provided evidence of harmony or imbalance in personality development and discussed the relation of innate and environmental factors to a harmonious or uneven development. She studied the results of analytic observations of young infants which "have demonstrated that it is the individual mother's interest and predilection which act as stimulants. In the beginning of life, at least, the infant seems to concentrate on development along those lines which call forth most ostensibly the mother's love and approval. . . ." Kris (1955) and Provence and Ritvo (1961) have also demonstrated from observations of infants in institutions that harmonious development was dependent on a relationship with the mother.

Nagera (1963) described the use of the Profile by the Diagnostic Research group at the Hampstead Clinic and stressed that in the Profile, "pathology is seen against the background of normal development and its possible variations." In this paper and in his later study (1964), he stressed the theoretical and clinical importance of distinguishing between arrest and regression in following the vicissitudes of drive development. Discussing the libidinal drive (1963), he commented, "it is not always easy to determine clearly how much of the libido one sees at a particular pregenital fixation point is present there as a result of the regression and how much has always remained fixated at that point and has never moved forward." Nagera nevertheless underlined the prognostic importance of distinguishing between libidinal arrest and libidinal regression since "it is no doubt easier to help the forward movement of libido that has regressed than of libido that has always been arrested at earlier stages. In assessing the total personality it is of value to have a relative estimate of how much of the libido was able to move forward to the phallic phase, even though it may at present be seen in a regressed state. It is important to know that at some time most or part of the libido has moved forward and made its contribution at the proper time to the development of the ego and to the personality as a whole."

Discussing how the clinical differentiation between drive arrest and regression may be made, Nagera (1964) indicated the value of a very careful developmental history of the child. He pointed out that when a pathologically activated fixation point "exists in a child it betrays itself by the excessive activity of the component instinct or instincts involved in the fixation." He suggested that such fixation points indicate a certain degree of arrest in drive development. In discussing the clinical manifestation of these pathological fixation points Nagera introduced the term "contamination" to indicate how "oral and anal conflicts reveal themselves at the phallic-oedipal stage." This contamination, he suggested, is revealed by the expression of fantasies, appropriate to the phallic phase in oral or anal terms. In regressive phenomena, on the other hand, the drives have at one point or another reached a higher level of development but, as a result of conflict at these higher levels, were forced back to earlier developmental positions.

A detailed developmental history was equally important, Nagera suggested (1963), in tracing the development of ego functioning and in the recognition of defects, as well as the unevenness or precociousness in development. Where ego defects were manifest, history should help determine "whether there is a primary disturbance based on an ego defect (organic damage being the possible substrate in many cases) or whether there is a developmental disturbance of the particular function or functions under consideration. In the latter case the cause might well be the lack of proper and adequate mothering. In this case the environment has failed in its releasing and stimulating function necessary for the proper development of the ego functions and apparatus."

Anna Freud (1965) elucidated many aspects of regression under the heading "Regression in Normal Development." In discussing ego and superego regression she pointed out that the regressive processes here operated according to different principles from those of drive regressions. In contrast to drive regressions, the retrograde moves on the ego scale did not lead back to previously established positions since no fixation points existed. Instead they retraced the way, step by step, along the line which was pursued during the forward course. This was borne out by the clinical finding that, in ego regression, it was invariably the most recent achievement which was lost first.

In a later paper Nagera (1966) re-examined the concept of infantile neurosis and showed that certain types of conflict described by Freud were not necessarily "neurotic conflicts" but conflicts around adaptation. Nagera first discussed "developmental interferences" that disturb the typical unfolding of development. The term may be reserved, he suggested, "to describe those situations that involve gross external (environmental) interference with certain needs and rights of the child. Frequently in such demands no account is taken by the environment of the child's lack of ego capacity to comply or cope with them." "Developmental conflicts" are experienced by every child to a greater or lesser degree either when certain specific environmental demands are made at the appropriate developmental phases, or when internal developmental and maturational levels are reached where specific conflicts are created. Nagera restricted the term neurotic conflicts to those "that take place among the different psychic structures, id, ego and superego, the latter either as a total structure or in early childhood more frequently its precursors." These conflicts between opposing forces can, Nagera pointed out, "occur very early on in the life of infants. We distinguish them from neurosis proper in that the latter is a much more complex organization and as such appears for the first time at a much later stage in the child's development."

II. DIAGNOSTIC CONSIDERATIONS

While our research group fully appreciated the diagnostic value of a careful developmental history, our experience suggests that in many instances such a history cannot be obtained at the time of the initial evaluation. Frequently the mother's anxiety or particular use of defenses at this time interfered with her power of meaningful recall. For example, it is not unusual for a mother to present sincerely a picture of an easy toilet-training period and only much later to recall the troublesome reality. Dr. Anny Katan (1959) showed that the initial impressions of a young child's disturbances based on the history given by the mother and her conscious reactions to the child's difficulties might be misleading in some important respects. She discussed the diagnostic opportunities provided by the therapeutic nursery school where day-to-day observations could be made. She stressed particularly the value of these observations for understanding the mother-child relationship, for determining whether the child's conflict is between himself and his environment or already internalized. Dr. Furman explained in Chapter 1 that the original assessments of the nursery school children included in the follow-up study were made by the staff in joint seminar discussions. These were based on two-month observations by teachers and therapists in the nursery school, as well as the therapists' impressions from weekly interviews with the mothers. The records of these observations were used by the members of the research group as the basis for constructing the first two profiles on each child.

These relatively long-term observations of each child's development, as well as the age range of our nursery school population, led us to focus on certain aspects of the metapsychological picture. Since we were dealing initially with a group of children between the ages of three and five, we wanted to estimate the extent and the ways a child's conflicts, manifest at the phallic stage, might interfere with the resolution of the oedipus conflict. Although, in our genetic assessment of the child, we distinguished between the effects of libido that did not move forward from a fixation point and the effects of libidinal regression, our predominant interest was assessing the amount of interference, whether caused by arrest or regression, seen in the child's object relationships, ego functioning, defense structure and superego formation (see Chapter 6).

In the review of the literature, Nagera's observations on the differential influences of arrest and regression on libidinal drive development were quoted. Here we wish to include some of our reflections on the development of the aggressive drive. The direction of the aggressive drive (towards self or object) and its modes of expression are studied in relation to the child's libidinal development and his level of ego functioning. For example, phase-appropriate manifestations of aggression in the oral-sadistic phase, will be screaming and biting. In the anal phase, when the child can walk and move arms more purposively, but before speech development allows another mode of expression, aggression will be discharged in kicking, throwing tantrums. In assessing the aggressive drive development of the child, we want to know, for instance, whether a child of three and a half, who has good command of speech and habitually shows anger in a preverbal form such as hitting and biting, ever progressed beyond this stage. We also want to know how the parents regarded and handled his expression of aggression. When a child still expresses aggression almost exclusively by physical means, it may be that, for reasons such as uncertainty or fear of verbal aggression, the parents did not help the child to verbalize. In such instances, a change in handling on the parents' part can frequently lead the child to take a progressive step and express aggression in a more age-appropriate way. We should only recognize arrest when the child remains unable to express aggression age-appropriately, even with parental help and sanction. We can recognize regression when a child previously used more advanced forms of expression of aggression and then abandoned them for earlier ones, reverting, for instance, from verbalizing to hitting or from hitting to biting or screaming. In assessing the aggressive drive it is also meaningful to distinguish between "content" and "form." The form, verbalization, for example, may be more advanced than the content, which may, for example, consist of sadistic teasing. This discrepancy may be due in one case to an arrest, in another case, to a regression.

The relation between fixation and arrest in drive development, libidinal and aggressive, is well illustrated by one of our children, Ben,[1] who at four and a half was still clinging and dependent on his mother. His aggression was always expressed by biting, hitting, yelling, as well as by refusing to eat in anger. This behavior had persisted since a separation from his mother and the birth of a sibling when Ben was twenty months.

In distinguishing between arrest and regression in object relationships we took as our starting point the developmental line "Dependency to Emotional Self-Reliance and Adult Object Relationships," formulated by Anna Freud (1963). In assessing the object relationships of the child we needed to know whether he ever reached the phase-appropriate level of object constancy, the preoedipal or oedipal stage and so on, or whether he remained fixated at an earlier stage. Regres-

---

[1] This case is discussed in more detail in Chapter 6.

sion was apparent if the child were unable to maintain himself at a level he had once attained.

In assessing the superego development of a child we first considered whether there was an age-appropriate balance between internal and external control. In younger children, before the resolution of the oedipal conflict and the consequent internalization of a more or less autonomous superego has been achieved, we are interested in those superego precursors which pave the way for later superego formations. The appearance and use of particular ego defenses, such as reaction formation, imitation, identification, and introjection, are significant here (Anna Freud, 1965). Where an appropriate balance between internal and external control does not exist, for instance, when a five-year-old is unduly dependent on external control, we have to consider especially the ego defenses, ego functioning and parental expectations, both past and present. Delays in development of secondary-process thinking, an inability to anticipate or appreciate the relationship between cause and effect, interfere with the process of internalization. Insufficient expectations, hostility or punitive attitudes or great inconsistency on the part of parents may also interfere with this process. While internalization normally occurs during the resolution of the oedipal conflict, complete superego autonomy is not achieved during childhood. Temporary regressions often occur in latency while, in adolescence, the superego, as the internalized representative of the parents, may be ejected as part of the attempt to break the incestuous tie with them.

III. DIAGNOSTIC CLASSIFICATION

The Research Committee has in general followed the classification suggested by Anna Freud (1962): the divergencies have been introduced to meet our particular needs.

We have found that the special population of the research project, i.e., a group of children who were between the ages of three and six years at the time of the first profiles, presented us with certain diagnostic problems. There was also a wide age spread at the time of the follow-up study, ranging approximately from seven to seventeen years.

The Committee spent the most time considering the children in our study whose disturbances did not appear age- or phase-appropriate, on the one hand, and did not fit into the category of neurosis or character disorder on the other. All of these children as we saw them at the nursery school showed partial arrests caused by pathological fixations. Some, in addition to these arrests, showed the beginnings of regression from the phallic or oedipal stages. All had symptoms maintained by pathological defenses and, in most cases, there was secondary defensive interference with ego functioning.[2]

We found ourselves in some difficulty when we came to our third (follow-up) profile on the children. We found some who had pathological formations that were not phase-appropriate, yet did not have a neurosis or character disorder. They were much fewer and were rarely the same children whom we had placed in this group when they entered nursery school. We further observed that these children, in spite of some symptoms, were progressing adequately in most areas, for example, in school. This was in contrast to children with a neurosis or character disorder.

We reached the conclusion[3] that there was an important difference between those children with the pathological formations described above, who had not yet completed the oedipal phase, and those who were already in latency or adolescence. In the former, the neurotic conflicts endangered the proper resolution of the oedipal conflict. In the latter,

---

[2] The conflicts of these children resembled those described by Nagera (1966) as follows: "Some developmental conflicts cannot be solved . . . and when development proceeds further, they remain behind as unresolved conflicted areas. In this way what should have been a transitory developmental conflict becomes a permanent neurotic conflict" [p. 49].

[3] This conclusion was formulated by Dr. Anny Katan.

once the oedipal stage was passed, the existence of some neurotic conflicts did not prevent further progressive development. These children were alike however, in having conflicts which were neither transitory nor phase-appropriate and because of this similarity we included both groups in a new diagnostic category, Group III. With this group we specified whether the child is an under-five or has reached latency. The characteristics of the children in this group are described in more detail in Chapter 6 ("Description, Evaluation and Follow-up Cases Treated via the Mother").

We had particular difficulty in assessing the disturbances of three of the children in the first profile. These were children whose disturbances involved drive and ego development, object relationships and economic factors to a marked extent. The rigidity of their defenses was particularly striking. In spite of this, structuralization in terms of ego and superego development did not lead to a neurosis. We nevertheless extended the description of Group IV to include these children, as well as those with neurosis and character disorders because of a similarity in the overall involvement and in the rigidity of defenses.

The five children with psychosomatic disorders presented special diagnostic problems since they showed great variation both in personality structure and in degree of pathology. It was decided to include each child in a special diagnostic group (Group VI) until it was possible to make a definitive diagnosis relating to the total personality of each child. The reasons for this decision are discussed in Chapter 7 ("Psychosomatic Disorders").

The diagnostic grouping of the children in the study is as follows:

I. In spite of some manifest behavior disturbances the personality growth of the child is essentially healthy.

II. Pathological formations (symptoms, defenses, economic

factors) are products of developmental conflicts, which are age- or phase-appropriate.

III. The pathological formations (symptoms, defenses, economic factors) are not phase-appropriate. An under-five child is placed in this group when the neurotic conflicts appear to endanger the proper resolution of the oedipal conflict. A latency child or an adolescent placed in this group has some neurotic conflicts which, however, are not incapacitating to further development.

IV. The "Neurosis and Character Disorder" group includes some young children whose structuralization is inadequate to the formation of a neurosis and whose pathology shows over-all involvement of drive and ego development, object relationships and economic factors.

V. Arrests and regression of drives are paralleled by arrests or regression in ego and superego development, i.e., disturbances of a borderline, psychopathic or psychotic nature. Children in this group show a lack of the usual progression in drive development (co-existence of all pregenital drives in almost equal measure). In the area of ego functioning they show particular impairment in the synthesizing and reality-testing functions and in the capacity for secondary-process thinking.

VI. Psychosomatic disorders.

VII. Primary organic deficiencies or very early deprivations leading to defective or retarded personalities.

VIII. Destructive process at work (organic, toxic, psychological, and so on) effecting a disruption of mental growth.

Table 1 in the Appendix shows the diagnostic groupings of the children two months after entry into nursery school, when leaving nursery school or kindergarten and during the follow-up study.

6. Description, Evaluation and Follow-up of Cases Treated via the Mother

ELIZABETH DAUNTON

I. USE OF PROFILE MATERIAL IN ASSESSING CHILDREN TREATED VIA THE MOTHER

While the diagnostic assessment of a child, contained in each of his three profiles, provided an overall basis for comparison, a more detailed study of the first and second profiles revealed the changes—in some cases, the absence of change —and developments within the personality structure which had occurred during his stay in the Hanna Perkins Nursery School.

A detailed study of the first two profiles provided the means (1) to examine the results of the treatment of the child via the mother in individual cases and (2) to compare the results of this treatment between the children of the different diagnostic groups.

The third (follow-up) profile showed whether the changes indicated in the second profile had been maintained.

Study of Individual Cases

After an initial study and comparison of the three profiles in each case, the research group decided to construct a Developmental Chart which would show whether a child had reached the age-appropriate level in each area, at a given time (i.e., at entry into nursery school, on leaving nursery school or kindergarten and on follow-up). This chart shows the levels of drive development and ego function and the presence or absence of pathological fixation points. These fixation points indicate that an abnormal amount of energy is bound to a particular developmental phase, which may be mainly due either to an arrest or to a regression. The heading, "General Economic Factors," estimates the capacity of the child to cope with frustration, to handle anxiety, and to sublimate. It also shows whether the predominant tendencies are progressive or regressive.

This chart clarified the developmental position of the child in all areas with one exception. Pathological fixation points at one or more pregenital levels were noted in all the children who were treated via the mother except for one case, the only child in Diagnostic Group I. Yet the children showed a wide divergence in the overall metapsychological picture, ranging diagnostically from Group II to IV. It was therefore decided to assess further both the quantitative aspects of the pathological fixations, i.e., how much of a child's drive energy was currently invested at the prephallic levels of development, whether due to arrest or to regression and the extent to which they affected the different areas of the personality. In the latter, we investigated whether the arrest at, or regression to, prephallic levels pertained to the drives or to object relationships or to ego functions or to all three.

The results of this assessment are shown in a Phase Dominance Chart (see Appendix). This chart refers to the child's status on the first profile. Phase Dominance means the predominant, instinctual level of the child. The chart differentiates phallic-oedipal phase dominance, contamination dominance at the phallic-oedipal level, anal phase dominance and oral phase dominance.

A child may be assessed as showing a "phallic-oedipal phase dominance," yet he may show some behavior from earlier levels, e.g., some thumbsucking or wetting. "Contamination dominance at the phallic-oedipal level" means a predominantly phallic-oedipal stage, which is, however, extensively "colored" by prephallic drives. "Contamination" is to be distinguished from (1) the normal overlapping of instinctual phases, and (2) the coexistence of all instinctual levels in almost equal measure. A child whose anal or oral phase is considered dominant may still show signs of phallic interests.

In assessing the status of the aggressive drive the same criteria used in assessing the libido were applied, but the predominance either of "content" or of "form" was also noted. For example, a child may express his anger verbally, a "form" indicative of the phallic-oedipal level, but the "content" of his aggression may be sadistic teasing and controlling, which is related to the anal level.

The level of object relationships is assessed in three areas: relationship with the mother, relationships with the teachers, relationships with peers. A child may, for example, maintain a sadomasochistic relationship with his mother but his relationships with the teachers and peers may be of a phallic nature.

In assessing ego functions only those demonstrably impaired by the prephallic drives were named and examined. In some instances, for example, the defense structure was characterized by excessive reaction formation; in others, gross oral-anal difficulties led to the instinctualization of an ego function thus impairing its adequate development, by inhibition or by insufficient investment with neutral energy. Such impairments were distinguished from ego regressions, which did not seem germane to the assessment.

The Phase Dominance Chart is therefore concerned only with those ego functions clearly affected by prephallic disturbance of drives, it does not provide a comprehensive picture of the child's ego functioning. The Developmental Chart assesses the age-appropriate use of defenses and records their interference with ego functioning.

II. COMPARISON OF RESULTS OF TREATMENT VIA THE MOTHER IN DIAGNOSTIC GROUPS I-IV

A study of all the chart data (Developmental and Phase Dominance) of children who were in the same diagnostic group on the first profile showed the common features, the areas of strength or weakness, and the exceptional cases among the group. A comparison of the first and second developmental charts of children in the same initial diagnostic group indicated the response of the group to the treatment work. Their response could then be compared with that of other diagnostic groups. The following are the results of the comparative study of each diagnostic group.[1]

Group I (In spite of some manifest behavior disturbances, the personality growth of the child is essentially healthy.)

Albert is the one representative of this group and will be described here in detail.[2]

First Profile. When Albert (and his twin sister) entered nursery school at two years, nine months, all aspects of his development were age-adequate. Albert was accepted because his mother felt she would need help with the upbringing of twins and because we were particularly interested in the nature of the twin relationship and its effects on the development of both children.

Second Profile. On leaving nursery school, Albert had moved to Group II. Albert remained free from pathological fixation points and continued to reach age-adequate levels.

---

[1] Chart on page 320 in the Appendix illustrates how the Developmental Charts of all children in the same diagnostic group were compared.

[2] The discussion of this case has been kindly contributed by Mrs. Joanne Benkendorf.

His tolerance of frustration in the area of aggression and his ability to tolerate anxiety were more limited and at times he resorted to defenses, which interfered with object relationships and ego functions. Albert had retained some of the earlier features of the twin relationship, where the twin served as the object for projection and displacement and as the much needed accomplice for sharing his guilt. These features could also be extended to friendships.

Follow-up Profile. Albert maintained the diagnosis of the second profile. In early puberty, he no longer needed the twin relationship to cope with his superego anxiety and guilt feelings; he could master them more independently.

Group II (Pathological formations are products of developmental conflicts which are age- or phase-appropriate.)

First Profile. The four children in this group were characteristically age-adequate in libidinal development, although two showed unevenness in libidinal distribution. All showed adequate ego functioning and defenses; they were rated age-adequate or advanced both in sublimation potential and in frustration tolerance in relation to neutralized activities. Progressive tendencies were predominant in all cases. In superego development, three of the four children showed an age-appropriate balance between external and internal control. The difficulties of the group were in the areas of aggressive drive development, in frustration tolerance in relation to drives and in the ability to tolerate anxiety. Although the children had an appropriate range of defenses, these at times were overwhelmed.

In object relationships, these children had greater difficulties in peer relations (inadequate in three out of four cases) than in relations with parents and teachers (inadequate in one out of four cases).

Study of the genetic development of the children showed no impairment of individual ego functions by the prephallic drives. However, each showed periodic restriction of ego functioning through defense activity.

Alice, for example, who had joined in all activities and played with other children while her mother was at school, began to limit her interests when her mother was not there. She confined herself to activities such as difficult puzzles and swinging and demanded the teacher's exclusive attention. She transferred to the teachers her longing for exclusive care, which she felt her mother now gave to her younger sister at home. As a result of her conflict, her ability to pursue many activities, either on her own or with other children, was restricted.

Second Profile. Three of the four children were now in Group I. Each of these three showed improvement (age-adequacy) in the areas of aggressive drive development, in frustration tolerance in relation to drives and in their ability to tolerate anxiety without recourse to rigid defenses. They showed ego functioning free from secondary interference by defenses, were age-adequate in object relationships and in superego formation. In each case there was an alleviation of conflicts. Of the three children, one, Alvin, showed signs of some unevenness of libido distribution between self and objects.

In the second profile, the fourth child, Bertha, was diagnosed as Group III, because she had some neurotic conflicts expressed in bodily symptoms. This child progressed in her ability to verbalize, particularly aggression, and in her frustration tolerance. However, she still showed some unevenness in the libidinal distribution between herself and objects and directed some aggression against herself. There was some secondary interference in ego functioning because of a tendency to withdraw from situations that aroused anxiety. A disturbance in the mother, precipitated by a family event, interfered with the progress of treatment, which had hitherto developed favorably.

Follow-up Profile. Three of the children maintained the diagnosis of the second profile. Two remained in Group I and Bertha, discussed above, in Group III. The diagnosis of the fourth child, Alvin, was again Group II. It was considered that this boy's greater difficulties in adolescence, as well as a tendency to turn aggression against himself, were predominantly linked with the serious, chronic illness of a parent, which had been recently diagnosed.

DIAGNOSTIC TABLE OF FOUR GROUP II CASES

First Profile	Second Profile		Third Profile		
Group I	Group II	Group III	Group I	Group II	Group III
4	3	1	2	1	1

Group III (The pathological formations are not phase-appropriate. An under-five child is placed in this group when the neurotic conflicts appear to endanger the proper resolution of the oedipal conflict. A latency child or adolescent placed in this group has some neurotic conflicts, which, however, are not incapacitating to further development.)

First Profile. There were few areas of strength or difficulty common to all 24 children in this group. All the children, however, had some disturbance in object relationships and many showed some restriction of ego functioning because of defense activity. In the area of the drives, many showed difficulties more with aggression than with libidinal development. While the children varied widely in their areas of difficulty, they were alike in their uneven development, the distinguishing feature of Group III. Because of the research group's interest in the progressive and regressive trends in development, we noted that the 24 in Group III were nearly evenly divided on that score: in 12 cases progressive trends were predominant and in 11 cases, regressive trends were predominant. In one case, the trends were evenly matched.

A detailed study of the 24 children in this group, showed that 12 were age-adequate in libidinal development and the other 12 showed "contamination" of the phallic phase by prephallic drives.

Of the 24 children, 22 showed disturbances in aggressive drive development. In 16 cases there was a predominant prephallic fixation. In four cases, there was contamination of the phallic phase by the prephallic drives, while the conflicts of two children were mainly on the phallic level.

The effects of pathological fixation or "contamination" of the prephallic drives on ego functioning were assessed separately from the effects of defense activity.[3] Twenty-two of the children showed either no ego involvement or slight to moderate involvement in at most two areas (i.e., speech and motility). Ben, whose case is discussed below, was a child whose speech was impaired by instinctualization at the prephallic levels. Nineteen of the 24 children showed some restriction or inhibition as a result of defense activity. For example, Bill frequently warded off anxiety by excited behavior which stood in the way of his learning. It impaired his capacity to pay attention and at times his ability to perceive and test reality, which plunged him into dangerous activity. He would repeatedly pile the big blocks dangerously and could not learn from previous experience of the blocks falling.

The children in this group showed disturbances in object relationships. One child had difficulties only with peers, the others had more extensive difficulties: they showed disturbances in two or three kinds of relationships (mother, teachers, peers). In superego development, only nine children showed an age-appropriate balance between external and internal control.

As regards economic characteristics, the children showed

[3] This point is discussed more fully above in the study of individual cases and in the Phase Dominance Chart.

less age-adequacy when their frustration tolerance was assessed. Two children showed adequate frustration tolerance for both the libidinal and aggressive drives and six other children showed adequate tolerance for one of the two drives (three libido, three aggression). Ten of the 24 children had adequate frustration tolerance for neutralized activities and eleven showed adequate sublimation potential.

When the 12 children in this group who showed predominantly progressive trends were compared with the 11 who showed regressive tendencies, the basic difference apparently was in the nature of the defensive structure. The defenses of the children with progressive trends were more flexible and allowed for some degree of mastery while those of the children with regressive trends led to restriction and impoverishment of the personality. The following case examples have been chosen to illustrate this difference, as well as to convey the unevenness of development characteristic of children in Group III.

Candace, age three and a half, had the symptoms of occasional withholding of feces, stammering and thumbsucking. Libidinally she had reached the phallic phase, but a tendency to regress showed in her provocatively messy eating, as well as in other symptoms. Since she could not yet verbalize her aggressive feelings, she expressed them instead in symptoms.

Although Candace reacted to some situations regressively, she had other defenses at her disposal, such as passive into active, which allowed for some mastery of situations and conflicts. In the sphere of superego development she needed the presence of mother or teachers to maintain control. Candace was in many ways still anchored to her relationship with her mother or mother substitutes. She was well liked by her companions at nursery school but away from it she did not play with other children and had not yet made the shift from egocentricity to companionship. By contrast Candace was a child who showed great maturity in ego functioning. She could verbalize thoughts and fantasies and had an excellent ability to tell stories. She also enjoyed many nursery school activities, especially games. Progressive tendencies appeared predominant in Candace.

Ben, age four years, three months, suffered from a severe separation anxiety in relation to his mother, father and next younger brother; he was also afraid of noises and fights. At 20 months he had been separated from his mother at the birth of a sibling and had responded with serious loss of appetite lasting two months and with clinging behavior. He was just beginning to talk when this separation occurred. Ben had probably reached the phallic level when he entered nursery school, since he showed an unwillingness to try activities which he felt he could not do as well as others. However, his relationships were largely sadomasochistic and dependent. Ben's aggression was both expressed and inhibited in a chaotic manner on all levels. Biting, hitting, yelling angry words, refusing to eat and inability to defend himself were typical manifestations. Ben showed disturbances of ego functioning in certain areas. Both large and small muscle control were poor for his age, and at school he mumbled almost unintelligibly. It seemed that his speech had not evolved as a neutral activity because it was so much affected by the strong oral fixation dating from his traumatic separation from his mother at 20 months of age. Evidence from home and school of his reasoning ability, verbal capacity, understanding of situations pointed to above normal intelligence. Ben's most prominent current defenses were avoidance, denial, ego restriction, displacement, projection and regression. His use of a number of primitive defenses made for a lack of mastery. His defenses also interfered with his ego achievements to a considerable extent. For instance, he made very restricted use of toys and materials.

Ben's superego development could not be fully assessed at this stage. It was striking that the control of his behavior did not depend on the parents; he appeared in better control, though anxious, when without his parents.

In his relationships at school Ben could not accept adult substitutes nor could he make relationships with other children because he was afraid of them. Ben's frustration tolerance was poor in relation to the drives and neutral activities. He had hardly any neutral achievements at his disposal and those he had were used more for defense than for enjoyment. His anxiety tolerance was also poor. Regressive rather than progressive tendencies appeared predominant in Ben because of a marked lack of the defenses leading to mastery.

Second Profile. On leaving nursery school or kindergarten, eight of the 24 cases were diagnosed as Group I, 10 as Group II and three as Group IV. Three cases began psychotherapy while still in nursery school and were not evaluated in the second profile.

Of the three Group IV children, two began analysis after leaving nursery school or kindergarten (see Chapter 8). The third child, Calvin, had presented the special problem of a child with a severe organic impairment. The role of the defect in the total metapsychological picture could not be adequately understood at this stage and a correct diagnostic classification had therefore proved impossible. Calvin's school-leaving diagnosis remained unchanged at the time of the follow-up.

All 18 children diagnosed as Group I and II showed a predominance of progressive tendencies on leaving school, whereas seven of the 18 showed predominantly regressive tendencies on the first profile. There was a striking consistency in overall development, in contrast to the earlier characteristic unevenness.

The main changes were as follows: (1) In the areas of drives —all the children were now age-adequate in their libidinal and aggressive drive development. (2) In defense organization

—all the children showed age-adequate defenses. (3) Superego —all the children had an age-appropriate balance between external and internal control. (4) In their object relationships—14 children had no outstanding problems in this area, while four still had difficulty in one type of relationship (mother, teachers, peers). (5) Economic Factors—14 were assessed age-adequate or superior under each of the headings. Of the four who were not age-adequate, one child had one area of difficulty (frustration tolerance of the libidinal drive), two had two areas of difficulty (in one case, frustration tolerance for neutralized activities and sublimation potential and in the other, frustration tolerance for libidinal drive and tolerance of anxiety). One child had three areas of difficulty (frustration tolerance for neutralized activities, sublimation potential and tolerance of anxiety).

Follow-up Profile. Seven children remained in Group I and four of the children who were in Group II in the second profile were now diagnosed as Group I. One child, Ben, now in Group II (previously Group I) had in the meantime suffered a most painful trauma: witnessing the death of a parent. Four children remained in Group II.

Two children in Group II on the second profile were now in Group III. One was Judy, who was followed up shortly after the beginning of puberty. She had a problem in handling aggression at home other than through interplay, which was characteristic in her family. Certain regressive tendencies, absent in latency, appeared to be a reaction to the beginning of puberty. However, she was placed in Group III because of the prominence of pregenital features in her relationship with her mother.

The other child was Laura who was difficult to assess because the follow-up interviews took place a few months after she had undergone major surgery for a congenital defect. Between leaving school and the follow-up she had had many difficult experiences of serious illness within her family but her development continued to be progressive. She was placed in Group III because of a symptomatic restlessness, inability to stay still and tendency toward self-depreciation.

DIAGNOSTIC TABLE OF 19 GROUP III CASES TREATED VIA THE MOTHER[4]

First Profile	Second Profile			Third Profile			
Group III	Group I	Group II	Group IV	Group I	Group II	Group III	Group IV
19	8	10	1	11	5	2	1

Group IV (Neurosis and character disorder.)

First Profile. Of the 23 children in this group, 15 had analytic treatment during or after nursery school (see Chapter 8). Of the eight who did not have direct treatment, some already had an established neurosis, with the others, structuralization was inadequate to the formation of a neurosis (see Diagnostic Classification).

All the children in the group had had serious developmental interferences which led to libidinal arrest at a number of fixation points. The ensuing conflicts greatly affected several areas of the personality. Rigidity of defenses was a predominant characteristic. However, it was the degree of involvement rather than the specificity of areas affected that distinguished the children in Group IV from Group III. This difference is reflected in the assessment of the progressive versus regressive tendencies in the two groups. In the first profile, 12 of the 24 children in Group III were assessed as progressive while none was rated progressive in Group IV. In seven cases regressive tendencies predominated; in

[4] The 19 cases in Group III treated via the mother were the original 24 cases less the three who went into psychotherapy and the two who went into analysis.

one case, progressive and regressive trends appeared evenly matched.

Second Profile. All the children in Group IV retained this diagnosis on the second profile and the estimate of predominance of progressive or regressive trends remained unchanged.

Follow-up Profile. The diagnostic status of the eight children who did not receive direct treatment remained unchanged at the time of follow-up. While there were some areas of improvement in individual cases, the outstanding characteristic was the persistence of pathology.

Let us take Marie as an example. She entered nursery school at age three years, six months with a severe speech disturbance. Her speech development was retarded although she was able to make herself understood verbally. She refused to speak to anyone outside her family, had a strong sadomasochistic relationship with her mother and had frequent temper tantrums. Marie also had many acute fears. Besides the speech difficulty, Marie's control of motility was variable and her reality testing was not age-appropriate. Her defenses severely restricted her ego functioning and object relationships, interfered with her ability to learn and prevented close contacts with people. Marie had low frustration tolerance in all areas and was often overwhelmed by anxiety.

Work with the therapist enabled Marie's mother slowly to give up the sadomasochistic interplay with her child, to recognize the aggressive component in her speech disturbance and to encourage verbalization instead of tantrums. Later the mother showed an understanding of her daughter's oedipal conflict and helped Marie with some of her feelings in this area. The mother, however, found it difficult to allow Marie to enjoy independent success.

When Marie left nursery school, she showed much more adequate functioning and greater mastery in a number of areas. Her speech was fairly fluent and understandable and she could use it to communicate with teachers and peers; her motor control also was now very good. However, Marie still experienced difficulty at all levels of libidinal and aggressive development. She had achieved much better mastery of her aggression and was well capable of giving it verbal expression, but her longstanding conflict over ambivalence tended toward symptom formation, withdrawal from relationships, especially with peers and adults outside the family. She seemed to enjoy few activities for their own sake although she liked success.

At follow-up in early puberty, Marie showed libidinal arrest and regression, which contributed to the persistence of the same symptoms and inhibitions. Her school performance was generally poor, she had many phobic symptoms, her relationships with peers were restricted and she appeared indifferent about her lack of friends. But Marie showed improvements in some areas. She used her good motor coordination to master many sports, which she now enjoyed for their own sake. She also had no undue reaction to entering puberty and showed interest in understanding her physical development.

III. DISCUSSION OF RESULTS OF TREATMENT VIA THE MOTHER FOR CHILDREN IN DIAGNOSTIC GROUPS I-IV

Of the 24 children initially included in Group I-III and treated exclusively via the mother, 21 showed diagnostic improvement on leaving nursery school or kindergarten. (The exceptions, Albert, Bertha and Calvin, have already been discussed individually.)

At follow-up 13 of the remaining 21 children maintained their school-leaving diagnosis of Group I or II. Four others who had been in Group II then moved at follow-up to Group I. (The four children who did not maintain their school-leaving diagnosis, Alvin, Ben, Judy and Laura, have already been discussed.)

We were particularly interested in the 16 children who were initially in Group III and diagnosed as Group I or Group II on leaving school and maintained this improvement at follow-up. This favorable development was possible for 16 of the 19 cases in Group III whose treatment was only via the mother (see table on page 300). These 16 children, at the beginning of nursery school, had considerable difficulty in maintaining themselves at the phallic or oedipal level, owing to their neurotic conflicts. Their drive development, defense organization, object relationships and economic functioning were severely impaired. Seven of the children at that time showed regressive trends owing to inadequacies in the defensive structure (including insufficient defenses, predominance of primitive defenses or excessive reliance on one defense), which led in turn to an impairment of ego functioning.[5]

IV. CONCLUSIONS

We wish particularly to emphasize the sustained improvement of the 16 children in Group III. This improvement has convinced us that treatment via the mother can be the appropriate treatment for a significant proportion of children under five whose disturbances are of greater severity than transitory developmental conflicts.

[5] The chapter on Treatment via the Mother has described how the task of modifying the defensive structure and alleviating the fixations was approached.

7. Psychosomatic Disorders

ROBERT A. FURMAN, M.D.

I. DIAGNOSTIC ASSESSMENT

In our work with young children with psychosomatic disorders we have been impressed by the great variations in their responses to our therapeutic efforts. In some instances it apparently has been possible to effect a complete eradication of the psychosomatic disease; in others, despite prolonged and intensive work, the underlying pathological process has remained essentially unaffected. Treatment programs have strengthened the child's personality and enabled him to deal more effectively with the consequences and burdens of his disease, but the disease has remained basically unchanged.

We have also been impressed, as many others have been, that the psychosomatic symptom itself has been of quite limited value as the basic diagnostic factor. An example is children with asthma; some have apparently been cured in treatment via the mother, while others have shown little change after treatment via the mother and prolonged analysis. The symptom has been the same but the children have responded almost as if they had entirely different diseases.

These experiences led us to seek a diagnostic assessment of psychosomatic disorders based on metapsychological considerations. From the outset, however, we felt that such an assessment could not consider only psychological factors and could not be expressed in psychological terms alone. Psychosomatic diseases by their very nature, have vital components

231

other than psychological ones (the organic disease, the medical management, for example). We directed our efforts, therefore, towards establishing a metapsychologically sound method of assessing what we most wanted to know in each case: What are the possibilities for psychological treatment directly influencing the basic disease process?

Such a diagnostic assessment would have the disadvantage of being partly descriptive rather than purely metapsychological. But if these diseases cannot be defined only in terms of their psychopathology, the proposed assessment may represent a realistic acknowledgment of this fact. At the very least it may offer an acceptable avoidance of the diagnostic dilemma presented by these cases with their two sided pathology. In addition, an assessment of the treatability may help to resolve certain most difficult clinical problems. For example, in some cases where it was possible to affect the underlying disease process favorably, it was crucial to the success of the therapeutic psychological program that all other treatment regimens be discontinued. But it is not reasonable to insist on this drastic step when there is a doubt or suspicion that the underlying organic process will not be eradicated by the psychological treatment.

Again it should be stressed: Our formulations are based on evaluating the possibilities for psychological treatment directly influencing the actual disease process, and this emphasis in no way depreciates any treatment program, psychological or medical, that helps a child cope with his disease and its consequences or strengthens his personality by helping him to resolve conflicts peripheral to his psychosomatic disorder. Actually, any diagnostic assessment that can enhance our evaluation of these disorders can only lead to a better utilization of all the available therapeutic approaches.

When we began this task, we did not know any means of assessing psychosomatic disorders that seemed applicable to the under five age group. Our approach was to derive our formulations directly from the clinical material available. Our thinking throughout was basically influenced by the work of A. Katan (1961) and E. Jacobson (1954). Only when our formulations were acceptable to the group as properly representative of our clinical experience, did we begin a survey of the material available in the literature. The results of this survey will be presented briefly below.

Any formulation of a diagnostic assessment of psychosomatic diseases must begin with a definition of these disorders and must include some theoretical considerations used in understanding the mechanism of operation of the psychic factors. The assessment should, as stressed above, give an evaluation of the possibilities for therapeutic psychological intervention and, although our point of departure is the child under five, should ultimately be valid or applicable for the patient of any age.

The definition and theoretical considerations detailed below do not represent our definitive, final viewpoint. Also, we are aware that our thinking differs greatly from many formulations currently available in the literature. We present our basic thoughts at the start of our discussion primarily to orient the reader to the working hypotheses that have served as the bases for our formulation. The clinical material that led to their acceptance is presented briefly towards the end of this chapter.

Definition

A psychosomatic disorder has two essential characteristics: (1.) there is definite evidence from the outset of pathological, organic change within the body which can lead to permanent tissue damage (Margolin, 1953); (2.) psychic factors play a significant role in the etiology of the disorder.

This definition should distinguish psychosomatic disorders from normal processes, functional disturbances, hysterical disturbances and from illnesses where the disturbance in the emotions is a response to and not a contributing cause of the disease. Inherent in this definition is the concept that the emotional disturbance is not the sole or necessarily even the primary etiological factor.

Theoretical Considerations

There does not appear to be any theory regarding the mechanism of action of the psychic factors in psychosomatic disease that is acceptable to all. But there apparently are enough factors about which there is sufficient general agreement for them to serve as a basis for a diagnostic assessment. These might be summarized briefly as follows: In a psychosomatic disease psychic energy deviates from the usual channels of discharge and expresses itself in a harmful way in a body organ whose pre-existing weakness enables it to serve as the site of expression. Although purposely vague, to minimize what could be distracting controversial theoretical considerations, this sentence helps provide a basis for a diagnostic assessment. This formulation suggests certain areas for further attention:

1. The body organ affected and the disease process active there—the organic factor.

2. The usual channels for discharge of psychic energy—the psychic factor. Evaluation of this factor would require focussing attention on the psychic economy and the agency most in control of its usual channels of discharge, the ego. The psychic factor seems therefore to have an economic aspect and an ego aspect.

3. The relationship between the organic factor and the psychic factor—the relationship factor.

Areas for Further Study

1. *The Organic Factor*

In evaluating the organic factor we are not exploring somatic compliance, the peculiar inherent ability of some organs or organ systems in some people which readily lend themselves to the expression of certain affects or drives. Rather we are attempting to examine all those aspects of the organic phase of the disease that may have a bearing on psychological treatment. It seems generally true that the more severe the disease process, the more difficult it will be to treat. It also seems generally true that the severity of the illness is evaluated in part by considering its duration, the presence or absence of remissions, the degree of organic damage it has caused.

But the severity of the organic manifestations of the disease has a significance beyond the obvious equation that the more severe disease is the more difficult one to treat. Our experience indicates that in the cases that have responded most favorably, the organic disease has been used by the personality as the avenue of discharge for an unacceptable affect or drive derivative, the organic disease apparently at the service of the personality for defensive or expressive purposes. In the cases that have responded least well it was as if the site of organic disease attracted to itself or utilized for its own harmful ends a less differentiated type of psychic energy which the personality had not had any opportunity to influence or moderate. The majority of our cases have fallen somewhere between these two extremes with varying admixtures of the characteristics of each. It has been our impression that a severely diseased organ tends to attract or divert to itself a large amount of the undifferentiated energy that is so difficult to influence, and does so in proportion to the extent of the organic damage.

We have also felt it more difficult to treat an illness involving a body part that is never free of vital physiological functioning, respiratory and gastro-intestinal tracts for example, as compared to one involving a less crucial area, such as the skin. Psychosomatic problems which have an apparently strong hereditary element may well prove less accessible to psychological influence for a number of possible reasons. Something that has proved difficult to evaluate has been the significance of multiple psychosomatic complaints. In some instances this has seemed to indicate a degree of flexibility or fluidity of the pathological processes that has augured well for treatment. In others, if one symptom has yielded to treatment programs only to be replaced by another, the impression has been created of a basic (organic) disability of great tenacity.

From experience it would also seem important to know what medical regimen is currently being employed, what success it has had and what psychological traumata have been associated with prior medical experiences. Therefore, in evaluating the organic factor, the following should be considered:

a. organ site of the disease process
b. severity when active
c. degree of existing damage
d. has it been unremitting since onset
e. frequency of episodes, if episodic
f. duration since onset
g. multiple psychosomatic complaints
h. family history
i. response to medical treatment
j. current medical program
k. psychological traumata resulting from prior medical programs.

2. *The Psychic Factor*

(a) *The Economic Aspect.* In psychosomatic disease it seems reasonable to consider that psychic energy that is usually either neutralized and fused and directed outwards has remained or become defused, unneutralized and directed inwards. In considering the energy aspect it seems important to evaluate the state of maturation of the economic development.

In making this evaluation for young children the profile supplies ready access to the crucial information. An indication of a satisfactory level of drive fusion will be available if object relations are predominantly on a phallic level and if there is an age-adequate development of the superego and/or its precursors. Also readily available is an estimate of the maturational development and distribution of the libidinal and aggressive drives. A section evaluating drive neutralization is specifically available. Each of these components, drive fusion, drive maturation, and drive neutralization should have equal weight in the overall assessment.

The economic aspect can be evaluated by considering the following questions:

    a. Drive fusion
       i. level of object relations
      ii. level of development of superego and/or its precursors
    b. drive maturation and distribution
       i. libido
      ii. aggression
    c. drive neutralization
       i. sublimation potential

(b) *The Ego Aspect.* As with the economic aspect, here also the profile provides the necessary information. In the section on the ego there are assessments of the ego functions vital to our considerations, synthetic function of the ego, secondary process thinking, reality testing, speech, motor control, as well as a description of defenses utilized by the ego and the ego's ability to tolerate anxiety. Although the latter is listed in the profile in the section on economic consideration, for the purposes of this evaluation it seems proper to include it here. In considering the defenses, an overall assessment of their range and age appropriateness should be made. In considering specific defenses, those of regression and aggression turned against the self should be specially noted. The inclusion of this latter mechanism does not mean to imply that the psychosomatic process is being viewed as an example of aggression turned against the self. Rather our current formulations would consider the destructiveness in the disease process the result either of an energy that has not yet been differentiated into aggression and libido or of an aggression that has never been directed outwards and could not therefore be directed onto the self in a defensive maneuver to protect an external object. The mechanism is included here because the resolution of a psychosomatic disease may be complicated if the disease process is secondarily used as a convenient site from which aggression can be turned against the self.

In the consideration of the ego aspect then, the following elements would need to be assessed:

a. ego functions:
    i. synthetic function
    ii. reality testing
    iii. secondary process thinking
    iv. speech
    v. motor control
b. defenses
    i. range
    ii. age-appropriateness
    iii. regression
    iv. aggression turned against the self.

3. *The Relationship Factor*

In evaluating the relationship between the organic and psychic factors we are in effect trying to determine the nature and degree of influence the emotional elements have on the body processes in question. It is sometimes possible to learn from the history that at the time of onset, or perhaps later with specific episodes, a direct relationship could be observed between emotional elements and the activation of the somatic pathology. If this is so, then it is important to investigate the degree of correlation between these factors as well as the psychological factor that is correlated. Concerning the latter, for example, a disease process activated because of a difficulty with a specific feeling, say anger, might be quite different from a disease process activated by a specific situation, say separation, and again quite different from a process activated by a major physiological or psychological change, such as puberty. The absence of a history of such a relationship between the psychic and organic factors may signify that treatment which has a favorable influence on the psychic factor will have little or no direct bearing on the basic disease process.

The age of onset of the disease has, we believe, a vital significance here. In general the younger the child has been at the time of onset of his difficulty, say under a year or even six months, the less direct has been the relationship discernible between the psychic and organic factors. And this should not be surprising, for the earlier the onset of the psychosomatic disease process, the less differentiated will be the energy involved and hence less subject to the influence of the personality. It would seem to follow logically that the less influence the personality has on the energy involved in the psychosomatic process, the less will be the influence on the organic disease of any psychological treatment approach.

In addition the younger the child at the time of onset of the disease, the earlier in his life will psychic energy have had an alternate route of discharge thereby being denied the ordinary processes of maturation: discharge to the outside, fusion and neutralization. The more psychic energy has been denied these usual maturational experiences, the more difficult will be any therapeutic psychological efforts. Not only will it be necessary for the therapist to try to promote more appropriate avenues of discharge for this energy, but also it may be necessary to participate in a process not unlike an educational one in supporting the maturational experiences that have been missed. For example, unusual attention might have to be devoted to initiating and supporting the development of various sublimations.

Therefore in assaying the relationship factor, the following questions need to be answered:

    a. age of onset

    b. degree of correlation between emotional and organic factors

    c. emotional factors correlating.

Evaluation of the Studied Areas

The next question concerns the utilization of the information culled from the developmental profile by the study of the three areas outlined above. For our purposes it was helpful to use what we called an assessment sheet for each case, simply listing the questions to be considered in assessing the various factors. The questions pertaining to the organic factor and those for the relationship factor were answered descriptively with whatever word or phrase seemed most appropriate. Those pertaining to the psychic factor were recorded as "age-appropriate," "not age-appropriate" or "markedly not age-appropriate." For the evaluation of an adult perhaps the designations "mature," "immature" and "markedly immature" would be comparable.

In the final overall assessment of the three factors (organic, psychic, relationship) we used just three descriptive designations: favorable, unfavorable or very unfavorable. That is, when each of the three factors is reviewed in turn, do they reveal a situation that is favorable, unfavorable or very unfavorable for psychological treatment being able to eradicate or to influence fundamentally the basic psychosomatic disease process. Only experience exceeding that currently available could indicate how many designations would be optimum and what designations might be more appropriate.

In discussing each factor we have tried to indicate the items that seem to have particular significance: severity of the organic pathology in the organic factor; age of onset in the relationship factor, for example. And we have tried to indicate the rationale for assigning a particular importance to each item. With the psychic factor the final assessment will be a composite, equally reflecting both component aspects, the economic and the ego. With the economic aspect also the final assessment should reflect almost an equal influence of its three component parts.

In the evaluation of the three main factors we have used our assessment sheets only as aids to our thinking and judgment. They have allowed us to collect and arrange our information on these different aspects of this complex problem so that we could focus our full attention on each individual element in turn, relatively unimpeded by the endless complexities inherent in the psychosomatic problem. What is obviously vital is not the assessment sheets or the descriptive words but rather our initial approach to the problem, the selection of the three factors enumerated, and information we have sought to evaluate each area.

Our current impression would be that if any one factor is considered very unfavorable, it is most unlikely that psychological treatment will be able to effect the basic psychosomatic pathology. If the component factors are predominantly favorable, treatment by way of the mother in the child under five should have a most reasonable expectation of success. If the component factors are predominantly unfavorable, our current expectation would be that after preliminary treatment via the mother a psychoanalysis might well prove necessary. This is a most tentative impression and treatment via the mother would, of course, be subject to the influence of all the limiting factors described in Chapter 4.

The Diagnostic Assessment vs. the Developmental Profile

It should be stressed that the diagnostic assessment of psychosomatic disorders proposed here is not considered as an alternative to the developmental profile. Rather it is an ordering of the material essentially available only from the profile in a particular way to suit a particular group of cases and in this sense is viewed rather as a tentative extension of the profile.

The formulations concerning psychosomatic disease which we have used postulate the operation of the psychological factor essentially as either an economic arrest or an economic regression. And the information available in the diagnostic assessment should make it possible to differentiate between the two and to make an estimate of the quantity of psychic energy that is pathologically fixated. If further experiences should validate this hypothesis, it would then be possible to include all the psychic factors operating in the psychosomatic disorder within the profile in those sections dealing with drive development, ego development, economic considerations and most particularly fixation points. With the organic part of the disease process always present in an active psychosomatic disorder, however, the diagnostic assessment should continue to prove a needed adjunct to the profile.

In one case presented below, that of Gretchen, it was possible for her psychosomatic problem to be considered simply as representative of one of a number of fixation points to which she regressed. The diagnostic assessment was, in this instance, an evaluation of a rather easily definable sector of this girl's total psychopathology. She was therefore considered both with the other Group III cases, where her total personality structure placed her diagnostically, as well as with the children with psychosomatic disease.

With our four other cases it was not possible at the time

of the initial profile to make a diagnostic categorization in addition to that of psychosomatic disease. The diagnostic assessment, in these instances, then represented an evaluation of a portion of the child's psychopathology, a portion whose limits were hard to define in a picture whose overall structure was difficult to comprehend clearly. We were interested in why this was so, why we could not simply integrate all the psychological data relating to the psychosomatic disease within the profile and arrive at one of the usual diagnostic groupings in addition to the more descriptive characterization of the psychosomatic disorder itself available in the diagnostic assessment. We believe there may be two explanations. First, the information available for the first two months' study of the children with psychosomatic disorders was usually focused most heavily on their organic disease. The anxiety about these disorders is most contagious and it was very easy for everyone to concentrate almost exclusively on what made the child wheeze or scratch and what we could do to help. Accurate historical information from the mothers, for example, about other aspects of the child's personality development was long delayed in becoming available to us.

Second, when the children with active psychosomatic disease started in school they were children under the stress or threat of an acute illness. It was difficult to evaluate at first whether some of their pathological formations represented transitory reactions to real, recent or current external stresses, their organic illnesses, and its treatment, or were component parts of their usual psychological make up. In all instances this situation had been clarified by the time the data was inspected for the second profile. The difficulties with the diagnosis at the time of the initial profile did not represent an inadequacy of the profile, but rather an unusual difficulty in obtaining the observations and information needed to complete the profile properly.

The Literature

In the introduction to this section it was mentioned that our work with children with psychosomatic disorders has been primarily influenced by the thinking of A. Katan (1961) and Jacobson (1954). The basic considerations about verbalization which Dr. Katan described have been found most particularly applicable with children who have psychosomatic disabilities. The usual benefits accruing to the ego from the maturational effects of verbalization seem augmented with these children by the advantages inherent in the acquisition or broadening of a channel of discharge other than the body and its processes. It was in trying to understand the cases that did not respond to our efforts that we found particular help in Jacobson's concept of "energetic regression." This she describes as "leading not only to resexualization and reaggressivization of the neutral energy of the ego, but even to partial regressive transformation of the libido and aggression into primary undifferentiated energy." This proposition offered us a means for understanding the difference in responsiveness of our treated cases on the basis of different levels of maturity of the psychic energy involved, and from this thinking has evolved the diagnostic assessment that has just been described.

It is not our aim at this point to present an extensive survey of the psychoanalytic literature on psychosomatic disorders, a task so admirably done by Schur (1955) but a relatively few years ago. Rather it would seem pertinent to see if our thinking, which is based primarily on clinical experiences with under-fives with asthma and skin disorders is matched by any who have worked with other age groups or different psychosomatic entities.

Our efforts at defining this group of diseases had been well anticipated by Margolin (1953) and Kubie (1953). Margolin's exposition of the stages of pathological change of these disorders led us to amplify our original definition and his belief that a "psychophysiological process does not arise *de novo* in the mind" aptly phrases the key thinking about the etiological role of the emotions which we had incorporated into our definition. Kubie, in a paper in the same volume, stressed effectively the great difficulty in distinguishing the processes that arise secondarily to the psychosomatic disorder from those which are a primary part of the disorder, a difficulty we also tried to stress. Both investigators had formulated classifications of these diseases, Kubie on the basis of the role played in the psychic economy of the organs affected and Margolin on the level of the psychophysiological development represented by the specific disorder. Margolin then correlated these levels of development with the type of therapy most applicable to the specific cases. In this way he also presented a diagnostic assessment based on the accessibility of the disease to treatment.

Before considering our own assessment in the light of Schur's *Comments on the Metapsychology of Somatization* (1955), it would seem appropriate briefly to mention three other authors. Tarachow (1945) used the phrase "physioneurosis" and emphasized the lack of specificity of these disorders in terms of symbols, a proposition that is basic to the energetic concept which has appealed to us. This concept has, incidentally, been described beautifully by Winnicott (1954) who wrote "one of the aims of psychosomatic illness is to draw the psyche from the mind back to the original association with the soma." The third investigator to be mentioned is M. Sperling who has written extensively about psychosomatic disorders, particularly ulcerative colitis, in children who in general were a bit older than those whom we report (1949). She has described what she feels to be one factor in the genesis of the psychosomatic disorders, the child's relationship with his mother, and has delineated three characteristics common to these mothers in their relationships with their children: (1) the carry-over of an unresolved emotional conflict from childhood and the acting out of this conflict with the child; (2) projection of part of the mother's personality onto the child; (3) a need for control over the child that is so intense that the child is treated as if he were a part of his mother's own body. Although we had no cases of ulcerative colitis in children in our current group, we were impressed that we had seen this particular combination of factors in the mother-child relationship not infrequently in instances where the children did not have psychosomatic disorders. Also we had at least three children with psychosomatic disorders in our current group where our experience with their mothers was sufficiently extensive to justify our saying that the characteristics described by Sperling did not exist. We would feel more at ease if we considered Sperling's observations as a most appropriate description of one mechanism that may operate to contribute to the development of psychosomatic disorders, rather than of a pathognomonic factor of any particular specificity.

Schur's point of departure in his extensive study is the anxiety reactions of the ego which he feels constitute an ego function subject to varying degrees of regression. He describes an interdependence between ego functions (such as secondary process thinking), level of neutralization of energy and the resomatization of the response to anxiety. When there is what many have called a physiological regression there will be a prevalence of primary process thinking, unneutralized energy and resomatization of the anxiety response. Although he begins with the ego, his very complete description soon encompasses many of the factors we considered when we began with the energic aspects of the regression and later explored the ego and economic aspects active in the mediation of this regression.

Schur stresses the ego functions of reality testing, secondary process thinking, motility, integration; he emphasizes the relationship between the level of ego functioning and the ego's capacity to neutralize aggression; he states that once organic damage is present it will become the focal point for the convergence of many pathological mechanisms; and he feels that the outcome of this situation will depend on the severity of the organic disease and the level of emotional health of the individual.

It seems significant to us that Schur working with adult patients with skin disabilities should evolve formulations so like those we come to, many years later, from work with young children with asthma and skin disorders. This conveys to us that the theoretical background of our diagnostic assessment must have a sufficiently sound basis to warrant the continued study of this method of approach to these disorders.

II. CASE EVALUATIONS

There are five children with psychosomatic disorders in the cases available for the follow-up study. Despite the great variations in the severity of their personality disabilities it seemed wisest to discuss them together in a separate section in recognition of their common problem.

They form a most instructive group because, although each came to school with the psychosomatic complaint as the primary presenting symptom, most of their similarities ended at this point. Examination of the evaluation of the component factors considered in the assessments of their psychosomatic disorders reveals that they represent examples of almost every gradation we considered possible.

The cases will be discussed first as a group, comparing their pathologies to illustrate the various aspects of the diagnostic assessment. Then they will be approached individually, exploring what transpired in the therapeutic work and what the follow-up has revealed of the significance of any changes that had occurred. To facilitate our considerations the most basic data about these five children has been summarized in the accompanying table.

SUMMARY OF THE CHILDREN WITH PSYCHOSOMATIC DISORDERS

Name	Gretchen	Craig	Chuck	Yvonne	Timothy
Age	4-3	4-0	4-2	3-9	3-10
Psychosomatic Symptom	allergic rashes	asthma	eczema	asthma	asthma
Organic Factor	unfavorable	favorable	unfavorable	unfavorable	very unfavorable
Psychic Factor	favorable	unfavorable	favorable	unfavorable	unfavorable
Relationship Factor	favorable	favorable	unfavorable	unfavorable	very unfavorable
Profile Diagnoses	3-2-1	4?-4-4	3?-2-2	3?-4	?-4
Treatment	via mother	via mother	via mother	via mother-psa.	via mother-psa.
Duration of Follow-up	6 years	11 years	5 years	still in analysis	just finished analysis

Diagnostic Assessment

1. *Organic Factor.* Craig, the four-year-old asthmatic, was the only one of the group whose organic factor was considered favorable. He had for about a year experienced weekly or monthly episodes of asthma which had lasted a matter of hours and had been reasonably moderated by oral medication. The diagnostic skin tests for allergic sensitivities had been terrifying to him and had constituted the only trauma accompanying his medical care. Timothy's asthma, by contrast, had been essentially unremitting for over three years and for six months had ceased to respond consistently or effectively to any medication. For this latter period he had rarely been free of an audible wheeze. He already had a rather marked emphysema and his growth was thought impaired by his disorder. He had endured numerous hospitalizations, beginning at six months and occurring almost monthly throughout his second year. His organic factor was considered to be very unfavorable.

Yvonne's organic factor was thought to be unfavorable, lying somewhere between the extremes presented by the two boys. Although her asthmatic attacks had occurred for over three years, there had been a period of a year without such episodes. The attacks themselves were severe as they were incapacitating for two or three days, responding slowly to conservative medical management. There had been no hospitalizations or traumatic experiences associated with her medical care and there was no suggestion of permanent disability. She alone of the three children with asthma had a strong family history of psychosomatic disorders.

2. *Relationship Factor.* These same three children can be used to illustrate the widest possible variations in the relationship factor. Craig's first asthmatic episode occurred at three years and almost all his attacks came at times when an expression of jealousy would have been most appropriate.

The relatively late onset and the close correlation with a specific feeling made his relationship factor seem favorable. Both Yvonne's and Timothy's asthma started very early, at six months of age, but while Yvonne's episodes correlated very closely with times of separation from her mother, it was almost impossible to detect any correlation for Timothy. For Yvonne the relationship factor was considered unfavorable and for Timothy as very unfavorable.

3. *Psychic Factor.* The psychic factor for all three asthmatic children was considered as unfavorable, with each component aspect, ego and economic, being so characterized. Craig will be used to contrast with Gretchen, the little girl with recurrent allergic skin rashes, whose psychic factor was judged to be favorable, both component aspects being so evaluated.

Craig, at four years showed little evidence of a phallic level of object relations as he tried to involve one and all in sado-masochistic interplays. His difficulties in functioning apart from adult supervision suggested an inadequate superego development for his age. Both these findings indicated a difficulty in drive fusion. Although he was struggling with phallic anxieties, his libido had never ceased its involvement with anal conflicts and his aggressive drive also did not give evidence of age-appropriate maturation. There was evidence of an unusual propensity to turn aggression against the self. His sublimation potential was considered as age-adequate. This state of his economic development was felt to be unfavorable because of the difficulties in drive fusion and drive maturation and may be contrasted with Gretchen who was considered as favorable in this area.

Gretchen seemed to have an almost age-appropriate degree of drive fusion. She had phallic relationships with all save her mother where difficulties with separation did not seem to indicate primarily a failure of drive fusion. After but two months in school, separation could be well tolerated when it represented a reasonable demand. When without adult supervision, also for a reasonable time, her functioning continued in an age-appropriate fashion. Her libidinal development was on an age-adequate phallic-oedipal level and, although she was not verbalizing aggression at the time of entry to school, it was basically directed outwards. Her sublimation potential seemed most age-appropriate. The favorable assessment for Gretchen's economic development was based on the evidence of essentially age-appropriate drive fusion, maturation and neutralization.

With regard to the ego aspect both Craig and Gretchen primarily employed defenses which were predominantly not age-appropriate, an excessive amount of reaction formation applied both to cleanliness and to aggression in Gretchen's case, for example. Both had difficulty in tolerating an age-appropriate degree of anxiety and both used some regression in times of anxiety, although in neither child was this considered in excess of what might be expected at four years of age. The contrast between the two in the ego area reveals itself in examination of the ego functions. Gretchen had no impairment of reality testing, secondary process thinking or synthetic function. Craig was capable of secondary process thinking and reality testing and they were considered age-appropriate although his anxieties could readily interfere with both. But he seemed to have a difficulty in utilizing prior experience in so many areas and to such an extent that it seemed to exceed what could be anticipated under the burden of his anxiety. This was manifest in school situations of learning and relationships with peers and in life situations of slightly varied new experiences. For these reasons the synthetic function of his ego was deemed not at an age-appropriate level. Because of this involvement of ego functioning, his ego factor was considered as unfavorable in contrast to Gretchen's more favorable assessment.

4. *Profile Diagnoses.* In addition to offering illustrative

examples of the various aspects of the factors involved in the psychosomatic diagnostic assessment we have proposed, the data on these same five children may also serve to show some of the questions involved in seeking appropriate diagnoses from the data available at the time for which the first profile was constructed. The group varied greatly in the ease with which the original therapist felt he could initially make an overall diagnostic assessment. With Gretchen and Craig, whom we have just been discussing, it was not so difficult. Gretchen's rashes seemed to appear if regression in habit training did not adequately solve the conflict distressing her. Craig had nightmares of being chased by men, stuttering and was unable to be active in a group of peers. Gretchen seemed to be a not unusual diagnostic category III child with pathological formations, her enuresis and her defenses for example, which were not age-appropriate and seemed not directly related to her rashes. Craig's rather all-pervasive passivity made him very suspect of belonging to category IV, neurotic or character disorder, and it seemed this difficulty had strong roots which well antedated the onset of his wheeze.

With Chuck, the four-year-old with eczema, and Yvonne we originally were aware that each had just one other difficulty in addition to their psychosomatic ones, and this was a separation problem. Timothy, the severe asthmatic, initially had one other symptom predominating, a marked sleeping disturbance.

It was difficult with these three children at the outset to decide how much of these other difficulties was a direct consequence of their psychosomatic problems. Chuck had just recently endured a severely traumatic two weeks' hospitalization in which he had been literally tied down in bed, to prevent scratching, and literally torn from his parents who had been allowed only brief twice-weekly visiting. How to decide if Chuck's difficulty with separation represented a response to this recent trauma or an inherent weakness in his personality? The same was true regarding Yvonne who had been terrified by the severity and, at that time, apparently unpredictable onset of her wheezing episodes. With Chuck the mother's anxious preoccupation with his eczema long precluded any accurate historical information. With Yvonne accurate reporting was also long delayed, although a different mechanism was operating with her mother.

Timothy's anxiety at night seemed at the outset related to a fear of dying because of his wheezing. The realities of his great breathing distress and many emergency hospitalizations made it impossible in the first two months to assess the neurotic aspects of this night difficulty. And during this time the energies of the mother and staff were so involved in dealing with the crises of his asthma, that it was difficult to try to observe and evaluate him apart from his asthma.

Initially, Chuck was felt probably to belong to category III diagnostically, as had Gretchen, and this was ultimately verified as correct. Yvonne was tentatively diagnosed with the first profile as being in category III, but subsequent observation and information, perhaps more than her later development, ultimately placed her in category IV. When Timothy's development just before beginning analysis was assessed, almost a year after starting school, it was felt that there was an adequate basis for placing him also in category IV along with Craig and Yvonne. These difficulties in making a diagnostic evaluation of the personality apart from the psychosomatic disorder at the time of their initial profile may diminish as noted above as our experience increases with these children.

III. INDIVIDUAL CASES

Gretchen—Allergic Rashes

Although Gretchen has been introduced in the discussion in the preceding section on the psychic factor, it is best to begin a resume of her case by directly quoting part I of her first profile, Reasons for Referral and Symptomatology. "Gretchen was referred at four years because of allergic rashes of two years duration, bed wetting and a recent eating difficulty. Three months before her referral Gretchen had developed a particularly severe rash which covered her from head to toe and was complicated by respiratory difficulties. Over a period of three months before her referral Gretchen had had a series of allergy tests of which she was exceedingly frightened. The mother was also concerned that Gretchen was overly careful about being clean and neat and that, while there were often arguments between Gretchen and her younger sister, Gretchen's attitude to her was excessively protective."

Gretchen's first two years seemed to have gone remarkably well despite the mother's allergies which prevented her caring for Gretchen in her first few weeks and despite a slight clubfoot which had required casts on both legs between five and eight months. Shortly after her second birthday and just before the birth of her sister, toilet training was started. This went poorly with many difficulties manifested in Gretchen's soiling. It was during this period the rashes first appeared.

The mother returned to part time work when Gretchen was two and a half years old and the soiling became worse. Spanking at this point ended the soiling but the day and night wetting became more consistent. When Gretchen was three, the mother got some help regarding the wetting from a local agency and Gretchen became dry by three and a half. A few months later the mother and father left for a ten-day vacation to which Gretchen responded first with a return to day and night wetting and second with the marked exacerbation of her skin rash.

The earliest work with the mother revealed a repetitive pattern, manifest in regard to the soiling or wetting and the anxiety attacks. Because of her own past experiences, the mother had a dread of loss of control, saw Gretchen's difficulties in these situations as a loss of control, would become anxious and then would turn the child's care over to her husband or the maid. When she became conscious of this pattern, the mother could alter her reaction and begin to explore Gretchen's feelings at these times, encouraging her to put them into words: the fear of the doctors, the anger that seemed expressed in the wetting, for example. The latter was difficult for both mother and child and the nursery school teachers helped Gretchen not to have "to like everyone and everything" when she obviously did not feel that way.

With this verbal outlet available for her feelings, Gretchen was able to surrender in large part her reaction formation (evident in her excessive emphasis on cleanliness and her exaggerated concern for her sister), her denial and reversal (evident in happily liking everyone at school, even those who had just done her injustices). Her skin became clear and her bed dry by early winter and an apparently allergic coryza responded to dietary exclusion of wheat and bananas that was discontinued in early spring.

Gretchen's oedipal development came more to the fore and was most understandingly managed by her mother including the aggression to the mother. Concern was aroused in the spring when Gretchen developed a fear of dogs which could be linked to her observations of boys urinating. This area was, by contrast, quite difficult to work through and when Gretchen left school there was a question about the course this aspect of her development would take. But the impression persisted that because of her greater freedom with her aggression, as well as other feelings, and because of the change in her defensive structure the gains represented by her dry bed and clear skin might continue.

During the first few of the six years which elapsed between the end of nursery school and the follow-up evaluation Gretchen's mother made a number of contacts with the therapist. The story that unfolds is most interesting because

Gretchen had psychic difficulties and somatic difficulties in the nature of hypersensitivity reactions to external stimuli but no psychosomatic symptoms. In the first grade she had some difficulty learning to read. In the second grade some episodic bed-wetting and anxiety attacks at times of separation combined with the learning trouble to lead to a treatment recommendation which could not be effected. The dog fear had vanished at this time and her therapist felt that the penis-envy conflict which seemed focused in this difficulty had not been resolved, had temporarily succumbed to her repression, and was a basic factor in the then current symptomatology.

The contacts with Gretchen's mother became less frequent at this point. At the time of the follow-up it was learned that the eneuresis, anxiety attacks, and study problem were apparently markedly improved. The resolution of these difficulties is difficult to evaluate, but one factor may have been a further maturation of her defenses. The parents took three trips abroad during this interval. Gretchen coped with these in part by asking to go away to camp in the summer. There were many other examples of such reliance upon passive into active, identification and repression (she had forgotten some of her parents' trips) which seemed to have become her dominant defense mechanisms.

At the time of the final follow-up it was also learned that in the third grade, after a kidney infection, Gretchen had a most severe, acute sensitivity reaction to sulfa drugs which required an emergency hospitalization. In the summer after the fourth grade she developed rheumatic joint symptoms severe enough to require crutches for three months. This had followed a period of repeated upper respiratory infections. The healing of this seemed complete and there has been no recurrence after other infections or after another summer at camp.

At the time of follow-up it was impressive how well

Gretchen had recently managed the unfortunate experience of witnessing the death of her best friend's brother in an automobile accident. Her affective response had been both appropriate and manageable. She seemed functioning well in all areas as an appropriate prepuberty child whose only difficulty seemed an over-vigorous use of repression particularly in dealing with aggression. This seemed to have secondary manifestations in some difficulties in reading and at times in adequately expressing herself.

It is difficult to avoid the impression that although an organic propensity to hypersensitive reactions persists (sulfa reaction, arthritic episode) and although some psychic difficulties remain, the absence of psychosomatic reactions indicates that the maturation of her personality has contributed to what seems to have been an inability of psychic factors directly to trigger organic reactions. External factors did trigger this reaction (sulfa drug, presumed streptococcus infections) but not psychic ones.

Craig—Asthma

Some aspects of Craig's situation on entry to school are already known from the descriptions available in the second section of this chapter where all aspects of his diagnostic assessment were presented and compared with the other children's. Although he had had a chronic cough since infancy, only at three years did he begin the breathing difficulty diagnosed as asthma. Dietary restrictions and a series of regular injections had by age four produced no significant improvement. At three and a half he had been hospitalized for a week with a febrile illness, had received numerous lumbar punctures and had been allowed only twice-weekly visits from his parents. Nightmares had ensued about men who tied him up, cut him up and shot him. For three weeks prior to school entry he had stuttered, following an episode in which his usually patient father had struck him in response to a prolonged nagging provocation. He had trouble playing with peers, teasing the weaker ones, being terrified of the stronger ones.

Only gradually did this latter aspect of his development come to the fore. Although his mother was distressed by his apparent ill health and crybaby attitude, she was pleased with his refined manner and was confused if he was described as robustly healthy. It was most difficult for her to agree to dispense with the weekly injections which were so frightening to Craig, fearing a great worsening of his condition. She reported his genitals had been underdeveloped since birth and that at two and one half years he had received a series of hormone injections with the prognosis given for further normal development. Both she and Craig had great concern over this aspect of his growth.

The history of his first years seemed significant in that his father had taken a perhaps unusually active role in his care, giving him his early morning and evening bottles, often changing his diapers, helping him dress and undress. Father took charge of training at age two, teaching him by demonstrations. It was about this time that the mother became pregnant with what was to be his sister and only sibling and was confined to bed for three months. Craig turned to his father more and more for his care, and when his father was present, would reject his mother's advances to him to turn away to the readily-accepting father. A few weeks after his sister's birth the mother was holding her during dinner. Craig reached for a dish on the table and the mother stopped him. An argument ensued which culminated in a coughing spell and then his first wheezing attack.

It is significant that the parents' distress about his passivity had not been more pronounced. The mother was hurt by his turning away from her and was most guilty that something she had done had caused this rejection. When she could understand that his turning away reflected his hurt at missing her then her intellectual curiosity could be aroused to explore his recent symptoms. Both parents worked diligently at new educational approaches, instituting a policy of bathroom privacy, for example. They reviewed with him his hospitalizations, explaining the realities of their inability to be with him and of the procedures he had endured, sympathizing with his dreadful feelings at that time and connecting them to his nightmares. The father apologized for having struck Craig, showed the boy his part in it and related his stuttering to this episode. They discussed with him his angry jealousy of his sister, its relationship to his wheezing and tried to encourage his bringing these feelings in words. The response to these endeavors was dramatic in the cessation of his coughing, wheezing, nightmares and stuttering.

But, in contradistinction to Gretchen, there was no change in Craig's defensive pattern. He could not use verbalization adequately to help master any of his basic difficulties, and he could not give up his constant provoking of sadomasochistic interplays in which he was always on the losing or bullied end of the relationship. Even in nursery school he constantly needed to be rescued from the boy who fulfilled the role of bully for him, a pattern that persisted in his early public school years. The parents tried to cope after he left nursery school by changing his school class but to no avail. This area of his development was unavailable for therapeutic work and attempts to explore it revealed difficulties within the family that precluded further work.

At the time of follow-up, with Craig almost 17, it was not surprising to find him having difficulties in achieving at school, involved in struggles within his family, protesting their supposed restrictions of him, stoutly maintaining his wish to be away from home but focusing on a college quite nearby. He tended to blame his learning difficulties on his home or the school. On the surface he had a fondness for girls and had one such close relationship. But he did indicate some

dissatisfaction with his present status and considered possibilities for a future treatment. Most significantly, from our
current viewpoint, he had experienced no recurrence of
cough or asthma. He had no allergies except a sensitivity to
nuts and had had a severe reaction recently when he had
eaten some inadvertently.

Again, as with Gretchen, the somatic predisposition persists (the allergy to nuts) as do psychic difficulties, but as far
as we know no psychosomatic difficulties have recurred. Again
it is as if some barrier has been instituted or reinstituted that
precludes the triggering of the somatic process by psychic
factors. Craig has apparently blocked this channel of egress
for psychic energy by more tightly binding it within his
characterological defenses. It would not be surprising if his
cough and asthma were to recur temporarily if he now had
an analysis as he has not been able to find the more healthy
outlets that Gretchen achieved. But it still remains that the
work with him via his mother restored an inner balance and
he has experienced no return of his asthma.

Chuck—Eczema

Chuck was most briefly introduced in the section on diagnostic classification where reference was made to the difficulties in assigning him a profile diagnosis for the time of entry
to nursery school. He had been referred to us from the hospital where a two-week stay had greatly improved his eczema
even at the cost of the psychic strains it had placed upon him.
It is important that he was admitted to the hospital by the
seventh physician the mother had consulted about his eczema
in the two and a half years of its existence.

There had been difficulties for Chuck and his mother literally from the moment of his birth, which had been an un-
anticipated and, to the mother, terrifying Caesarean section.
Two months later a breast abscess caused an end of nursing
and two months after that the mother had a pneumonia com-

plicated by a severe allergic penicillin skin reaction. Three months later, at nine months, training started which was a struggle until at 20 months, at Chuck's insistence, his parents took off his diapers and allowed him to use the big toilet. But the mother was still wiping him, as well as dressing and bathing him, at four years. The eczema, which started exactly in the middle of the training struggle, was a particular source of anxiety to the mother because of her own recent allergic reaction and because of the father's eczema of 20 years' duration. This was yet another stimulus to her anxiety about Chuck, already so great because of all the unfortunate events associated with his first year.

The mother was an extremely literal person and her concrete type of thinking made the work with her difficult. When asked about longing or sadness in connection with her feelings about Chuck starting school, she had no response. But when asked if she missed him, she had such a flood of affect she wondered why the therapist had never asked before about such an important feeling. Later on, when Chuck's skin cleared after months of hard work, she was convinced it was a miracle and it was most difficult to dissuade her of this and to get her to use Chuck's progress with him to further support the work.

During the two and one half years Chuck had his eczema before coming to school, the disease and its care had been most difficult for him. He had been twice excluded from stores when his appearance frightened the proprietors that he might have a contagious disease. He had been on cortisone in his third year until his body weight had literally doubled. After the drug was discontinued the mother vividly remembered his standing before the mirror feeling his face saying "Now I am me again." During and after the cortisone period, when his face was broken out, he would hide from guests in the home and from peers who wanted to play with him. Just before his hospitalization he had so furiously scratched his back that he had gouged off bits of flesh on the door catch. It was this severity of the eczema that had prompted the drastic measures employed in his hospitalization and they had been successful in that he had only erythema and some induration of his cheeks, arms and behind his knees when he started school.

The emphasis at the start of the work was on the separation problem the mother and child shared. Chuck dealt with the situation in a controlling way, either refusing to leave his mother or leaving when he was ready, after delaying to count the buttons on her coat a number of times, for example. He also used passive into active in abruptly leaving her on other days. When the teachers or his mother tried to help him with his feelings around separation he either withdrew physically or else emotionally with no evidence of any recognition or acknowledgment of what was said to him. His every fiber seemed to say "if it's unpleasant, I'll say it isn't there." At times when anger was anticipated his skin would flush and he would soon be scratching. Later, as some of his denial lessened and he could acknowledge what was said to him, he would just start scratching without there being a preceding skin blushing. The scratching stopped when he could verbalize his feelings and his skin became essentially clear for good after about six months at school. During this period his self-imposed dietary restrictions offered an avenue to discuss his previous dietary restrictions; his insistence on the miracle of his clear skin offered entry to the earlier miracle of his body changes with the cortisone; and his focus on the then-current name of the nursery school—The University Hospitals Nursery School—gave a chance to review his hospitalization.

A further word about his defenses is in order. We were all impressed initially with the limited range of defenses at his disposal, the very controlling type of passive into active and denial predominating. As sublimations and verbalization became available as outlets for him, we began to see a wider range of defenses, some of which concerned us. He began to use his excitement to ward off some unpleasant affects, to use projection and some obsessive mechanisms. The problem was complicated by his mother's difficulty in approaching libidinal difficulties and by her pregnancy which began during the latter part of the school year. Although the father could help in dealing with Chuck's questions and fears in the libidinal area, we were concerned about this side of his development and what it might mean for his future progress. We just hoped that the progress he had made with mastery of his aggression and with verbalization would be adequate to keep his eczema inactive.

Chuck's follow-up study five years later was most instructive. There had been no suggestion of any eczema or any other psychosomatic difficulties whatsoever. He was experiencing some difficulty achieving fully in school but still obtained B and C grades. He was easily excited or distracted in school and the mother had returned to the therapist when Chuck was in the second grade because of some sex play with his peers. But in his home situation with its limited support of sublimation and its limited means of dealing with the libidinal side of a child's development, he seemed to be making a most reasonable adjustment. It was of particular significance to learn of the fate of his obsessive mechanism. It had started before leaving school with arranging his rock collection each night in a certain order before retiring; the rocks had then been replaced by toy cars, also in careful order; then he began making model cars and the care and order went into the intricate tasks performed in putting the cars together; and finally he began sharing with his father the care and maintenance and interest in the family car. A similar pattern of development was discernible in his excited play with his boy friends which ultimately moved to organized games and then to sports in what seemed a well sublimated outlet.

With Chuck, as contrasted with Gretchen and Craig, no organic predisposition remains in evidence of the old psychosomatic problem. And despite some psychic difficulties he seems to have found new ways of coping which may preclude a return of the earlier mode. Most remarkable with Chuck, and here paralleling Gretchen, it would seem as if the work via his mother had initiated a process of development of his defensive apparatus which continued in the years after he left school.

Yvonne—Asthma

This little girl was referred to briefly in the discussion on diagnostic assessment both in describing her organic factor as well as in discussing profile diagnoses. She was a very apprehensive and rather sad child when she was referred from another nursery school at three years and eight months because of the severe separation reaction she had endured at attempting to start school, a reaction that had culminated in a severe asthmatic episode. She had experienced episodic wheezing during her first six months, of sufficient intensity to have interfered with her feeding. These attacks seemed to subside, only to return with severe exacerbations at one year, eighteen months and again at two years. The asthmatic episodes at one and two years coincided with separations from the parents for vacation trips and there had been at least eight separations of two or more days during the first eighteen months. The mother always insisted that the asthmatic episodes be treated symptomatically and had resisted suggestions for extensive study.

At the time of admission it was known that although Yvonne had achieved bowel control and daytime bladder control by two and a half, these had not been accomplished easily and full night bladder control had been attained only just prior to starting school. It was also known at this time

that there was a sleep problem with Yvonne frequently going to the parental bedroom when she was frightened at
night. These visits to their bedroom had been allowed by the
parents and there was a suspicion of at least one primal scene
exposure. This rather lax policy regarding bedroom privacy
was in sharp contrast with the policy regarding the bathroom
which had been one of strict privacy. Questions about sexual
matters had been avoided by the mother as this was then an
area of apparent difficulty for her.

As we got to know Yvonne at school, it was striking to observe her troubles on each libidinal level, seeming to correspond with the history of the impediments to development
in feeding, training and phallic matters. She was a very clinging little girl who attempted to be most controlling of her
mother. She was in a constant food interplay at home, one
which she attempted to bring to school and its mealtimes.
She was also a very provocative child who had destroyed some
of her mother's cherished possessions in the home, with severe
outbursts and scenes the inevitable consequence. She likewise attempted to bring the same sadomasochistic interplay
to her relationships with the teachers and peers and did bring
to school a marked reaction formation that greatly inhibited
her use of play materials. She had not attained a phallic level
of object relationships and the separation from her mother
at school, although prolonged over many weeks, was accompanied at its beginning with recurrent episodes of asthma.
There was no verbalization of aggression with a great deal of
kicking and hitting and some scratching of herself as well.

In addition to the mechanisms of reaction formation and
controlling demandingness, Yvonne easily regressed at times
of stress, projected a great many of her troubles onto her
mother and would withdraw into solitary play at other times.
These mechanisms interfered greatly with her relationships at
school, with her ability to sublimate, but were inadequate to

control her anxiety which broke through in paniclike states at times of separation, often followed by asthmatic attacks.

The work with Yvonne by way of her mother revealed some rather unexpected insights into her situation. Although the mother was most adroit with her use of language and at times a most astute observer, she apparently had difficulty with true affects, both in perceiving and discussing them with her daughter. Educational policies that were consistently applied by both parents were at this time difficult to effect and these two factors combined to contribute to limited success with the initial treatment approach.

During the year Yvonne increasingly brought evidence rather directly of her inability to control her excitement and, following a bit of uncontrolled sexual behavior with a neighbor boy, had an asthmatic attack which seemed directly related to this episode. As this difficulty was explored it became clear that there were at present and had been for an unknown period of time similar episodes of sexual acting-out which proved most difficult to limit and control. The new awareness of this stress on Yvonne gave broader understanding to her separation difficulties and increased the already quite clear need for an analysis.

The work via this mother had in this instance brought little change to Yvonne's personality structure, but rather had been most effective in fully clarifying the need for an analysis and in preparing the parents and Yvonne for this new approach to her difficulties. From the standpoint of her psychosomatic problems, there had been essentially no change in the frequency and severity of her asthmatic attacks and a recurrent eczema appeared to complicate the picture. She has been in analysis about four years now and her analyst advises us that as Yvonne has progressed in her analytic work there has been a very definite amelioration of the psychosomatic symptoms but that the asthma has not been eliminated.

Timothy—Asthma

The background of Timothy's asthma has been sketched in the description given in the prior discussion regarding the organic and relationship factors. Reference was made there to the early onset of his wheezing, which occurred for the first time without a concomitant respiratory infection when he was six months of age. This was the date of his first hospitalization and the start of a six-month period of fairly constant mild wheezing. By a year he had been weaned from two bottles and weighed 25 pounds. His second year saw an increase in the severity of the wheezing that led to five hospitalizations in the first six months and three more in the latter six months. At 18 months he was started on cortisone and an allergy desensitization program. Weaning was completed at this time and first efforts at training were abandoned when they seemed to correspond with the onset of his sleep problem. By the time he was two he weighed 22 pounds, a loss of three pounds from a year before.

Early in his third year training was accomplished. When he was 28 months, the mother delivered a full-term defective baby who died within 48 hours. Although Timothy had earlier been allowed to feel the baby's intrauterine movements, he was told that it was all a mistake, there had never been a baby there. His wheezing ceased at this time for two months but was beginning to recur in moderate severity over the last half of this year. Shortly after his third birthday the asthma became severe and constant and refractory to medication, with his sleep problem paralleling it in severity.

Timothy's mother gave the impression that all the anxiety and duress to which she had been exposed had been extremely difficult for her. It seemed at first as if it was hard for her to be warm or gentle with him. As we got to know her better, it became clear that her major mechanism at times of anxiety was to be as active as possible and she had been giving him adrenalin injections under the physician's instruction. But this mechanism had been of limited value in many stressful situations and she had not been able to accompany him to the hospital, for example, when he was admitted. She was always able, however, to be with him day and night after the first crisis of admission was past. The father had always gone with Timothy to the hospital and had taken over at nights when his wife had been exhausted.

At three years and ten months, Timothy was miserable about starting school. He tried boldly to send his mother home the first day, but was quite unable to cope with school and all it involved. He was a dawdler, a provoker, a demander: "You do it for me, I won't do it. You make me." He wanted only mother to do things for him, would only play the games he wanted and when he wanted. He was most upset when he got the least bit dirty. He reported all meals and what he considered teachers' injustices in great detail to his mother. During his first four weeks at school each asthmatic attack came when a demand or wish of his was frustrated. He could be verbally angry, but seemed to use this as a means to avoiding anything physical, as he could not defend himself when it was appropriate. He was extremely clever at doing puzzles.

The work with his mother focused on three areas: the night problem, the dead baby and later, preparation for his analysis. As his fear of dying at night in the asthmatic attacks became clear to everyone and the mother could discuss this with him, the nights ultimately became characterized by nightmares once or twice weekly whose content he could relate to his mother. This was great progress from the screaming, coughing, wheezing episodes that had occurred almost nightly. The work had naturally approached many of his separation feelings as well as a full discussion of the baby who had died. It was a strenuous period for his mother who had to cope with her own feelings and fears each step of the way before she was able to assist him, but she persevered with great tenacity. It is not surprising that her new approach to his difficulties was at this time rather dependent on her contact with the therapist.

Towards the end of the year his asthma had moved from being constant and uninterrupted to somewhat episodic with the precipitating anxiety discernible in some instances. He would cough briefly when informed of music time, which he hated, or begin to wheeze in telling the teachers his father was away. It was on this basis that the need for a treatment was shown to and accepted by the parents. By the time he neared his treatment Timothy had begun to manifest phallic level problems and concerns and had seemed able to use verbal aggression more appropriately. He could play well away from his mother and take pride in what he had accomplished. His eating seemed fully independent. He could join the other children in games not of his choosing and could successfully get them to join him at times. He could use all media freely and the demanding dawdling was greatly diminished.

But these gains were most tenuously held. After functioning well on the level just described for even as long as two weeks, he would very speedily regress to solitary play with a return of almost all the earlier modes of behavior. It seemed as if some aspects of his personality had been partially freed for further maturation and development and that this progress seemed to be paralleled by some diminution in the intensity of his asthmatic responses. It was hoped that an analysis could complete this process or at least further it to the point that his asthma would cease to be such a dominant influence in his life.

These expectations could not be realized. His analyst reports as follows: "In the first three years of Timothy's treatment much of the work consisted of analyzing the defensive aspects of his wheezing as a means of warding off anxiety and also relating the wheezing to underlying affects and instinctual derivatives. Consequently there was a marked decrease of the wheezing that functioned in this way. When the wheezing no longer served as a substitute for affects and instinctual derivatives, it became increasingly apparent how often it began as a response to external physical factors, such as changes in humidity." Timothy had many gains from his analytic work, but there was no fundamental improvement in his asthma. It seemed as if all the psychic energy involved in the psychosomatic process that was available for rechanneling or modifying was tapped during the earlier phases of his treatment, beginning with the work via his mother. It was not a limitation of the method that precluded the further progress which we had expected and hoped for, but rather seemed a limitation imposed by the nature of his basic disease process.

IV. DISCUSSION OF THE INDIVIDUAL CASE MATERIAL

These then are the cases available for report in this study that have stimulated our thinking about psychosomatic diseases. Some detail of the course of the illnesses has been presented to document two observations of ours that were mentioned at the start of the discussion of the diagnostic assessment: 1. the great variation in response to our therapeutic efforts; 2. the limited value of a symptom descriptive diagnosis, such as "asthma."

In addition, perhaps these brief descriptions can illustrate why the concepts used in the formulation of the diagnostic assessment for classification particularly appealed to us. Gretchen illustrates well one extreme regarding the mechanism of action of the psychic energy involved in psychosomatic diseases referred to in discussing the organic factor. Her rash started at two years of age at the time of great stress, the training struggle towards the end of her mother's pregnancy. It seemed as if when the soiling provided an inadequate avenue of expression for her feelings, her skin then offered an alternate or additional site of discharge. The same was true in the latter half of her fourth year when she responded to a separation from her parents, first by regressing to day and night wetting and then, later, by a severe exacerbation of her rash. She seems in this way to present a good example of the personality using a pre-existing site of body weakness, origin unknown, perhaps hereditary, as a site of discharge of psychic energy which the personality has had difficulty in mastering. The same seemed true of Craig, whose wheezing began at a time of great stress when his characterological defenses seemed inadequate to the task of binding the energy with which they were coping.

Timothy, the last child described, seems well to illustrate the other end of the spectrum. It was clear that at some times his personality utilized his asthma as a site of discharge or means of expression of unwelcome affects his other defenses could not contain. But it is equally clear that some other mechanism of action regarding the psychic energy was primarily involved here. In this instance it seemed some of the energy could not be influenced psychologically because it was bound within the asthma itself and because it was of such a primitive, undifferentiated nature.

It would seem logical to anticipate that in instances where the psychosomatic outlet was being used by the personality as a route of expression for unwelcome affects or instinctual derivatives, it would be possible to interrupt this process by providing the personality with alternate means of mastery or expression. And this outcome seems amply demonstrated with Gretchen, Craig and Chuck. In Craig's instance it was as if the intolerable stresses of the time were reduced and ameliorated so that his pre-existing defenses, despite their pathological nature, were then adequate to their task without further utilization of the psychosomatic outlet. In his case the lack of recurrence of his asthma raises a question the answer to which is not readily available.

With Chuck and Gretchen, however, the lack of recurrence of their symptomatology provokes no such question. With both children it was possible to initiate and observe the development of progressively more age-appropriate means of dealing with psychic energy. It is striking with Chuck that all evidence of any psychosomatic predisposition has disappeared, although perhaps his puberty will tell a different story.

It would also seem logical to anticipate that if some of the psychic energy involved in the psychosomatic process is of an undifferentiated nature that has never been under the influence of the personality, an energy that is bound in the diseased organ itself, then this process would be little capable of being influenced psychologically. And this seemed true with Timothy, as mentioned above.

These considerations about the nature of the psychic energy involved with these cases has been the cornerstone of our thinking. They account for what we primarily seek in examining the organic factor, the areas we scrutinize in examining the psychic factor and they are what we basically evaluate in what we call the relationship factor. These considerations seem at the moment to have provided a reasonable basis for the study of this group of diseases because their pursuit has led us to a rather logical end. They have led us to study psychosomatic disease by studying the psychic factor, the somatic factor and the relationship between the two.

It is most difficult with such a small series of cases, even if they are dynamically studied and then followed for so long, to be certain of our understanding of what has unfolded. It is never possible, once a treatment program starts, to know what the natural course of the disease would have been. We know when the children started with us what their course had been to that point. We know what changes transpired personalitywise and what changes did or did not appear concomitantly in their psychosomatic processes. But besides being unable to be aware of the natural course of these diseases, we cannot isolate a number of factors, such as the effect of cessation of the medical regimens. By their very nature these regimens are apt to be most frightening, disturbing particularly to those children whose situation is predominantly one of a personality already overtaxed in its task of dealing with certain feelings and instinctual derivatives.

8. The Role of the Nursery School with the Children Who Received Direct Treatment

RUTH OPPENHEIMER

This section of our study concerns the 28 children who went into direct treatment and the role the nursery school played in relation to that treatment. It is not meant as a report on or an evaluation of the treatment these children received. It would be impossible to evaluate which gains a child eventually made were due to his therapy and which were due to the nursery school program. We want to consider here the help obtained by child, parents and therapist in having treatment start in the nursery school setting; and also how therapist and school worked together and complemented each other.

For this reason we did not undertake follow-up profiles for the children who received direct treatment. We felt that a diagnostic follow-up profile would not show us in what specific way the nursery school had helped these children. Moreover, some of the children are still in analysis, and it would

---

The material for this section is taken from the Diagnostic Profiles, the summary notes on the work with the mothers preceding treatment, the summaries on the role of the nursery school before and during treatment and the retrospective evaluations of initial profiles, all compiled by the therapist of each child.

be most difficult to make a meaningful diagnostic assessment of them.

In cases where the child was in the nursery school for more than a few months before treatment was started, a second diagnostic profile was worked out just before the child started therapy, in order to see if any changes had occurred. In addition each therapist listed the ways in which treatment had been influenced by the fact that the child attended nursery school. The therapists also noted how the initial profiles agreed or differed from impressions gained in therapy.

Many of the children we shall be discussing were known to require direct treatment on admission. These were the most disturbed children, of whom it was seen from the start that they were suffering from disturbances characteristic of the diagnostic categories IV or V. The majority entered treatment within a few months of admission to nursery, while in a few cases preliminary work had to be done with parents or children to prepare them for treatment.

In a different group of cases treatment via the mother was attempted initially, but was found to be insufficient. These cases have already been mentioned in the chapter concerned with the technique of the work with the mothers. In some the disturbance turned out to be more serious than was thought originally. During their stay at the nursery a more detailed and more complete diagnostic picture could be arrived at through observations by the teachers and further insights obtained from the work with the parents. In addition, a disturbance seen in the first place as partly due to external conflicts and developmental stresses, often manifested itself as an internalized neurosis when the child reached the height of phallic and oedipal conflicts.

In the cases of treatment of the under-five via his mother in which it was difficult to assess if either the mother's limitations or the child's pathology would preclude successful work,

276

Ruth Oppenheimer

we could feel safe in the knowledge that should this method
fail, the child could get direct treatment. This was a reassurance to the therapist working with the mother, for example, in cases where a mother might be able to work effectively with the child on his defenses but was not able to deal
with the underlying conflict. We found these mothers very
relieved when their child could get direct therapy.

I. CASE MATERIAL

Beginning of Treatment in Relation to Nursery School

During the 11 years covered by this study 28 children who attended our nursery went into direct treatment, 24 into analytic treatment and four into three-times weekly psychotherapy.
Twenty-one of the 28 children started treatment while actually in the nursery and one boy started during our kindergarten. Of the remaining six, four children started from six
to 12 months after leaving our school and two started analysis
before entering the nursery school.

TABLE I

Beginning of Direct Treatment for 28 Children

Before Nursery School	Concurrently or during Nursery	During Hanna Perkins Kindergarten	6-12 months after leaving our school
2	21	1	4

Both children who began their treatment prior to nursery
school were suffering from physical handicaps. Robin was
blind in one eye and Orson suffered from severely clubbed
feet. It was felt that they needed treatment in order to prepare them to deal with the reactions of the other children in
the nursery to their handicap.

In the four instances where treatment started within the
year after leaving school the mothers had been worked with
and in two instances an attempt had been made to treat the

children via their mothers. In these two cases the diagnostic picture was not completely clear at the time of entry to the nursery: Yvonne belonged in the psychosomatic category; and Doug was thought to be a category III case, but under the full impact of phallic and oedipal conflicts during the end of the nursery year his disturbance was diagnosed as a case of infantile neurosis (category IV).

The other two were recognized as belonging to the neurotic category soon after entry to nursery school. Both these children entered the nursery school late, being four years, six months and four years, 10 months, respectively on entry. The time they remained at the nursery was devoted to preparing the mothers for the treatment of the children.

Diagnostic Categories

Diagnostically 15 of the 28 children were thought to suffer from infantile neuroses (Category IV) on admission to nursery school. Two belonged to the psychosomatic category and six were in diagnostic category V. All went into analysis with a single exception to be described below. There was little doubt in our minds at the time of beginning school that these children would require direct treatment, although there was a question in some of the cases whether the parents could accept it.

The remaining five cases were in Group III at the time of admission. In two instances the diagnosis changed to Group IV during their stay in school: Doug, mentioned above, and Ethan. In Ethan's case, too, the year of work via the mother clarified the extent of his pathology and showed the mother's limitation in working with him. The other three children in category III were taken into psychotherapy; they will be discussed below.

There was only one other case where the diagnostic category changed prior to treatment, this time from category V to IV. Sam had suffered from episodes of bizarre movements of his body. He had been diagnosed and treated as an epileptic for some years. Medical re-examination eventually ruled out any organic involvement and resulted in referral to our nursery school. Our initial evaluation showed that Sam's movements were related to emotional distress in specific situations and were but part of his overall disturbance of extreme withdrawal and infantility. In her work with the therapist his mother was helped to cope with her guilt and anxiety which enabled her to discuss the boy's difficulties realistically with him especially his movements and numerous fears—and also to change her educational measures. Within five months the therapist reported that Sam now was a mature, intelligent, neurotic boy with many anxieties with which he coped mainly by obsessional means and a number of compulsions.

TABLE II

Diagnostic Grouping of Children

Categ. III stayed III	Categ. III changed to IV	Categ. IV stayed IV	Categ. V changed to IV	Category V stayed V	Psychosomatic (Category VI)
3 (Psychotherapy)	2	15 (one of these a psychotherapy case)	1	5	2

The Psychotherapy Cases

Of the four children who went into psychotherapy three belonged to category III and one to category IV.

All these instances arose in the first years of our work and we ourselves have been puzzled to find that during the last few years we have not encountered cases suitable for psychotherapy rather than treatment via the mother or psychoanalysis. We have tried to think about the four cases in terms of why they were selected for a different kind of treatment than the children are at present.

All four children were suffering from acute internalized conflicts on the phallic level which showed signs of a possible pathological solution. In the case of Hugh, the Category IV case, this pathological solution had already become established in the form of a dog phobia. However, unlike such phobias in many children we were concerned with later, the disturbance in this case did not seem to interfere as much with the functioning of his ego in most areas. Much of this boy's disturbance had been reached in work via the mother who had been able to do an unusual amount of successful work on some of the child's conflicts. Those which remained were seen as circumscribed areas for therapeutic work and it was thought possible to resolve them in three-times weekly therapy. This assumption proved to be correct.

In the category III children, a particular difficulty prevented working through the mother in each case. In Don's case, his mother had suffered from the same symptom— eneuresis—up to the age of nine. She felt excessively guilty about the child's problem. In the case of Nancy, it was also found that the problems of mother and child were in the same area, so that the mother could not work on them with Nancy. Drew's home background and mother were extremely disturbed and treatment via the mother proved impossible. Probably different selection methods, account for our not having such a case nowadays.

The fact that at that time we had not yet coordinated the therapeutic and educational aspects of the program to the same extent may have caused us to take these children into direct treatment sooner. In addition our time for working with and through the mother was more limited since we now have the extra kindergarten year.

Looking at the Diagnostic Profiles Retrospectively

The therapists agreed that on the whole the impressions gained of child and mother prior to treatment gave a fairly accurate picture of their psychopathology. Analysis, of course, clarified details and origin of the conflicts and allowed more specific insight into the disturbance of the child, but in most areas we were struck by the consistency of our first and later impressions.

However, there is one area in which much was added to our previous knowledge of the child and his environment. This was in the field of exposure to sexual stimulation. Our findings here were impressive: two children had actually been seduced, five had been exposed to primal scene observations —one of these was of an extramarital relationship. Nine children were found to be consistently overstimulated by a seductive parent, while four frequently saw one or the other parent out of control. Family secrets in the form of marital discord, extramarital relationship and alcoholism transpired in three cases. Two children had their autoerotic activities interfered with in a way which proved traumatic to them.

All this material was unknown at the beginning of treatment and had been avoided, kept secret or repressed by the parents in spite of a close working relationship with the therapist. Although suspected in some cases, this information could only be learned from the analysis of the child and in all cases it was found to play a major part in his disturbance.

II. ROLE OF THE NURSERY SCHOOL IN PREPARATION FOR TREATMENT

In previous chapters we described the ways our nursery school has helped all children. In this section we want to show how the school has helped the child and parents in preparation for and during the child's treatment. Naturally, the ways in which the children who did not get direct treatment benefited also helped the children in treatment, but here we will consider only the additional gains in relation to the treatment program.

In the first place the school helped enormously in observations which led to a clarification of the diagnostic picture of the child. This was already seen during the first two months, during which material for the first profile was collected. Much of a child's behavior looked very different from the point of view of neutral observers than from that of the parents when they reported on the child. Often a parent was not struck by a peculiarity in a child's behavior in the family setting, where there were no other children to whom he could be compared. On the other hand a teacher could evaluate some of the children better when they could see the interaction between mother and child, while the therapist could get a clearer picture of the environmental causes contributing to the manifestation of a disturbance in the child.

Most of the therapists noted the observations, which led to the decision for direct treatment, as of the greatest help. It became possible to see how much conflict remained between mother and child, and how much the child had internalized. Sometimes it took considerable time to see this clearly in children coming from a chaotic home. Drew, mentioned already, came from a very disorganized home; his father had left when the boy was less than a year old. He lived with his grandmother, mother, an eight-year-old aunt and a 16-year-old uncle. There were perpetual fights between his grandmother and his mother. His father visited once a year on Drew's birthday, but the boy was never told who the visitor was. On several visits father and mother started fighting. When these facts became known, Drew's uncontrolled aggressive behavior could easily be seen as an identification with the aggressor.

In many cases we found that the mothers' own disturbances obscured their observations. Symptoms shared by mother and child were not thought important enough to be reported by some mothers, or mothers were unable to see them. Several mothers were excellent observers in some areas, but could not see disturbed behavior in others; e.g., many could see and deal well with difficulties relating to the early oral and anal phases, but were unable to observe phallic difficulties.

Three main areas where nursery school observations showed that mothers had "blind spots" and were unable to separate their own conflicts from those of the children were those of disturbances in separation, difficulties in toilet training and in eating habits. Here the nursery school proved very helpful in sorting out whether the conflicts belonged to mother or child or both, and how much of it was internalized in the child.

In Oliver's case, his inability to separate from his mother was seen to be due largely to the difficulties his mother had in letting him go and her need to make him feel guilty when he was able to enjoy himself apart from her. The mother received support from the teachers while clarifying these conflicts with the therapist. Oliver was helped in treatment by being shown realistically that this problem was as much his mother's as it was his.

In other cases mothers had their own difficulties about separations which caused them to deny them in their children. Yvonne's mother felt very guilty because she had suddenly taken the child away from home without preparation, after which Yvonne had suffered an asthmatic attack. Fred's mother's defenses against her own feeling in regard to separation made her unable to realize her son's feelings. In these cases the teachers were most helpful in verbalizing the feelings with the children and enabling them to see the conflict.

We had five soilers in our group of children. When they entered nursery we were not sure how much this symptom was a conflict with the external world. In these cases we were struck to see to what extent mothers would put up with the soiling symptom and try to make excuses for the child. Here the task of the nursery school was to present this symptom to both mother and child as the child's problem, and to make it more of a conflict to the child. The teachers set an example for the mothers in the educational handling of the soiling symptom. Often school was the first place where the child became responsible for cleaning himself up. In some cases, where toilet training had been delayed and the child had not been aware of much conflict he was helped to resolve the problem, but in all the cases we are concerned with here, much of the problem had been internalized and required direct treatment.

The third area where the school's observation gave us significant information concerned eating disturbances. Often these were not noticed by mothers who were in the habit of providing any food the child wanted. Only in the nursery setting were food fads and intolerances noted and the child realistically confronted with his difficulty.

Over the years we had a number of children, of whom not much had been expected at home. Well-meaning parents were anxious lest they expected too much of their children. When these children came up against expectations adequate for their age, they were found to have many difficulties of which the parents had been unaware. This was found especially in cases of very disturbed children, where often parents found it impossible to face up to the extent of the disturbance and made special allowances for the child to deny their own disappointment. An example is Ricky, who was referred to our nursery at the age of three years, six months because of bizarre behavior and complete withdrawal at a previous nursery where he was thought to be autistic. His mother maintained that at home he behaved in a perfectly normal manner, was outgoing and happy. No one who saw this child running around in circles talking to himself in nonsense language and making bizarre movements with his hands could possibly believe this. In preparing him for treatment the therapist found that his mother's feelings over having such a disturbed child caused her to deny his difficulties or to attribute them to outside events. This family did not lead a social life, and further work with the mother showed that unconsciously she kept away from any situation where Ricky might be compared to other children.

A further task of the nursery school and the therapist during the period preceding treatment was the assessment of the parents' ability to support treatment. We found ourselves here in a very fortunate position: parents through the work with the therapists became very well aware of what treatment of the child would mean, and demand of them. Some parents for whom this was difficult went into therapy themselves. A group of children to whose parents direct treatment of the child was recommended, but who for various reasons could not accept it, has been mentioned already (see chapter 3).

Up to the present all the parents of the children who have had treatment have supported it as well as could be expected. We can probably say that knowledge of our school and of our aims has sorted out the parents who could and who could not support treatment, so that there were no cases where children started treatment and were removed before substantial work had been done.

By the time these children started treatment the parents were well prepared. Teachers and therapists had presented the child's problem realistically by expecting age-adequate behavior and by comparing the child to others. They had helped a number of mothers to change their handling of the child in order to make the child realize the conflict and the need for help. The child's symptoms could no longer be accepted by the family.

For many mothers a longer period of preparation for the child's treatment was necessary. They needed to work through with the therapist their feelings of disappointment that their children needed therapy. Some mothers found it very hard not to be able to treat the children themselves. Often these mothers were helped by seeing that other nursery children were in treatment too; it helped to relieve their guilt feelings, on which they were then able to work with the therapist and that made it possible for them to accept the need for direct treatment for the child. It is our practice to see mothers of young children in analysis on a regular weekly basis. We find this to be an intrinsic part of the analysis of a young child for a number of reasons.

We rely on the mothers of the under-fives to give us reality material which the young child does not bring to the analysis. Moreover, we may need them to clear up past history. Acting out of analytic material at home is bound to occur in the young child, and it is of great help to the therapist if he can get to know of this and the child be helped to bring material back to treatment. Most important is to have the mothers keep up with the changes in the young child, which may necessitate a different attitude towards some manifestations of behavior, in order to prevent a loyalty conflict in the child. We have to bear in mind that the internalized conflicts may be in part an outcome of the conflicts between the instincts and the demands of the environment. Analysis of the conflict alone without a modification of environmental demands does not help the young child. Edith Buxbaum (1954) has stressed the need for work with the mother of the under-five by the child's therapist and the need for mother as well as therapist allowing the child a different way of approaching his conflicts.

In the same way as the parents were prepared by having the problem presented to them realistically, so the children themselves were shown the difficulties by the teachers. They worked to help the child experience some conflict about his symptom and a wish for help. In this way teachers saved therapists much hard work.

Some children had to be helped by the teachers towards verbal communication as a prerequisite to therapy. The role verbalization plays in analytic treatment is known to all analysts. Anny Katan (1961) has pointed out to what extent preparation toward verbalization by parents and teachers can help treatment and can save valuable treatment time. Among our children a few had no speech at all. In these cases we found that the family had minimized the child's need to express himself verbally by anticipating his need and by accepting nonverbal behavior instead. The school presented a more realistic situation by not making it so easy for the child to communicate in ways other than speech. Slowly these children began to express themselves verbally.

Another group of children used speech, but not for the purpose of communication. These were our most disturbed children—all the category V cases—who talked to themselves in a nonsensical, bizarre way most of the time. These children were helped by teachers to use speech for the purpose of communication. Often it was difficult for the teachers to establish a relationship with them based on verbal communication, to which these children were not accustomed. But we found that once this process had been started these children could be helped in therapy.

Apart from the children who could not communicate in words at all, most of the children had difficulties in expressing their feelings verbally. During the period prior to treatment the teachers worked with these children by verbalizing affects for them and translating some of their actions into words. This was found to cut down the child's acting out considerably, both before and during treatment.

In one case the nursery school was of specific help in preparing a child for treatment. Here the mother found it impossible to do it, owing to difficulties of her own. She was a mother who shared the symptoms of dog phobia and eating disturbance with the child. With the mother's permission the teachers were able to talk to the child in a realistic manner about his need for help with these conflicts.

III. ROLE OF THE NURSERY SCHOOL DURING THE
CHILD'S TREATMENT

The length of stay in the nursery school of the 23 children
who started treatment before or during nursery school varied
from four months to one year and eight months after beginning of treatment. Four children had an additional year in
kindergarten.

In discussing the role of the school during the child's treatment we want to consider the help derived by the child, by
his parents and by the therapist.

Helping the Child

First, a number of children were so disturbed that they
would not have been accepted at any ordinary nursery
school. In this group were all the children who belonged in
our diagnostic category V, the children whose behavior was
bizarre and who did not communicate verbally, who were
withdrawn into their own world of fantasy and whose ways
of interaction with others took on the most primitive forms.

There were also a few children in the neurotic group who
were at times so overwhelmed by anxieties that it would have
been impossible for them to attend an ordinary nursery. An
example is Orson, whose therapist described his behavior in
the following way: "He was quite unable, at age four, to
orient himself as a part of a group of children—rather, he
approached them with extreme rigidity which soon gave way
to hitting, kicking, grabbing—with little or no provocation.
Similarly, his initial 'too good' restrictive behavior with
adults soon gave way to strenuous and persistent physical attack, out-of-control messing and destruction, biting, kicking,
spitting, and running or involving himself in dangerous
activities—inviting chase. Without a considerable degree of
objectivity and professional (analytic) understanding the
teachers would have been unable to tolerate the constant,

almost daily strain that Orson's behavior imposed upon them (for the first year and much of the second year).''

Some other children were helped by being able to be away for hours from a sadomasochistic interplay with their mothers, which in turn helped these mothers to get some relief and enabled them gradually to deal better with the children when they were with them.

For children like these and for others with a very disturbed home background or very disturbed parents the nursery school provided controls, which proved of invaluable help to treatment.

The school's support of reality has already been mentioned in regard to preparation for treatment. During treatment, too, teachers continually provided a background which made it difficult for the child to deny his problems. Conflicts were experienced by the child at school and the teachers tried to motivate the child to take his problems to treatment instead of allowing him to act them out in school.

Throughout the child's stay in the nursery he was helped with the verbalization and expression of affect. But our teachers were also aware of a child's tendency to act out analytic material in the school setting. This knowledge enabled them to refer whatever the child "spilled over" back where it belonged, i.e., therapy. This was observed most clearly in the case of a couple of soilers, children with anal problems who tended to put the wrong thing in the wrong place.

Nursery activities were important for supporting a child's ego functions at all times, but became especially important when energy was freed in treatment and became available for sublimatory activities. Our school was especially helpful in timing demands which could be made on the child as an outcome of treatment. Therapists and school could work in close cooperation. The teachers also were most helpful in using educational measures advised by the therapist, e.g., how to handle a symptom like soiling.

School was an important place for the child in regard to making social relationships—as treatment enabled them to do so.

In some cases specific help was given to a child in a specific area by the teachers, e.g., one child and his mother who were caught up in a very sadomasochistic interplay found it extremely difficult to go to the analytic hour together. Both were greatly relieved when a teacher would take the child, until the analysis had progressed sufficiently for both mother and child to handle this independently.

For another child the school supplied protection from much unhappiness and emotional deprivation by communicating his needs to his parents.

For the most disturbed children with impaired reality testing the school tried to help make a differentiation between treatment and outside life; this was found to be a most difficult task in some very sick children who tended to act out their conflicts in any setting or situation.

Helping the Parents

With the most disturbed children the parents were helped greatly by being able to be away from the child for part of the day. It allowed them some respite from being continually drawn into the child's conflicts, and enabled them to deal better with the child for the remainder of the time. This was especially so in the cases of a strong sadomasochistic relationship.

Teachers helped the parents to see the child as well as their own part in his disturbance objectively by sharing assessment of the child with them. Many parents would experience much relief from their guilt through discussing the child with the teachers and be able to see the child more objectively. Furthermore, the school continued to supply a model for educational handling of the child. Some parents had difficulties in handling the child after some of his defenses had been removed in treatment, when they had to face up to the child expressing some conflicts and feelings which had previously been repressed. These mothers would get much support from the teachers and from seeing how teachers handled these situations. Moreover, school supplied an additional place where the children could show these difficulties. In some cases work on the defenses freed a great amount of aggression and it was difficult for the parents to tolerate this. School was able to relieve the home situation by providing a place where the child could express some of it appropriately.

Helping the Therapist

All therapists agreed on the valuable contributions the teachers' observations made to the ongoing treatment. It made many of us fully aware of how distorted a picture one can get if one relies on the reports from parents alone. Many symptoms go by unnoticed in a setting accustomed to living with a disturbed child. It has been mentioned above how important the teachers' objective observations were toward obtaining a clear diagnostic picture of the child; in the same way these contributions helped greatly toward a correct assessment of the child's reactions to treatment. In addition, observations were recorded and well documented by teachers. This was helpful for therapists, as records could be used to verify analytic material in cases where the original mother-guidance worker was not the child's analyst. This also helped in the case of one particular child whose mother died shortly after he started analysis.

Teachers helped treatment by sharing their knowledge of the child and their observations with the therapist and by encouraging the child to take his problems to therapy.

They also relieved the therapist by giving objective advice on educational matters to parents or by underlining a suggestion made by the therapist in regard to these. They could also provide educational measures advised by the therapist to the parents and to them and in this way we could make sure that they were the same at home and at school.

IV. SOME DIFFICULTIES INHERENT IN THE NURSERY SCHOOL SETTING

Having described the many ways in which the nursery school was invaluable, a few instances should be mentioned where the setting created difficult situations.

Parents and children at times found it difficult to separate therapy from school, the close association of the programs tending in some cases to encourage "spilling." With the children the teachers found it not too difficult to show them the displacement and to encourage them to take the problem back to therapy.

It was more difficult for the teachers to deal with displacements of feelings parents had about therapy. The father of one child would keep her out of treatment whenever he was angry with the therapist, when nursery school was not in session. With school in session he would keep her away from school instead. This instance could be worked out by the therapist, but often it could not be seen quite as clearly by the school, and because of the close association with treatment school became a prime target for displacements of this kind.

For some of our most disturbed children—especially the category V children with very impaired reality testing, the contact with other very disturbed children tended to add a pull towards regressive behavior. Children with similar disturbances were found to get considerable gratification from associating with each other, and this was found quite difficult to manage.

Moreover, the flexible attitude on the part of the teachers and the special attention they gave to these children when they were most disturbed, tended to be exploited by them, as they got better during therapy. Examples of this are provided by Richard and Ricky, two of the most disturbed (category V) children we ever had in our nursery. Both of them were at the nursery for a full year before they started treatment, and were kept on an extra year after. In their first year they needed much special help to learn to communicate, and the teachers had to give them much special attention. Due to their particular disturbances they found it very gratifying and were reluctant to give this up as they became able to do so. They only made full use of their treatment after they came up against the demands of the outside world, i.e., public school. Ricky especially clung to his omnipotent ideas that he could change reality, as long as he was in our nursery, which had provided him with special attention during his first, most disturbed year.

These two boys were some of a number who initially would never have been tolerated in public school, owing to their disturbed and disturbing behavior, so at the time the only alternative was to keep them on for an extra year in the nursery. The difficulties this presented was one of the factors which led toward an expansion of the school to include a kindergarten class.

9. Role of the Nursery School in Relation to Total Child Analytic Program

EDWARD SCHIFF

The Hanna Perkins Nursery School provides a number of unusual opportunities to further the aims of child analysis. In addition it has an important function in the training of nonanalytic professional workers in the area of child development.

The nursery school fulfills a role in the child analytic setting by providing opportunities for clinical observations, facilitating the training of child analysts and creating a focus for research.

Direct observations of normal development, over an extended period (often between two to three years, from ages three or three and one half to six years) afford the opportunity to study the various changes during these crucial developmental stages. Many aspects of early personality development can be observed clinically in this way. Not only is normal development observed but pathology as well, with its many ramifications ranging from developmental interferences to developmental conflicts to fully organized internalized conflicts.

Observations in the nursery school itself of the mother-child relationship are made when the child is brought to school and picked up at the end of the day and when the

293

mother visits the school at various times of the day as planned by the teachers.

The total nursery school program, especially the weekly sessions of mother and therapist, afford a unique opportunity to study the mother-child relationship in a dynamic way and to understand the child's contribution to this relationship in a way which might not otherwise be possible.

The oedipal feeling of the child might be used as an example. Only in treatment of the under-five via the mother can one get the total view, through the mother's eyes, of the full impact on her of the child's oedipal feelings, what happens to them as the mother understands them and handles them with the child. The work with the mother, then, is an opportunity to understand, via the mother's observations, how the child copes with these feelings. By contrast in direct analytic work with the child his oedipal feelings may be divided between therapist and mother. Thus the mother may not experience the full impact of these feelings and therefore not deal with them fully herself.

Another facet of the clinical observations are those made by the mothers of their other children of various ages and how they cope with their development. The therapist's experience is consequently broadened as the mother is helped to deal with all her children, both older and younger than the child being treated. The other children in the family are often observed in this indirect fashion and derive considerable benefit from the mother's work.

In the training of child analysts all the factors discussed under the opportunities for clinical observation are available for the trainees, plus the additional opportunity to attend meetings, discussions and seminars and hence participate and learn. The child analyst in training observes in the nursery school setting many children under five both in a group and in individual activity. These experiences are often lacking in the training and professional background of the medical child analyst.

The school also provides a source of children under five for direct analytic treatment. As mentioned in other sections there are children who are admitted to the school about whom it is already known that analytic treatment will be necessary. There are other children who are seen to be in need of analysis after a longer or shorter period of observation and work with the mother.

The school has also been a source of latency children for analysis since it has been either advisable or unavoidable in some instances that the analysis be delayed until the child is in latency. As with the under-fives, these latency children have often been analyzed as supervised training cases. Because the school makes available for analysis these well prepared and well studied children, the training programs in child analysis have not been hampered by an inadequate supply of suitable cases.

The training of child analysts is further enhanced by the opportunity to observe and learn the educational aspects of development. Medical people (especially) often have little knowledge of the chronological steps in the development of ego activities and the timing of educational measures. For example, in the nursery school, ego achievements, such as a child being able to handle a zipper or button his coat or wash his hands or tie his shoes or help clean up something he has spilled, can be understood in the sequence of ego development, which determines the time when a child can master such skills.

Another function of the school toward the further development of child analysis is that its program, which includes children in analysis, serves as a continual focus for meetings and discussions by child analysts in the weekly seminars. In this way the school becomes not only a focal point for research in analysis but most importantly also a place where child analysts can meet to discuss their cases and share in each other's work and research.

There are a number of specific areas in which research has been done and more is planned. An example is the study of children's reaction to deaths of the mothers of a nursery school and a kindergarten child, studies in depth by various members of the nursery school staff including both teachers and therapists (Furman, 1964; Barnes, 1964; McDonald, 1964).

The relation of the nursery school program to the community deserves special mention. As a result of the school's providing analytic treatment for both under-five and latency children, analysis has become recognized in the community as a type of therapy that is necessary for certain childhood disturbances. This recognition has originated with the parents who have been involved in the analysis of their own children and the other professional workers in the community familiar with the nursery school.

The nursery school serves the community through its early detection and treatment of childhood disturbances, thereby aiming to prevent their later disruptive effects on society (family, school and social groups). Another community service provided by the school relates to the children in Diagnostic Group V, some of whom, without the nursery school and analytic treatment might have required long-term hospitalization and institutionalization.

The nursery school teachers themselves in conjunction with the child therapists spend considerable time in the special training of new nursery school teachers as they come to the center to work. The trained teachers, in turn, eventually help to train nursery school teachers in the community by participating in the programs of the Cleveland Association of Nursery Education. Another important community function provided by the nursery school, while not specifically analytic, is the opportunity to teach analytic concepts and the application of analytic principles to nonanalytic professional people.

The school provides a place for observation of young children, an opportunity to study their histories, and through discussion with teachers and attendance at seminars a way to integrate observations and concepts. Thus a number of people of different backgrounds are trained in child observation and understanding by the personnel of the therapeutic nursery school. Some of the professional people regularly attending are resident physicians in pediatrics, medical students in child psychiatry elective clerkships, fellows in child psychiatry training, psychologists, social workers and nurses.

10. Appendix

ERNA FURMAN

SCHEMA OF LINES OF DEVELOPMENT AND MASTERY OF TASKS

1. *Leaving Nursery School*

    (a) Functioning in nursery school in terms of the developmental lines indicated in first profile re "Entry to Nursery School."

    (b) Reactions to preparation for public school, e.g., ability to participate and learn in prekindergarten programs in the nursery school, response to visit at public school.

    (c) Child's handling of separation from nursery school.

2. *Adaptation to Public School*

    (a) Relationships to teachers and peers.

    (b) Observance of school rules and routines.

    (c) Formal learning and creative activities.

    (d) Current adjustment at home and in environments other than school, e.g., neighborhood, relatives.

298

AREAS FOR INVESTIGATION FOR THE FOLLOW-UP OF
CHILDREN IN LATENCY (PROFILE III)[1]

SCHEME FOR LINES OF DEVELOPMENT AND MASTERY
OF TASKS

Introduction

1. Latency period is defined arbitrarily in terms of school
placement, that is, "the latency child is one who is currently
attending elementary school."

2. The commencement of first grade is recognized as a
"developmental point" for which there are certain emotional
and intellectual prerequisites. However, there does not seem
to be any point of crisis similarly experienced by all children
until entrance into junior high. In the six years' span there
are undoubtedly experiences that represent a "crisis" for
individual children, but there's no uniformity in the nature
of these experiences. For this reason, the investigation outline
which follows is organized to apply to a child at any point
during the six years.

3. In evaluating adjustment during this period, the committee used Freud's (1909) remarks about the task of education as expressed in the case of Little Hans. He suggested that
the aim of education is "to make the individual capable of
becoming a civilized and useful member of society with the
least possible sacrifice of his own activity." This emphasizes
the two-sidedness of education: consideration for society and
consideration for the individual. Most parents and teachers
have these twin goals in mind. In terms of social criteria,
they want a child to be socially acceptable, to "do well," to
cause no trouble, to be considerate of others, and so on. In
terms of the inner self of the child as an individual, they want

[1] Proposed by R. Furman, E. Hosley, E. Daunton, M. Flumerfelt, and J.
Kessler.

RESUME OF DIAGNOSES OF ALL CASES, GROUPED ON BASIS OF INITIAL PROFILE
AND MODE OF TREATMENT

		Treatment via the Mother		Direct Treatment*	
Group I	1.	Albert	1-2-2		
Group II	2.	Alvin	2-1-2		
	3.	Alice	2-1-1		
	4.	Ann	2-1-1		
	5.	Bertha	2-3-3		
Group III	6.	Andrew	3-1-1	1. Don	3- ⊹
	7.	Betty	3-1-1	2. Drew	3- ⊹
	8.	Candace	3-1-1	3. Nancy	3- ⊹
	9.	Dorothy	3-1-1	4. Doug	3-4
	10.	Edna	3-1-1	5. Ethan	3-4
	11.	Eleanor	3-1-1		
	12.	Freida	3-1-1		
	13.	Gretchen	3-2-1 ↓		
	14.	Arthur	3-2-1		
	15.	Helen	3-2-1		
	16.	Hilda	3-2-1		
	17.	Ben	3-1-2		
	18.	Bert	3-2-2		
	19.	Jane	3-2-2		
	20.	Bill	3-2-2		
	21.	Janice	3-2-2		
	22.	Calvin	3-4-4		
	23.	Judy	3-2-3		
	24.	Laura	3-2-3		

Group		Name	
	6.	Frank	4-4
	7.	Fred	4-4
	8.	Gary	4-4
	9.	George	4-4
	10.	Harry	4-4
	11.	Harold	4-4
	12.	Herbert	4-4
	13.	Hugh	4-4 ±
	14.	James	4-
	15.	Lou	4-
	16.	Lem	4-
	17.	Robin	4-
	18.	Matthew	4-
	19.	Oliver	4-
	20.	Orson	4-
	21.	Peter	5-5
	22.	Richard	5-5
	23.	Ricky	5-5
	24.	Sam	5-4
	25.	Vivian	5-
	26.	Thomas	5-
	27.	Yvonne	PS 3?-PS 4
	28.	Timothy	PS -PS 4

Group		Name	
IV	25.	Louise	4-4-4
	26.	Margaret	4-4-4
	27.	Marie	4-4-4
	28.	Martha	4-4-4
	29.	Mary	4-4-4
	30.	Charles	4-4-4
	31.	Matilda	4-4-4
	32.	Myrtle	4-4-4
V			
VI	33.	Chuck	PS 3?-2-2
	34.	Craig	PS 4?-4-4
	13.	Gretchen	PS 3-2-1 ←

* Direct treatment means analysis unless otherwise noted.
± Cases treated by three-times weekly psychotherapy.

him to be self-confident, spontaneous and capable of enjoying himself in many ways.

4. The proposed outline for investigation starts with observable behavior, indicating by parenthetical remarks the derivation of the behavior in terms of personality structure. The material can be re-ordered into a form similar to the developmental profile. This particular scheme, organized to help interviewers, is analogous to the distinction between the manifest and latent content of dreams.

OUTLINE

I. *Family Relationships*

A. *Relationship to parents.* There should be some indication of preference for the company of the same-sexed parent, a sharing of interests, hobbies, and other activities. (Resolution of the Oedipus complex with identification.)

There should be little difficulty in coping with separation from the parents: willingness to go to school, ability to remain overnight with friends or at camp, little distress at parents' vacations, and so on. (Resolution of the Oedipus complex in terms of separation anxiety.)

There should be little overt evidence of romantic interest in the parents, such as wanting to get in their bed or expressions of fantasies. (Resolution of the Oedipus complex as manifested by repression.)

The child should be responsible in matters of self-care in terms of choosing clothes and matters of personal hygiene. He should find a middle ground between "fastidiousness" and "provocativeness"; he should not indulge in a teasing interplay with his parent. (Drawing away from the earlier intimate relationship with parent and indications of independence stemming from superego.)

The child should demonstrate some feeling for the parents and assumption of responsibility—show concern if they are ill or pleasure in giving gifts, material or otherwise. (Super-ego.)

B. *Relationship to siblings.* Here there should be diminution of bickering and expressions of jealousy and minimum bossiness. In other words, there should be less rivalry with siblings for the exclusive attention of the parents. (Oedipus complex resolution and superego functioning.)

II. *Relationship to Teacher and Authorities Outside the Home*

The child should be able to accept his status as a member of a group rather than seek individual attention (which would represent a displacement of the original oedipal wishes). At the same time, the child should be fond of authority figures and willing to have a positive relationship. (If contrary, the defense against oedipal attachments would be excessive.)

The child should have a differential reaction to different teachers, or substitutes, without being unduly traumatized by an uncongenial adult.

The child should be able to accept instruction and help, recognizing his own limitations with good grace.

III. *Relationship to Peers*

The child should have a definite preference for the company of his own sex. (A cardinal sign of latency.)

The child should have established some meaningful friendships which persist over some period of time. (An indication of some object removal from the oedipal figures.)

The child should be able to function in a variety of situations—where he excels as well as where he is not outstanding. (Ability to tolerate competition, indicating resolution of the Oedipus complex.)

The child should be able to function with his age mates both in the structured situation of controlled groups and in free situations and capable of "self-government" in spontaneous recreational activities.

IV. *Relationship to Work*

The child should have some pleasure and interest in school activities. (Sublimation.)

His achievement level should be commensurable with his mental ability. This can be ascertained by comparing mental tests and achievement tests. In addition, he should be judged by the teacher as adequately productive. (Ego ideal, sublimation, superego, freedom from anxiety or overwhelming conflicts.)

He should be reasonably independent in getting his assigned work done with a minimal interplay between child and adults.

He should be able to tolerate both success and relative failure.

There should be some indication of self-initiated interests, seriously pursued without external pressure. (Sublimation.)

V. *Relationship to Self*

A review of symptoms should be made, particularly those that represent a continued form of the problems for which the child was originally referred.

Child's reaction to stress should be assayed, assuming that he has experienced some crisis—parental illness, his own illnesses, injuries or disappointments. (Tolerance for frustration, resistance against the development of symptoms in the face of anxiety.)

The child's ability to express his feelings should be evaluated in terms of the affects of anger, sadness, anxiety, pleasure or love.

The child's feelings about himself should be evaluated in terms of self-confidence or realistic self-concept and whether he is a chronic worrier or overly conscientious. (Possibility of suppressive defenses of reaction formation.)

Some estimate should be made of his general character tendencies such as acting out or obsessional.

AREAS FOR INVESTIGATION FOR FOLLOW-UP OF PUBERTY CHILDREN (PROFILE III)[2]

SCHEME FOR LINES OF DEVELOPMENT AND MASTERY OF TASKS

Aim of Enquiry

To assess whether an individual child has reached the developmental stage of puberty and whether his/her personality deals with the pubertal conflicts with age-appropriate means. These means may extend over a wide range. Within it the relative flexibility of adjustment is more important than any specific forms.

Basic Aspects to Be Assessed

Object relationships. (1) Any puberty changes within family relationship?; (2) revival of pre-oedipal attachments; (3) degree of attempts at object removal.

Ego functioning in all areas. Study of the defenses is to be used to assess: (1) instinctual status, forms of drive expression and drive distribution; (2) attempts at object removal; (3) flexibility in dealing with conflicts. Mainly healthy defenses: displacement, reversal of roles, reversal of affect, sublimation, intellectualization. Mainly pathological defenses: withdrawal of libido to self, arrest at latency, regression to (a) latency, (b) continued impulsive acting out, (c) predominant use of primitive defenses (denial, projection, aggression turned against self).

Superego. (1) Identifications and ego ideals: Are they new? Are they outside the family? Are there rapid changes? Are they real, fantasy or a mixture of both? Do identifications affect ego? If so, what aspects—the whole ego or part? Are

2 Proposed by M. Barnes, J. Benkendorf, E. Furman, R. Oppenheimer, A. Rolnick.

the identifications with a group or with an individual? Gang formation or group ideals? (2) Guilt—self-denial, self-punishment, aggression turned against self, provoking punishment, asceticism, religion, depressive moods. (3) Self-esteem—ability to enjoy activities or achievements, or both; reactions to success and failure; appearance.

Outline of Specific Areas for Investigation

1. Current relationships within family. Is the child compliant, rebellious or independent? Is he consistent in any one of these attitudes or does his behavior show swings from one to the other? What are the manifestations of guilt? Areas: (a) daily routines: bathroom sharing, meals, TV sharing, chores, responsibility in family, responsibility for self (bodily, schoolwork, appointments, room); (b) outings: does he join family? Does he like to be with others or alone? (c) shopping (e.g., for clothes); (d) behavior with family when outsiders are present; (e) reaction to having done something wrong.

2. Is the current picture different from age 10 approximately? If so, what does parent attribute it to—external or internal factors?

3. Contacts outside the family. (a) Peers: sex, personal description and personality, individual or group, nature of relationship and shared activities; activities or special interest—pajama parties, overnights, canteen, dating, clubs; constancy of friendships, consistency of choice. (b) Adults: Are relationships real or fantasied? In (a) and (b), see how much the child is affected in regard to (1) bodily characteristics—clothes, hairdo, mannerisms, etc.; (2) mental characteristics—interests, ideals, skills; (3) degree of influence on moral actions. (c) Young children: siblings, babysitting, care for children in camp. (d) Animals: pets or fantasy preoccupations.

4. School (see Social Worker's Enquiry).

5. Hobbies and interests at home, such as creativity, new interests, dancing, religion.

6. Acting out—degree and continuity, in the home or outside, amount of gratification; the extent of the guilt. Is it a new manifestation? Is the outcome progressive or regressive?

7. Reactions to bodily changes. Girls: in regard to hair, breasts, size, weight, skin, menstruation. Boys: in regard to voice, hair, size, size of penis, skin, nocturnal emissions, and ejaculation.

Are reactions shown by exhibitionism, shame, secrecy, pain (menstruation), denial, regression? What are the attitudes to gym and swimming, use of make-up, care of skin, clothes, foundation garments?

8. Autoerotic activities—manifest or brought up for discussion or displaced (eating feasts, overeating, smoking, cleanliness or lack of, hyperactivity, exercises, insomnia).

9. Family environment and family's reaction to child's puberty.

Social Worker's School Enquiry for Puberty Children

1. Has there been any change in academic record since fifth grade?
   (a) Overall
   (b) In a certain subject
   (c) In consistency within a certain subject.

2. Has there been any change in *attitude to school?*
   (a) To learning in school, in homework, in tests
   (b) To teachers: Does child do better with male or female teachers? Does he single out special teachers for special likes and dislikes? Does this affect the performance? How dependent is child on teacher?
   (c) To authority and discipline: Is attitude positive or negative?
   (d) To peers: Does child mix with same or opposite sex? Is he leader, follower or loner? Does he participate in groups?

(e) Personal appearance

(f) Citizenship and effort grading

(g) Attendance

3. Creativity: projects in any subject, contribution of ideas, original ideas in literary output, art, drama, music.

4. Performance and attitude in special subjects: gym, health class or hygiene, home economics, science and math.

5. Extracurricular activities: Are there any and what are they? What is performance in these compared with academic performance? How long does interest persist? Dancing—bal-

ADAPTATION OF FLOOR PLAN OF THE HANNA PERKINS SCHOOL

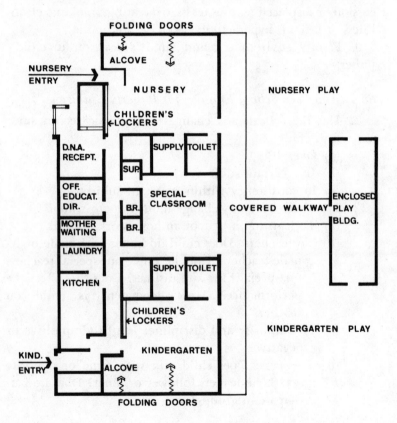

let or social dancing? Does child learn, show what he knows? Is he affected by presence of other sex? How does he dress?

6. Unstructured time: behavior during study hall, recess, in cafeteria, going to and from school.

SUMMARY OF INFORMATION ABOUT THE ROLE OF THE NURSERY SCHOOL IN CASES OF TREATMENT VIA THE MOTHER[3]

The members of the research committee extracted the basic data for each case from the therapists' summaries, specifically from the section describing the role of the nursery school. These data were then grouped and tabulated for 41 cases: 34 cases treated via the mother only; six cases in diagnostic category III with whom treatment via the mother was followed by individual psychotherapy or analysis; one case in diagnostic category IV, treated first via the mother, then by analysis. This case was originally also in category III before category IV was broadened to include this type of disturbance (see Chapter 5).

Help of Nursery School to Mothers

Helpful observations made by mother or presented to mother by teachers—20 cases.

School serving as model for education—19 cases.

Separation could not have been accomplished without help of school—8 cases.

Observations *of* mother by staff—5 cases.

Hours without child are helpful and necessary relief to mother—4 cases.

Helping mother to work through child's conflicts—4 cases.

Relationship with teachers acts as helpful support to

[3] By Erna Furman and Edward J. Schiff, M.D.

mother—10 cases. (Breakdown of this figure: 4—school supports mother's work with therapist; 4—school supports mothers in stressful reality of a longstanding nature, e.g., desertion of father; 2—school supports mother during short-term stressful reality crisis, child's hospitalization.)

Help of Nursery School to Child

Verbalization of feelings (such as sadness, anger or anxiety) —22 cases. Sublimations and skills—18 cases.

Basic education of drives (toilet training, out-of-control behavior, etc.)—11 cases. Of these, *two* children required specialized educational technique due to lack of speech and severe visual handicap.

Essential diagnostic observations—13 cases.

Help with extreme problems in peer relations—13 cases.

Help with separation beyond the usual—12 cases.

Providing a healthy and calm environment (in some cases this meant relief from interpersonal tensions with parents, in most cases it meant becoming acquainted with a normal setting in contrast to extreme pathology in the home)—12 cases.

Removing secondary gain of symptomatic behavior—3 cases.

Help with mastery of current stressful reality (hospitalizations)—3 cases.

Providing a model for identification with the mother's approval (in these cases the mother could not provide the desired traits but could tell the child she admired these traits in the teachers and hoped the child would emulate them)—2 cases.

Creating some insight in child (in lieu of mother)—3 cases.

Helping child to prepare for events (in lieu of mother)—1 case.

Positive use of group pressure as motivation for child to work out his troubles—1 case.

STUDY OF PARENTAL FACTORS HELPFUL OR LIMITING TO THE WORK[4]

In this study an attempt was made to tabulate the data on positive and negative factors in the parents to determine the changes in these factors during the period of work and correlate them with the course of the child's development. The members of the research committee used the individual case summaries as their source material, extracting from them the data for the following headings:

1. Assets of the mother facilitating the work
2. Limitations of the mother interfering with the work
3. Role of the mother as an educator
4. Turning points (for better or worse)
5. Role of the father.

These data were then collected and organized. At the beginning of each table there is a brief explanation of the principle for the organization of the data.

41 cases were included in this study: 34 cases treated via the mother only, six cases in diagnostic category III, with whom treatment via the mother was followed by individual psychotherapy or analysis, and one case in diagnostic category IV, treated first via the mother, then by analysis. This case was originally in diagnostic category III, before category IV was broadened to include this type of disturbance (see Chapter 5).

Education

An attempt was made to assess the mothers' abilities as educators at the beginning and end of the periods of work with her. The categories below were set up *a priori* as representing, hopefully, the major areas of education. The therapists'

[4] By Erna Furman and Edward J. Schiff, M. D.

and reviewing therapists' descriptions were then fitted into these areas. The 41 cases are grouped according to initial and subsequent diagnostic categories.

1. Twenty-one cases starting with category I, II or III and improving to (or maintaining original status at) I or II.

| | Instinct Education | | Sublimation | Handling of Reality |
	Aggression	Libido		
Before	21 No	19 No	6 No	16 No
	— Yes	2 Yes	15 Yes	5 Yes
After	— No	— No	1 No	— No
	2 Partial	5 Partial	1 Partial	
	19 Yes	16 Yes	19 Yes	21 Yes

2. Three cases starting with category 2 or 3 but ending in category 3 on follow-up diagnosis:

| | Instinct Education | | Sublimation | Handling of Reality |
	Aggression	Libido		
Before	3 No	3 No	2 Yes	2 Yes
			1 No	1 No
After	2 No	1 No	2 Yes	2 Yes
	1 Partial	2 Partial	1 No	1 Partial

3. Three cases starting with category III and remaining there prior to entering psychotherapy:

| | Instinct Education | | Sublimation | Handling of Reality |
	Aggression	Libido		
Before	3 No	3 No	1 No	2 No
			2 Yes	1 Yes
After	1 No	3 No	1 No	2 No
	1 Partial		2 Yes	1 Yes
	1 Yes			

4. Two cases starting with category III and becoming category IV:

Before	2 No	2 No	2 Yes	2 No
After	2 No	1 No 1 Partial	2 Yes	2 No

5. Twelve cases with category IV-IV-IV:

Before	12 No	11 No 1 Partial	9 No 3 Yes	12 No
After	10 No 2 Partial	10 No 2 Partial	8 No 1 Partial 3 Yes	10 No 1 Partial 1 Yes

Overall Results

1. Mothers in all diagnostic categories started with undistinguishable records as educators.

2. The children's improvement or nonimprovement appears directly correlated to the mothers' capability as an effective educator. In group "III to I or II," all mothers improved considerably as educators; in group "IV to IV" none did.

3. The mother's ability to change as educator cannot be assessed from these data. More mothers (15 out of 21) who were initially effective in the area of sublimation could change, fewer mothers (3 out of 12) who were initially effective in sublimation could not change, but this is not a very significant indication.

4. Of the areas listed, "sublimation" is the least important in terms of contributing to child's improvement. "Instinct education" is by far the most important, "handling of reality" ranks midway.

Fathers

Only those fathers whose role in the work with the parents was of more than average significance were included in this index, i.e., 27 out of the 41 cases. The categories below are based on a summary of the fathers' roles as described by therapists and reviewing therapists. No *a priori* index was made to classify the fathers' roles.

Category	No. of cases	Child improved	Not improved
I. Father significantly helpful	7	5	2
II. Father cooperates with program but his personality disturbance significantly affects child	10	6	4
III. Father does not cooperate with program and his personality disturbance significantly affects child	10	4	6

Results

The numbers themselves do not suggest a significant trend. Moreover, in all cases of improvement with "helpful" fathers, the mothers are described as functioning fully and well with only minor areas of difficulty. Similarly, in all cases of non-improvement with "uncooperative and/or disturbed" fathers, the mothers show serious and broad areas of difficulty. No single improvement or nonimprovement is described as primarily due to the father.

Turning Points (Positive and Negative) in the Work with the Mothers

The categories below are based on a summary of the therapists' descriptions. The first four categories denote positive turning points, the fifth category denotes negative turning points.

I. Mother gains insight into child's conflict after over-coming own resistance or rather, despite own resistance—16 cases: aggression, 4; aggression in relation to separation and penis-envy, 4; phallic conflicts, 3; need for control of child, 1; effect of a reality on child, 4.

II. Mother gains insight into her own problem, past or present, and is able to separate it from child or use it to em-pathize—9 cases: spontaneous recall of own childhood con-flict, 3; gaining awareness of fantasy about child, 3; aware-ness of sharing child's feelings now, 2; awareness of own pathology, 1.

III. Discussion of guilt with and by the mother—5 cases.

IV. Reality changes made in the home—3 cases.

V. Negative turning point: onset or severe worsening of parental psychological illness during course of work—4 cases: depressions, 2; obsessional neurosis coupled with severe physi-cal illness, 1; colitis, 1.

Results

It is striking that the biggest category comprises those mothers who were able to help their children in spite of the psychological hardship it must have caused them. It is not known from the summaries what helped them to do so (dis-tribution of narcissism in relationship to child, repeated ob-servations by mother and staff, therapist's drawing attention to the reality, relationship to therapist) or at what stage in the work.

Limiting Factors in Mothers

The groups are based on a summary of the therapists' de-scriptions. Some mothers are listed in several categories, some only in one. The major categories are almost equal numer-ically and represent essentially those areas that had been known to be important limiting factors (including aggression, phallic and oedipal phases, sadomasochism, shared problems, undue narcissistic involvement). "Gross educational inconsistency" was not expected originally.

No area (except overall gross parental pathology) is prognostically hopeless. In all of them there is a relatively even numerical distribution among "change" and "no change" or "partial change." From the diagnostic categories, it appears that the children's improvement tended to correlate with changes in the mothers' limiting factors, and vice versa. The data (see below, table entitled "Outcome") do not show what causes or deters change with any given factor.

OUTCOME

Assets in Mothers

Every description stresses the adequacy of libidinal cathexis of the child, i.e., the healthy aspects of the mother-child relationship. In addition, the following assets are listed in equal numbers: therapeutic facility, good educator, healthy guilt, ability to identify with N.S. center, ability to help child despite personal psychological strain or reality strain, or both.

DEVELOPMENTAL CHART[5]

The general purpose of this form is to see whether the child has reached the age-appropriate level in each area at a given time—that is, at entry to school, upon leaving school and at the time of follow-up.

The Roman numeral and letter headings on the left side are the same designations used in the profile and will help you match the question with the profile. There are 25 ques-

5 By Elizabeth Daunton and Erna Furman.

Limiting Factor Factor	No. of Cases	Change	No Change	Partial	Diagnostic Category
Major difficulty with aggression	13	8			3 or 2→1 or 2
			2		3-2-3, 2-3-3
				3	3-2-3, ps-4-4, 4-4-4
Over-all difficulty with libido	5	2			3 or 2→1
			2		2-3-3, ps-2-2
				1	3-2-1
Specific areas of difficulty with libido: 1. Phallic—boys	4	1			3-2-1
			3		ps-4-4, 4-4-4, 4-4-4
2. Phallic—girls	6	1			3-1-1
			1		4-4-4
				4	3-2-1, 3-2-1, 3-2-3, 3-3-
3. Oedipal phase	3	1			3-1-2
			2		3-2-3, 3-2-3
4. Sadomasochistic relationship	13		6		ps-4-4, 4-4-4, 4-4-4, 4-4-4, 4-4-4, 3-4-
		6			4-4-4, 3-2-1, 3-1-2, 3-2-2, 3-1-1, 3-2-1
				1	3-1-1
Shared conflict or defenses	13	3			3-1-1, 3-1-1, 3-1-1
			4		4-4-4, 4-4-4, 3-4-, 3-
				6	3-2-3, 4-4-4, 4-4-4, 4-4-4, 3-2-2, 3-2-1
Gross educational inconsistency	10	1			3-2-1
			5		all 4-4-4 and one 3-
				4	3-2-2, 3-2-1, 3-3-, 3-4-
Pathological guilt	6	3			3-2-1, 3-2-1, 3-1-2
			3		4-4-4, 4-4-4, 4-4-4
Narcissistic involvement (undue)	12	5			3 or 2→1 or 2
			5		4-4-4, 4-4-4, 3-, ps-4-, 3-4-4
				2	4-4-4, 3-1-1
Inability to mother consistently	3	1			3-2-2
			2		3-4-, 4-4-4
Mother's personality disorder seriously interferes in relation with child and work	7		5 major 2 partial		5 are 4-4-4 2 are 3-4-, 4-4-4
Mothers with depressive tendencies with two, depression was obstacle to the work (3-2-3, 4-4-4)	7		7		3-2-3, 4-4-4, 4-4-4, 3-2-2, 3-2-1, 3-1-1, 2-1-1

tions to be answered for each profile, or a total of 75 questions for each child with his three profiles.

The majority of the questions asked concern the age-appropriateness of the function or level of development. For brevity's sake, write "yes" in the proper place if the function or level was age-appropriate; if not, write "no."

The following information should be useful in answering the questions. The information is listed according to the question number found in the third column.

1. Libido level to be age-adequate at entry to school should be at least phallic; on leaving school, the oedipal conflict should have been reached.

2. Libido distribution—Is the libido evenly distributed between objects and self? Answer "yes" or "no."

3. Aggression—To be age-appropriate at entry to school there should be some verbalization, despite the incidence of hitting or tantrums.

4. Distribution of aggression—This question should be answered "yes" if the child's aggression is predominantly directed outwards and "no" if it is directed against the self in an unusual degree.

5. Ego intactness—This also should be answered "yes" or "no" though no question of age-adequacy is involved.

13. Defenses—Are they predominantly age-appropriate?

14. Ego free from interferences by defenses? Answer "yes" if the ego functions appropriately and "no" if there is secondary interference by defenses.

15. Superego—Is there an age-appropriate balance between internal and external control?

19. Fixation points—Is there an indication of marked fixation points—oral, anal or phallic fixation—due to pathology? The answer here in the column could be "anal, oral, phallic" so for brevity's sake use the letter A, O or P, or the word "None." *This designation should be used for the first column (Entry into Nursery School) only.* In the second and third

Child's name:	Case therapist:	Review therapist:

ITEM	No.	Age of child Enter N.S.	Age of child Leave N.S.	Age of child Follow-up
V. A. Instinctual development				
1. Libido level	1			
b. Libido distribution	2			
2. Aggression	3			
a. distribution of aggression	4			
V. B. Ego functioning				
a. intactness	5			
b. functions				
i. perception	6			
ii. memory	7			
iii. motor control	8			
iv. speech	9			
v. reality testing	10			
vi. integration	11			
vii. secondary process thinking	12			
c. defenses	13			
d. ego free from interference by defense	14			
e. superego	15			
V. C. Relationships				
a. members of family	16			
b. teachers	17			
c. peers	18			
VI. Genetic development fixation points	19			
VIII. General economic characteristics				
a. Frustration tolerance				
i. libido	20			
ii. aggression	21			
iii. neutral	22			
b. sublimation potential	23			
c. anxiety tolerance	24			
d. progressive vs. regressive	25			

DEVELOPMENT CHART DATA FOR NINETEEN GROUP III CHILDREN TREATED VIA THE MOTHER

FIRST PROFILE

	ANDREW	BETTY	CANDACE	DOROTHY	EDNA	ELEANOR	FREIDA	GRETCHEN	ARTHUR	HELEN	HILDA	BEN	BERT	JANE	BILL	JANICE	CALVIN	JUDY	LAURA
LIBIDINAL LEVEL	Y	Y	Y	Y	Y	Y	Y	Y	Y	Y	Y	Y	N	Y	N	N	Y	N	Y
LIBIDINAL DISTRIBUTION	N	Y	N	N	Y	Y	Y	Y	N	Y	N	N	N	N	N	N	N	Y	N
AGGRESSION	N	N	N	N	N	N	N	N	N	N	N	N	N	N	N	N	N	N	Y
DISTRIBUTION AGGRESSION	Y	Y	Y	N	Y	Y	Y	N	Y	N	Y	Y	N	N	N	Y	N	Y	N
EGO INTACT	Y	Y	Y	Y	Y	Y	Y	Y	Y	Y	Y	Y	Y	Y	Y	Y	Y	Y	Y
FUNCTION																			
PERCEPTION	Y	Y	Y	Y	Y	Y	Y	Y	Y	Y	Y	N	Y	Y	Y	Y	Y	Y	Y
MEMORY	Y	Y	Y	Y	Y	Y	Y	Y	Y	Y	Y	Y	N	Y	Y	Y	Y	Y	Y
MOTOR CONTROL	Y	Y	Y	Y	Y	Y	Y	Y	Y	Y	Y	N	N	Y	N	N	N	Y	Y
SPEECH	Y	Y	Y	N	Y	Y	N	N	Y	Y	Y	Y	N	Y	N	Y	Y	Y	Y
REALITY TESTING	Y	Y	Y	Y	Y	Y	Y	Y	N	Y	Y	Y	N	Y	Y	Y	Y	Y	Y
INTEGRATIVE	Y	Y	Y	Y	Y	Y	Y	Y	Y	Y	Y	Y	N	Y	N	Y	Y	Y	Y
SECONDARY PROCESS	Y	Y	Y	Y	Y	Y	Y	Y	Y	Y	Y	Y	Y	Y	Y	Y	Y	Y	Y
AGE ADEQUATE DEFENSE	N	N	N	Y	N	Y	N	N	N	Y	N	N	N	Y	N	N	N	N	Y
EGO FREE FROM																			
SECONDARY INTERFERENCE	N	N	N	Y	N	N	N	Y	N	Y	N	N	N	N	N	N	N	N	N
SUPEREGO BALANCE	N	N	N	Y	Y	Y	N	Y	N	Y	N	N	N	Y	N	Y	Y	N	Y
RELATIONS																			
PARENTS	N	N	N	N	Y	Y	N	N	N	N	N	N	N	N	N	N	N	N	N
TEACHERS	N	Y	N	Y	Y	Y	N	N	N	N	N	N	N	N	N	N	N	N	N
PEERS	N	Y	Y	Y	Y	Y	N	N	N	N	N	N	N	N	N	N	N	N	N
FIXATION POINTS	A	$^{O}_{A}P$	A	$^{O}_{A}P$	O	A	$^{O}_{A}$	A	$^{O}_{A}P$	$^{O}_{A}P$	$^{O}_{A}P$	$^{O}_{A}$	$^{O}_{A}P$	$^{O}_{A}$	$^{O}_{A}$	$^{O}_{A}P$	$^{O}_{A}$	$^{O}_{A}$	$^{O}_{A}$
ECONOMIC FACTORS																			
LIBIDO	I	A	A	A	?	I	I	I	I	I	I	I	I	I	I	I	S	I	I
AGGRESSION	I	I	I	I	?	I	I	I	I	I	I	I	I	A	I	I	S	I	A
NEUTRALIZATION	I	A	I	I	?	A	A	A	I	A	I	I	I	I	A	I	S	I	A
SUBLIMATION	I	A	?	I	A	A	A	A	I	A	I	I	I	I	A	I	I	I	I
ANXIETY TOLERANCE	I	I	I	I	I	I	I	I	I	A	I	I	I	I	I	I	I	I	I
PROGRESSIVE VERSUS																			
REGRESSIVE	R	P	P	P	P	P	P	P	R	P	R	R	R	P	R	R	P	R	P
DIAGNOSIS	3	3	3	3	3	3	3	3	3	3	3	3	3	3	3	3	3	3	3

SECOND PROFILE

	ANDREW	BETTY	CANDACE	DOROTHY	EDNA	ELEANOR	FREIDA	GRETCHEN	ARTHUR	HELEN	HILDA	BEN	BERT	JANE	BILL	JANICE	CALVIN	JUDY	LAURA
LIBIDINAL LEVEL	Y	Y	Y	Y	Y	Y	Y	Y	Y	Y	Y	Y	Y	Y	Y	Y	N	Y	Y
LIBIDINAL DISTRIBUTION	Y	Y	Y	Y	Y	Y	Y	Y	Y	Y	Y	Y	Y	Y	Y	Y	N	Y	Y
AGGRESSION	Y	Y	Y	Y	Y	Y	Y	Y	Y	Y	Y	Y	Y	Y	Y	Y	Y	N	Y
DISTRIBUTION AGGRESSION	Y	Y	Y	Y	Y	Y	Y	Y	N	Y	Y	Y	Y	Y	Y	Y	N	Y	Y
EGO INTACT	Y	Y	Y	Y	Y	Y	Y	Y	Y	Y	Y	Y	Y	Y	Y	Y	Y	Y	Y
FUNCTION																			
PERCEPTION	Y	Y	Y	Y	Y	Y	Y	Y	Y	Y	Y	Y	Y	Y	Y	Y	Y	Y	Y
MEMORY	Y	Y	Y	Y	Y	Y	Y	Y	Y	Y	Y	Y	Y	Y	Y	Y	Y	Y	Y
MOTOR CONTROL	Y	Y	Y	Y	Y	Y	Y	Y	Y	Y	Y	Y	Y	Y	Y	Y	N	Y	Y
SPEECH	Y	Y	Y	Y	Y	Y	Y	Y	Y	Y	Y	Y	Y	Y	Y	Y	Y	Y	Y
REALITY TESTING	Y	Y	Y	Y	Y	Y	Y	Y	Y	Y	Y	Y	Y	Y	Y	Y	Y	Y	Y
INTEGRATIVE	Y	Y	Y	Y	Y	Y	Y	Y	Y	Y	Y	Y	Y	Y	Y	Y	Y	Y	Y
SECONDARY PROCESS	Y	Y	Y	Y	Y	Y	Y	Y	Y	Y	Y	Y	Y	Y	Y	Y	Y	Y	Y
AGE ADEQUATE DEFENSE	Y	Y	Y	Y	Y	Y	Y	Y	Y	Y	Y	Y	Y	Y	Y	Y	N	Y	Y
EGO FREE FROM																			
SECONDARY INTERFERENCE	Y	Y	Y	Y	Y	Y	Y	N	N	Y	Y	Y	Y	Y	Y	N	N	Y	Y
SUPEREGO BALANCE	Y	Y	Y	Y	Y	Y	Y	Y	Y	Y	Y	Y	Y	Y	Y	Y	Y	Y	Y
RELATIONS																			
PARENTS	Y	Y	Y	Y	Y	Y	Y	Y	Y	Y	Y	Y	Y	Y	Y	Y	N	N	Y
TEACHERS	Y	Y	Y	Y	Y	Y	Y	Y	Y	Y	Y	Y	Y	Y	Y	Y	N	Y	Y
PEERS	Y	Y	Y	Y	Y	Y	Y	Y	Y	N	Y	Y	Y	N	Y	Y	N	Y	Y
FIXATION POINTS	AI	AI	AI	AI	AI	AI	AI	AI	AI	AI	AI	AI	A	AI	AI	AI	$^{O}_{A}$	AI	$^{O}_{P}$
ECONOMIC FACTORS																			
LIBIDO	A	A	A	A	A	A	A	I	A	A	A	A	I	A	A	A	S	A	A
AGGRESSION	A	A	A	A	A	A	A	A	A	A	A	A	A	A	A	A	S	A	A
NEUTRALIZATION	S	A	A	A	A	A	S	A	I	A	A	A	A	A	A	A	S	A	I
SUBLIMATION	S	A	A	S	A	A	S	A	I	S	A	A	A	A	A	A	I	A	I
ANXIETY TOLERANCE	A	A	A	A	A	A	A	A	I	A	A	A	I	A	A	A	R	A	I
PROGRESSIVE VERSUS																			
REGRESSIVE	P	P	P	P	P	P	P	P	P	P	P	P	P	P	P	P	R	P	P
DIAGNOSIS	1	1	1	1	1	1	1	2	2	2	2	1	2	2	2	2	4	2	2

THIRD PROFILE

	ANDREW	BETTY	CANDACE	DOROTHY	EDNA	ELEANOR	FREIDA	GRETCHEN	ARTHUR	HELEN	HILDA	BEN	BERT	JANE	BILL	JANICE	CALVIN	JUDY	LAURA
LIBIDINAL LEVEL	Y	Y	Y	Y	Y	Y	Y	Y	Y	Y	Y	Y	Y	Y	Y	Y	N	Y	Y
LIBIDINAL DISTRIBUTION	Y	Y	Y	Y	Y	Y	Y	Y	Y	Y	Y	Y	Y	Y	Y	Y	N	Y	Y
AGGRESSION	Y	Y	Y	Y	Y	Y	Y	Y	Y	Y	Y	Y	Y	Y	Y	Y	N	N	Y
DISTRIBUTION AGGRESSION	Y	Y	Y	Y	Y	Y	Y	Y	Y	Y	Y	Y	Y	Y	Y	Y	N	Y	Y
EGO INTACT	Y	Y	Y	Y	Y	Y	Y	Y	Y	Y	Y	Y	Y	Y	Y	Y	Y	Y	Y
FUNCTION																			
PERCEPTION	Y	Y	Y	Y	Y	Y	Y	Y	Y	Y	Y	Y	Y	Y	Y	Y	Y	Y	Y
MEMORY	Y	Y	Y	Y	Y	Y	Y	Y	Y	Y	Y	Y	Y	Y	Y	Y	Y	Y	Y
MOTOR CONTROL	Y	Y	Y	Y	Y	Y	Y	Y	Y	Y	Y	Y	Y	Y	Y	Y	N	Y	Y
SPEECH	Y	Y	Y	Y	Y	Y	Y	Y	Y	Y	Y	Y	Y	Y	Y	Y	Y	Y	Y
REALITY TESTING	Y	Y	Y	Y	Y	Y	Y	Y	Y	Y	Y	Y	Y	Y	Y	Y	Y	Y	Y
INTEGRATIVE	Y	Y	Y	Y	Y	Y	Y	Y	Y	Y	Y	Y	Y	Y	Y	Y	Y	Y	Y
SECONDARY PROCESS	Y	Y	Y	Y	Y	Y	Y	Y	Y	Y	Y	Y	Y	Y	Y	Y	Y	Y	Y
AGE ADEQUATE DEFENSE	Y	Y	Y	Y	Y	Y	Y	Y	Y	Y	Y	Y	Y	Y	Y	Y	N	Y	Y
EGO FREE FROM																			
SECONDARY INTERFERENCE	Y	Y	Y	Y	Y	Y	Y	Y	Y	Y	Y	Y	Y	Y	Y	Y	N	Y	N
SUPEREGO BALANCE	Y	Y	Y	Y	Y	Y	Y	Y	Y	Y	Y	Y	Y	Y	Y	Y	Y	Y	Y
RELATIONS																			
PARENTS	Y	Y	Y	Y	Y	Y	Y	Y	Y	Y	Y	Y	Y	Y	Y	Y	N	N	Y
TEACHERS	Y	Y	Y	Y	Y	Y	Y	Y	Y	Y	Y	Y	Y	Y	Y	Y	N	Y	Y
PEERS	Y	Y	Y	Y	Y	Y	Y	Y	Y	Y	Y	Y	Y	Y	Y	Y	N	Y	Y
FIXATION POINTS	AI	AI	AI	AI	AI	AI	AI	AI	AI	AI	AI	AI	AI	AI	AI	AI	$^{O}_{A}$	AI	$^{O}_{A}P$
ECONOMIC FACTORS																			
LIBIDO	A	A	S	A	A	A	A	A	A	S	A	A	A	A	A	A	S	A	A
AGGRESSION	A	A	S	A	A	A	A	A	A	S	A	A	A	A	A	A	S	A	A
NEUTRALIZATION	S	S	S	S	A	A	S	A	A	S	A	A	A	A	A	A	R	A	I
SUBLIMATION	S	S	S	S	A	A	S	A	A	S	A	A	A	S	A	A	I	A	I
ANXIETY TOLERANCE	A	A	A	A	A	A	A	A	A	A	A	A	A	A	A	S	R	A	I
PROGRESSIVE VERSUS																			
REGRESSIVE	P	P	P	P	P	P	P	P	P	P	P	P	P	P	P	P	R	P	P
DIAGNOSIS	1	1	1	1	1	1	1	1	1	1	1	2	2	2	2	2	4	3	3

See page 321 for legend →

columns for the second and third profiles, write either "unchanged" or "alleviated," the latter meaning the fixation was alleviated enough not to interfere with functioning and maturation.

20-23. Write "inadequate," "adequate" or "superior."

24. Anxiety tolerance—The answers are either "insufficient," "adequate," or "rigid" measures.

25. Write "progressive" or "regressive."

PHASE DOMINANCE CHART[6]

To assess the degree of dominance of the age-appropriate phase, it is necessary to determine the extent of interference in the personality of the existing pathological fixation points. The extent of interference is evaluated under three main headings initially: 1. libido, 2. aggression and 3. object relationships. In each of these areas, the reviewing therapist (after consultation with the case therapist, if indicated) evaluates and checks phallic-oedipal dominance, contamination dominance at the phallic-oedipal level, anal phase dominance or oral phase dominance. Only if there is phallic-oedipal

[6] By Erna Furman and Robert A. Furman, M.D.

1. Headings to Fixation Points
   Y = Yes   N = No
   ? = insufficient evidence

2. Fixation Points
   O = oral fixation
   A = anal fixation
   P = phallic fixation
   Al = alleviated

3. Frustration Tolerance and Sublimation Potential
   I = inadequate
   A = adequate
   S = superior
   ? = insufficient evidence

4. Anxiety Tolerance
   I = insufficient
   A = adequate
   R = rigid

5. Progressive vs. Regressive
   P = progressive
   R = regressive

dominance should one note any direct manifestations of pre-phallic phases, e.g., bedwetting, thumbsucking. Regarding aggression, the evaluation should include both form (for example, biting vs. hitting vs. verbalizing) and content (for example, shouting devouring threats, vs. teasing with threats vs. using aggression for appropriate self-defense). Under object-relationships, the evaluations should be made for relationships with the mother, the teachers, the peers.

The final point of evaluation is under heading 4—ego functions—which includes defenses as ego functions. List only those functions that are demonstrably affected by prephallic drives and rate them by degree of interference. Do not list functions interfered with by drives of age-appropriate phase.

The first space under heading 5—comments—is left for the therapist to list any points he wants discussed.

RECAPITULATION OF SOME OF OUR DEFINITIONS

1. By phase dominance is meant the predominant, not exclusive instinctual level. Therefore a child may be phallic-oedipal phase dominant, yet show some measure of thumbsucking or wetting. Similarly a child may be dominantly oral or anal, yet show isolated signs of phallic interests.

2. Phase dominance when applied to "contamination" or "oral" or "anal" does not distinguish between fixation and regression. It only assesses the current picture at intake and does not specify how the child got to the manifest stage.

3. "Contamination" means a predominantly phallic stage, which is so markedly colored or coated by prephallic drives that the phallic manifestations are not free. Contamination is to be distinguished from (a) normal overlapping of phases, (b) coexistence of all instinctual levels in almost equal measure, as is characteristic of atypical children in diagnostic group V.

4. Involvement of ego functions: The functions that were

PHASE DOMINANCE CHART FORM

Name of child:

Age of child:

Case therapist:

Reviewing therapist:

	Phallic-oedipal dominance	Direct manifestations of prephallic phases	Contamination dominance at phallic-oedipal phase	Anal phase dominance	Oral phase dominance
1. Libido					
2. Aggres. (a) content					
(b) form					
3. Object-relations (a) mother					
(b) teachers					
(c) peers					

4. Ego Functions: List ego functions impaired by prephallic drives, identify drive and rate.

Function	Drive	Slight	Moderate	Severe

named and rated were only those demonstrably impaired by the prephallic drives, e.g., predominance of reaction formation impaired defenses, or gross oral-anal difficulty inhibited or arrested speech. In many children other functions were impaired, either by phallic drives (e.g., prevalence of identification with the aggressor) or indirectly by other aspects of their disturbance (e.g., prevalence of denial, impairing defense structure). Thus this category of involvement of ego functions does not give a picture of the child's ego functioning but only assesses the areas that were clearly affected by prephallic disturbance of drives.

5. This index also does not assess the degree of pathology at the age-adequate phallic level, either in the area of instincts or of relationships and ego. Many children showed serious disturbances in the phallic phase, which could create a pathological fixation point. This does not show in this index.

5. Comments

CHART FOR ASSESSMENT OF
PSYCHOSOMATIC DISORDERS[7]

Factors	Items
O R G A N I C	1. name of disease 2. severity when active 3. degree of existing damage 4. whether unremitting since onset 5. frequency of episodes, if episodic 6. duration since onset 7. multiple psychosomatic complaints 8. family history 9. response to medical treatment 10. current medical program 11. traumata from prior medical programs
E C O N O M I C	Drive fusion 12. level of object relations 13. development of superego and/or precursors Drive maturation 14. libido 15. aggression Drive neutralization 16. sublimation potential
E G O	Ego functions 17. synthetic function 18. reality testing 19. secondary-process thinking 20. speech 21. motor control Defenses 22. range 23. age-appropriateness 24. regression 25. aggression against self
Relationship	26. age of onset 27. degree of correlation 28. emotional factors correlating

Organic Factor:

Psychic Factor:
    Economic Aspect
    Ego Aspect

Relationship Factor:

[7] By Robert A. Furman, M.D.

Bibliography

Alpert, A. & Krown, S. (1953), Treatment of a child with severe ego restriction in a therapeutic nursery. *The Psychoanalytic Study of the Child,* 8:333-354. New York: International Universities Press.
——— (1954), Observations on the treatment of emotionally disturbed children in a therapeutic center. *The Psychoanalytic Study of the Child,* 9:334-343. New York: International Universities Press.
Barnes, M. (1964), Reactions to the death of a mother. *The Psychoanalytic Study of the Child,* 19:334-357. New York: International Universities Press.
Benedek, T. (1959), Parenthood as a developmental phase: a contribution to the libido theory. *J. Amer. Psychoanal. Assn.,* 7:389-417.
Benjamin, J. (1959), Prediction and psychopathological theory. In: *Dynamic Psychopathology in Childhood,* ed. L. Jessner & E. Pavenstedt. New York: Grune & Stratton, pp. 6-77.
Benkendorf, J., Furman, E., & Rolnick A. (1955), A contribution to the education and therapy of young children with emotional disturbances. Unpublished paper.
Bibring, G. (1959), Some considerations of the psychological processes in pregnancy. *The Psychoanalytic Study of the Child,* 14:113-121. New York: International Universities Press.
Bonnard, A. (1950), The mother as therapist, in a case of obsessional neurosis. *The Psychoanalytic Study of the Child,* 5:391-408. New York: International Universities Press.
Burlingham, D. (1951), Present trends in handling the mother-child relationships during the therapeutic process. *The Psychoanalytic Study of the Child,* 6:31-37. New York: International Universities Press.
Buxbaum, E. (1946), Psychotherapy and psychoanalysis in the treatment of children. *Nerv. Child,* 5:115-126.
——— (1954), Technique of child therapy. *The Psychoanalytic Study of the Child,* 9:297-333. New York: International Universities Press.

Coleman, R., Kris, E., & Provence, S. (1953), The study of early variations of parental attitudes. *The Psychoanalytic Study of the
Child*, 8:20-47. New York: International Universities Press.

Freud, A. (1945), Indications for child analysis. *The Psychoanalytic
Study of the Child*, 1:127-149. New York: International Universities Press.

—— (1960), Unpublished lectures delivered in New York City.

—— (1962), Assessment of childhood disturbances. *The Psychoanalytic
Study of the Child*, 17:149-158. New York: International Universities Press.

—— (1963), The concept of developmental lines. *The Psychoanalytic
Study of the Child*, 18:245-265. New York: International Universities Press.

—— (1965), *Normality and Pathology in Childhood*. New York: International Universities Press.

Freud, S. (1909), Analysis of a phobia in a five-year-old boy. *Standard
Edition*, 10:5-149. London: Hogarth Press, 1955.

Friedlander, K. (1947), Psychoanalytic orientation in child guidance
work in Great Britain. *The Psychoanalytic Study of the Child*,
2:343-357. New York: International Universities Press.

Furman, E. (1957), Treatment of under-fives by way of parents. *The
Psychoanalytic Study of the Child*, 12:250-262. New York: International Universities Press.

—— (1964), Observations on a toddler's near-fatal accident. *Bull.
Phila. Assn. Psychoanal.*, 14:138-148.

Furman, R. (1964a), Death and the young child: some preliminary considerations. *The Psychoanalytic Study of the Child*, 19:321-333.

—— (1964b), Death of a six-year-old's mother during his analysis.
The Psychoanalytic Study of the Child, 19:377-397. New York:
International Universities Press.

Hellman, I. (1962), Hampstead nursery follow-up studies: I. sudden
separation and its effect followed over twenty years. *The Psychoanalytic Study of the Child*, 17:159-174. New York: International Universities Press.

Jacobs, L. (1949), Methods used in the education of mothers: a contribution to the handling and treatment of developmental difficulties in children under five years of age. *The Psychoanalytic
Study of the Child*, 3/4:409-422. New York: International Universities Press.

Jacobson, E. (1954), The self and the object world. *The Psychoanalytic
Study of the Child*, 9:75-127. New York: International Universities Press.

Katan, A. (1947), Experience with enuretics. *The Psychoanalytic Study
of the Child*, 2:241-255. New York: International Universities
Press.

———— (1959), The nursery school as a diagnostic help to the child guidance clinic. *The Psychoanalytic Study of the Child*, 14:250-264. New York: International Universities Press.

———— (1961), Some thoughts about the role of verbalization in early childhood. *The Psychoanalytic Study of the Child*, 16:184-188. New York: International Universities Press.

Kris, E. (1953), Unpublished report from the longitudinal study of personality development. New Haven: Yale University Child Study Center. (Presented at the 20th International Psycho-analytical Congress, Paris, 1957).

———— (1955), Neutralization and sublimation: observations on young children. *The Psychoanalytic Study of the Child*, 10:30-46. New York: International Universities Press.

Kubie, L. (1953), The problem of specificity in the psychosomatic process. In: *The Psychosomatic Concept in Psychoanalysis,* ed. F. Deutsch. New York: International Universities Press, pp. 63-81.

Lovatt, M. (1962), Autistic children in a day nursery. *Children,* 9:103-108.

Margolin, S. (1953), Genetic and dynamic psychophysiological determinants of the pathophysiological processes. In: *The Psychosomatic Concept in Psychoanalysis,* ed. F. Deutsch. New York: International Universities Press, pp. 3-36.

McDonald, M. (1964), A study of reactions of nursery school children to the death of a child's mother. *The Psychoanalytic Study of the Child,* 19:358-376. New York: International Universities Press.

Nagera, H. (1963), The developmental profile: notes on some practical considerations regarding its use. *The Psychoanalytic Study of the Child,* 18:511-540. New York: International Universities Press.

———— (1964), On arrest in development, fixation and regression. *The Psychoanalytic Study of the Child,* 19:222-239. New York: International Universities Press.

———— (1966), *Early Childhood Disturbances, the Infantile Neurosis and the Adulthood Disturbances.* New York: International Universities Press.

Neubauer, P. (1960), The one-parent child and his oedipal development. *The Psychoanalytic Study of the Child,* 15:286-309. New York: International Universities Press.

Pfeiffer, E. (1959), A modified nursery school program in a mental hospital. *Amer. J. Orthopsychiat.,* 29:780-790.

Provence, S. & Ritvo, S. (1961), Effects of deprivation on institutionalized infants. *The Psychoanalytic Study of the Child,* 16:189-205. New York: International Universities Press.

Rangell, L. (1950), A treatment of nightmares in a seven-year-old boy. *The Psychoanalytic Study of the Child,* 5:358-390. New York: International Universities Press.

Ruben, M. (1946), A contribution to the education of a parent. *The Psychoanalytic Study of the Child,* 1:247-261. New York: International Universities Press.

———(1960), *Parent Guidance in the Nursery School.* New York: International Universities Press.

———& Thomas, R. (1947), Home training of instincts and emotions. *Health Educat. J.* (London), 5:1-6.

Sandler, A., Daunton, E. & Schnurmann, A. (1957), Inconsistency in the mother as a factor in character development: a comparative study of three cases. *The Psychoanalytic Study of the Child,* 12:209-225. New York: International Universities Press.

Schur, M. (1955), Comments on the metapsychology of somatization. *The Psychoanalytic Study of the Child,* 10:119-164. New York: International Universities Press.

Sperling, M. (1949), The role of the mother in psychosomatic disorders in children. *Psychosom. Med.,* 11:377-385.

Tarachow, S. (1945), A psychosomatic theory based on the concepts of mastery and resolution of tension. *Psychoanal. Rev.,* 32:163-180.

Winnicott, D. (1954), Mind and its relation to the psyche-soma. *Brit. J. Med. Psychol.,* 27:201-209.